THE ULTIMATE FOOTBALL FACT AND QUIZ BOOK

Frank Nicklin

Cartoons by
Peter Coupe

STOPWATCH

Published by Stopwatch Publishing Limited

This edition published 1997

Printed and bound in Finland

Compiled by Jay Bigwood and with thanks to staff at
Hayters Sports Agency

© Stopwatch Publishing Limited
443 Oxford Street
London WIR IDA

ISBN I 900032 02 3

CONTENTS

THE ULTIMATE FACT AND QUIZ BOOK

FOOTBALL

Quiz Book

QUIZ CONTENTS

 **Quiz 1**

The Football
League

1. **Which 12 teams were the founder members of the Football League?**

2. Who won the first ever Football League title?

3. **With what club did Billy Southworth score the first ever double hat-trick in 1893?**

4. Which team won the first title of the Twentieth Century?

5. **Who won the league for the second year running, in 1903-04, by scoring 48 goals, one fewer than Liverpool who were relegated?**

6. Which team set a record of 14 straight league victories in the First Division, in the 1903-04 season?

7. **For which side did 22 stone Bill "Fatty" Foulke sign in the 1904-05 season?**

8. Which team won 14 consecutive matches in the second division in 1905-06 to set a record?

9. **With which club did Alf Common sign to become the first £1000 player in 1905?**

10. Who were the first southern club to lead the First Division in the 1906-07 season?

11. **For which London team did George Hilsdon score five goals on his debut in the 1906-07 season?**

12. For which Midlands team did West, Hooper and Spouncer all score hat-tricks in a 12-0 win over Leicester Fosse in 1909?

13. **Which team lost 9-1 to Sunderland in the 1908-09 season, yet still managed to win the First Division?**

14. In which season did Manchester United first play at Old Trafford?

15. **Which team scored 36 out of a possible 42 points in their last 21 games to secure promotion in the 1909-10 season?**

 **Quiz 1**   **The Football League**

16. Who won their sixth League title in the 1909-10 season?

17. **In which season did the League first pay money to the clubs finishing in the top places in the First Division?**

18. Before 1985, when was the last time that Tottenham beat Liverpool in the league at Anfield?

19. **In which season did Arsenal play their first League game at Highbury?**

20. Which team won the championship on only 46 points in 1915, the lowest total since the league was expanded to 20 teams in 1905?

21. **Which team scored a record 104 goals in their 1919-20 championship winning season?**

22. From which team did Leeds United take over Elland Road to play their home matches?

23. **Which team only managed to attract 13 spectators in their final home game of the 1920-21 season, after they were already relegated from the Second Division?**

24. Which club set a record when they went 42 League matches unbeaten from November 1977 to December 1978?

25. **For which team did Jimmy Evans become the first full back to be his side's top scorer, after scoring 10 penalties in the 1921-22 season?**

26. Which team finished the 1922-23 season with 42 points from 42 matches, 14 wins, 14 draws and 14 defeats, with 40 goals for and 40 goals against?

27. **For which team did Billy Smith score the first ever goal direct from a corner, in the 1924-25 season?**

28. Up to the start of the 1997-98 season, two clubs share the record of 29 unbeaten League games from the start of a season. Who are they?

29. **Which teams competed in the first League match to have been broadcast on radio, on January 22 1927?**

30. Which team paid Stockport County three freezers full of ice cream for a player in the 1926-27 season?

---

16. Aston Villa 17. 1910-11 18. 1911-12 19. 1913-14 20. Everton 21. **West Bromwich Albion** 22. Leeds City 23. **Stockport** 24. Nottingham Forest 25. **Southend** 26. Southampton 27. **Huddersfield** 28. Leeds (1973-74), Liverpool (1987-88) 29. **Arsenal and Sheffield United** 30. Manchester United (Hughie McLenahun)

 **Quiz 1**   The Football League

31. **Who scored nine goals in the last three matches of the 1927-28 season, to set a record of 60, which included 40 headers?**

32. When did the Football League celebrate its Centenary?

33. **Which club in the 1927-28 season was relegated with 38 points, the highest total for a club to go down, and were only 3 points behind Arsenal, 12 places above them?**

34. Which London club won the Third Division South in the 1927-28 season with a record 127 goals?

35. **In what year did numbers first appear on players' shirts in League matches?**

36. How old was Albert Geldard when he became the youngest league player, making his debut for Second Division Bradford Park Avenue in 1929 season?

37. **Which team finished runners-up in the Third Division South every year for six consecutive years in the 1920s?**

38. Which team won the First Division three years in a row, from 1923 to 1925, and finished runners-up for the next two years?

39. **Which team lost their first twelve games of the 1930-31 season?**

40. Who were the first team to leave the League in mid season, when they retired after six games in the 1931-32 season?

41. **With which team did Stanley Matthews make his League debut in the 1931-32 season?**

42. Which club was fined £250 for fielding understrength teams in the 1935-36 season?

43. **Which clubs played in the first televised League game, in August 1936?**

44. Which British club first signed an Argentinian, in 1937?

45. **In what League season was the arc at the front of the penalty area introduced?**

Quiz 1 — The Football League

46. When was the offside rule brought in to League football?

47. For which club did Len Shackleton score six goals on his debut in the 1946-47 season?

48. For which club did 52 year old Neil McBain become the oldest man to play in the League in the 1946-47 season?

49. In what season did the League's aggregate attendance reach its highest ever figure - over 41.2 million?

50. In what season was obstruction made an offence in League football?

51. For which club did father and son Alec and David Herd both play in 1951?

52. Tommy Lawton scored his 200th League goal on the opening day of which season

53. For which club did Peter Aldis score a 35 yard header, thought to be the longest ever, in the 1952-53 season?

54. Who signed 34 year old Tommy Lawton in the 1953-54 season?

55. For which club did Sam Bartram set a League record 500th appearance in March 1954?

56. Who set a League record of 401 consecutive games for Tranmere before missing a match in September 1955?

57. In what year did the first League game to use floodlights occur?

58. Who, in the 1956-57 season, set a League record of 30 games without a win?

59. Who scored 10 times for Luton Town against Bristol Rovers in a Division Three (South) match in 1936?

60. In what season did the Football League introduce a national Fourth Division?

46. 1925 47. **Newcastle** 48. New Brighton 49. 1948-49 50. 1948-49
51. **Stockport** 52. 1951-52 53. **Aston Villa** 54. Arsenal 55. **Charlton**
56. Harold Bell 57. 1956 58. Scunthorpe United 59. **Joe Payne** 60. 1958-59

 Quiz 1   The Football League

61. **In what year were Sunderland relegated to the Second Division for the first time since being formed in 1890?**

62. Which team beat Everton 10-4 in the 1958-59 season - the highest scoring First Division match this Century?

63. **Who became the youngest player to score five goals in a First Division match in 1958?**

64. Who reached 200 League goals in fewer matches than any other player, whilst playing for Middlesbrough in the 1950s?

65. **Who scored 59 goals in 37 League matches for Middlesbrough in 1926-27?**

66. Who led the PFA in their argument with the Football League over players' wages and contracts during the 1960-61 season?

67. **Which team won the 1962-63 championship and were labelled the "Cheque Book Champions"?**

68. Who retired in the 1963-64 season, aged 39, after making a record 764 appearances for Portsmouth?

69. **Who scored the fastest League goal in history in 1964, timed at 4 seconds, for Bradford Park Avenue?**

70. Who was the oldest player to have appeared in the First Division, aged 50 years and 5 days, in 1965?

71. **Keith Peacock become the first substitute to appear in a League match in 1965. Which club was he playing for at the time?**

72. Who scored 44 goals in the Fourth Division for Bradford Park Avenue in the 1965-66 season?

73. **Who took over at Hartlepools United to become the youngest manger in the League in 1966?**

74. In which season did all of the top three First Division clubs score over a hundred League goals?

75. **In what League season were goalkeepers limited to only four steps when holding the ball?**

Quiz 1 — The Football League

76. How many goals did Tottenham score when they won the 1960-61 First Division?

77. **Who scored one of his six goals against Sunderland with his hand in October 1968?**

78. Who scored his 200th League goal for his First Division club in November 1968?

79. **Which team went from the Fourth Division to the First Division and back to the Fourth division in nine years?**

80. Who were fined a record £5,000 for fielding an understrength team in 1970?

81. **In what year were Blackpool last in the top division?**

82. Which club had to name their Chief Scout on the substitute's bench, in September 1970, because of a depleted squad?

83. **Who made his 500th League appearance for Chelsea in January 1970?**

84. Which club drew a record 23 out of 42 First Division matches in the First Division in the 1978-79 season?

85. **Which club won 18 of their 21 away League matches in Division Three (South) in 1946-47?**

86. Who scored 52 League goals in 1960-61 for Peterborough United?

87. **Who made his 600th appearance for Leeds in 1972?**

88. Which clubs was involved in match fixing allegations, for the match which decided the title, in 1972?

89. **Who replaced an injured linesman in a game between Arsenal and Liverpool in 1972?**

90. When did the distinction between amateur and professional footballers cease to exist in the League?

 Quiz 1   The Football League

91. Who was banned for life following a match fixing scandal, only to resume playing for Sheffield Wednesday in the 1972-73 season?

92. In which year were Huddersfield relegated to the (old) Third Division for the first time in their history?

93. Which two clubs were promoted from the Second to the First Division in 1972?

94. Who were the Second Division champions in the 1961-62 season?

95. Which club was promoted to the First Division in 1964 and ended up as runners-up the following year?

96. Who came from four goals down at halftime to earn a draw in a First Division match against Port Vale in 1996-97 season?

97. Which two teams in a Division 2 match ended with five players sent off in February 1997?

98. Which team set a record with eight scorers in one match during a First Division game in September 1989?

99. Which club became the first to play 3,000 matches in the League, in 1975, and 3,500 in 1987?

100. Which season saw the switching from goal average to goal difference in the Football League?

101. Which Liverpool striker scored in 10 successive First Division matches from the last game of the 1986-87 season to the ninth of 1987-88?

102. During an unbeaten run of 29 matches, how many goals did Liverpool score against Coventry on New Year's Day 1989?

103. Which team was promoted to the Second Division in 1976, in only their fourth season in the Football League?

104. Which club asked their fans to sponsor them at the start of the 1976-7 season?

105. In which year were red and yellow cards introduced?

 Quiz 1 The Football League

106. Which two players reached the 770 match mark for Chelsea on the same day in 1978?

107. Who became the first player to reach 100 League appearances for four different clubs?

108. Which club was first to legally wear a sponsor's name on their shirts?

109. Which club was relegated from the First Division alongside Norwich in 1974?

110. In what year did the Football League introduce three points for a win?

111. In what year was the sending off of players for "professional fouls" introduced?

112. In what year did Robert Maxwell become chairman of Oxford United

113. In what year did the League sign a deal which led to the League Cup being renamed the Milk Cup?

114. Who became the youngest First Division scorer, aged 16 years 57 days in February 1984?

115. Who finished bottom of the First Division in 1984-85, winning only three games and scoring a record low of 24 goals?

116. Who was First Division top scorer six times in 11 seasons - between 1958 and 1969?

117. Who was the youngest hat-trick scorer in the First Division, at the age of 17 years and 140 days, in 1988?

118. When was the last year that Brighton and Hove Albion were in the top division?

119. When did Portsmouth last win the championship?

120. When did Burnley last win the old First Division?

106. Peter Bonetti and Ron Harris 107. **Alan Ball** 108. Liverpool
109. **Manchester United** 110. 1981 111. 1982 112. 1981-82 113. 1982
114. Jason Dozzell 115. **Stoke** 116. Jimmy Greaves 117. **Alan Shearer**
118. 1982-83 119. **1949-50** 120. 1959-60

 **Quiz 1**   **The Football League**

121. **Who were the runners-up when the new First Division came into operation?**

122. Who were the first new Third Division champions?

123. **At the end of what League season did Ian Rush and Gary Lineker both move abroad?**

124. In what season did Wimbledon first reach the top division?

125. **When did Kenny Dalglish score his 100th League goal for Liverpool?**

126. Who scored 37 League hat-tricks for Tranmere and Everton between 1924 and 1938?

127. **Who did Arsenal beat on September 8 1984 to put them top of the First Division for the first time since 1972?**

128. Which team recovered from a 4-0 half time deficit at Portsmouth to draw the match 4-4, in the Second Division, on New Year's Day, 1984?

129. **Which club was relegated from the First Division to the Fourth Division in four straight seasons from 1983-84?**

130. Which club postponed two matches in October 1985 on the advice of the police?

131. **Which club signed a 44 year old TV presenter as reserve goalkeeper in November 1985?**

132. Which two clubs were automatically promoted to the Premiership in 1996-97?

133. **How many players were sent off in English League football on December 14 1985 to set a record?**

134. In which club's ground did Middlesbrough have to play their first game of the 1986-87 season, when they were in the hands of the Official Receiver?

135. **Which club were the first to be relegated from the First Division in 1996-97?**

 Quiz 1   The Football League

136. When did Ian Rush score his 200th goal for Liverpool?

137. Peter Shilton made his 1000th League appearance playing for which London club?

138. In which season were two substitutes allowed to be used for the first time in the Football League?

139. Which club lost 2-1 to Notts County in August 1986, their first League defeat in nine months, and first home defeat in a year?

140. Which two clubs contested a 6-6 draw in a Division Two match on October 22, 1960?

141. Up to the start of the 1997-98 season, only two clubs have completed a Football League season unbeaten. Name them.

142. Who called off their match against Bolton, in September 1987, following a dispute over how many police were needed at the match?

143. Who set a club record of 13 straight League wins in September 1987?

144. When West Ham beat Newcastle 8-1 in a Division One match in April 1986 which player scored against three different goalkeepers?

145. Which goalkeeper set a new record in 1995-96 by keeping 29 clean-sheets for Gillingham in the Third Division?

146. Who was the first, and so far only, club to play in the Premiership, all four previous divisions of the Football League and in both sections (North and South) of the old Third Division?

147. Which club had two points deducted for calling off their first match of the 1988-89 season because of building works on their ground?

148. Who became the first player to score 50 goals for a League club since 1960-61 when he scored 52 for Wolves in 1987-88?

149. From the start of which season were artificial pitches banned by the League?

150. Who was fined a week's wages for a sit down protest at half time in his side's opening match of the 1990 season?

---

136. 18 March 1987 137. **Leyton Orient** 138. 1987-8 139. **Swindon Town** 140. Charlton and Middlesbrough 141. **Preston North End (1888-89) and Liverpool (1893-94)** 142. Tranmere 143. **Tottenham** 144. Alvin Martin 145. **Jim Stannard** 146. Coventry City 147. **Tottenham (points replaced with £15,000 fine)** 148. Steve Bull 149. 1991-92 150. Neville Southall

 **Quiz 1**   The Football League

151. **Which club had their coach was wheel-clamped and towed away during a match at Chelsea in November 1990?**

152. Which club hold the record for the lowest Fourth Division attendance, only 625, for a game against Wrexham in December 1990?

153. **Who was the first club to win promotion on penalties, following their Fourth Division play-off?**

154. Millwall were successfully sued by three fans from which club because of a poor view they had at The New Den?

155. **Which club had four players sent off in their match against Northampton in September 1992?**

156. Which league decided to experiment with kick-ins instead of throw-ins in the 1994-95 season?

157. **Who was the first player to accumulate 61 disciplinary points in a League season?**

158. Who was the first player to score 30 goals in an English season in three consecutive years?

159. **Which club went through five managers in the 1995-96 season?**

160. Which club's first home ground was Plumstead Common?

161. **Whose record League win is 12-0 against Loughborough in 1900, and record League defeat is 0-8, also against Loughborough, four years earlier?**

162. Whose record League victory is 12-2 in a match against Accrington Stanley in 1892?

163. **Which club's highest League victory is 8-1, against Middlesbrough in the First Division in 1953?**

164. Which team set a club record when they beat Portsmouth 10-0 in Division One in 1928?

165. **Which club's record defeat is 1-9 by Birmingham in Division Two in 1959?**

 Quiz 1   The Football League

166. Who is currently Liverpool's highest scorer in one season, with 41 goals?

167. Which side won the first eleven games of their double winning season?

168. Whose record League victory is 10-1 against Huddersfield in November 1987?

169. Which club won their first ever League game 7-0 in 1892?

170. How many teams go into the play-offs every season?

171. Who did Middlesbrough beat 9-0 in 1958 to record their highest ever League victory?

172. Which 1997 Premiership club was originally called Stanley?

173. For which club does Wally Ardron hold the record for most League goals scored in a season, having scored 36 in 1950-51?

174. Who is the oldest League club in England?

175. What is the highest position that Oxford have ever finished in the top division?

176. Which club's record League attendance is 35,353 for their match against Leeds United in 1974?

177. Which club's record defeat is 1-16 against Southbank in the Northern League in 1919?

178. Which club played their first football league game on September 3 1892, when they won 1-0 away at Notts County?

179. Which club, who formerly played at the Antelope Ground, were runners-up in the 1983-84 First Division?

180. Who were the runners-up in the 1982-83 First Division championship?

166. Roger Hunt 167. **Tottenham** 168. Manchester City 169. **Manchester City** 170. 12 171. **Brighton and Hove Albion** 172. Newcastle 173. **Nottingham Forest** 174. Notts County 175. 18th (1985-86 and 1986-87) 176. QPR 177. **Scarborough** 178. Sheffield Wednesday 179. **Southampton** 180. Watford

 **Quiz 1**   The Football
League

181. Which club lost 1-9 to Brighton and Hove Albion in 1965, their record defeat and Brighton's record win?

182. Who were the four clubs who played in the 1996-97 First Division play-offs?

183. Who beat Halifax 13-0 in 1934 to record their biggest League win?

184. For which club is Harry Hardy the only player ever to have received an England cap?

185. Which club played in Europe seven times but never played in the (old) First Division?

186. Which team has a record league victory of 9-1 away at Newcastle and has spent every season bar one in the top two divisions?

187. Which club established their record League win of 9-0 against Bristol Rovers in 1977?

188. Who were the two clubs that produced the record score for a First Division match in 1948 at Maine Road?

189. Who has made the most League appearances for Watford, with 415 games?

190. Which club inflicted West Ham's worst defeat, 2-8 in 1963?

191. Which club was known as Thames Ironworks FC when they were set up in 1895?

192. Which player has made the most League appearances for West Ham?

193. Against which team did Geoff Hurst score six goals in West Ham's record equalling 8-0 win in 1968?

194. Which club's best ever placing in the League is fourth in the old third Division in the 1985-86 and 1986-87 seasons?

195. Which club was formed in 1889, but only turned professional in 1964, and entered the League in 1978?

Quiz 1

The Football League

196. Who became the costliest player to leave Wimbledon in June 1995 and how what was the transfer fee?

197. Which club's record League victory was set at only 4-0 when they beat Scarborough in 1993?

198. When the Football League split into two divisions in 1892, which club first won the new Division One?

199. In what year did the Third Division North and the Third Division South combine to create one league?

200. After Liverpool, who won most (Old) First Division titles?

201. Which two clubs won the original Second Division the most, with six wins each?

202. In the 1988-89 season, Liverpool lost only one game after New Year's Day. Who beat the?

203. On which ground did Arsenal win the double in the 1970-71 season?

204. Who finished second when Tottenham won the League in 1961?

205. When was the last time that Tottenham were relegated?

206. Who was Tottenham's top goal scorer in 1979-80, with 19 goals?

207. Who beat Tottenham 6-0 at White Hart Lane in a League match in 1935?

208. Have Tottenham and Arsenal ever met in a League game outside the top division?

209. When was the first Arsenal/Tottenham League match?

210. Against which club did Argentinians Ossie Ardiles and Ricardo Villa make their Tottenham debut?

209. December 1909 210. Nottingham Forest
Wednesday **205. 1976-77 season** 206. Glenn Hoddle **207. Arsenal** 208. No
202. Arsenal, in the last game of the season **203. White Hart Lane** 204. Sheffield
199. 1958 200. Arsenal (10 times) **201. Leicester City and Manchester City**
196. Warren Barton, £4m **197. Wycombe Wanderers** 198. Sunderland

 **Quiz 1**   **The Football League**

211. How long did it take Ricardo Villa to score his first League goal?

212. Who saved two penalties in a match against Liverpool in March 1973?

213. Who won Chelsea's Player of the Year award in 1976 and 1977?

214. Who is Chelsea's second highest scorer of League goals?

215. What is Chelsea's longest unbeaten run in a season?

216. What was the score when Manchester United beat West Ham to secure the 1966-67 title?

217. Who was Manchester United's leading scorer when they won the 1964-65 and 1966-67 titles?

218. Which club twice held Manchester United to draws durinh the Red Devils 1966-67 title winning season?

219. Only one club took maximum points at Old Trafford in Manchester United's 1966-67 title winning year. Name them.

220. Against which club did George Best score his first league goal?

221. Where did Manchester United win their only away game in the 1986-87 season?

222. Who scored the only hat-trick in Manchester United's 1985-86 season?

223. Against which club was Chelsea's record home attendance of 82,905 set in 1935?

224. Who has an average 0.78 goals per game for Chelsea, a club record?

225. Which team finished bottom of Division Three in 1996-97 to be relegated to the GM Vauxhall Conference?

 **Quiz 2**

**The Premiership
1992-93**

1. **Which Premiership favourites were beaten 4-2 by Norwich on the opening day of the season after leading 2-0?**

2. Which game was the first to be broadcast live on satellite television?

3. **Which two unfancied clubs had the only 100 per cent records after two games?**

4. A late goal against Southampton from which new signing gave Manchester United their first win of the season?

5. **Which Tottenham player was accused by the FA with feigning injury, the first case of its kind?**

6. Who scored a hat-trick for Leeds as they crushed Tottenham 5-0 in August?

7. **Which club's opening four defeats completed the worst start to the season in the manager's 17-year reign?**

8. Which team opened their £8m Centenary Stand in September?

9. **Which defender scored his first League goal for Liverpool in their 1-1 draw with Southampton in September?**

10. Which Manchester United striker broke his leg against Crystal Palace in September?

11. **Who was the Sheffield United goalkeeper sent off in their game against Spurs in September?**

12. Which Chelsea defender damaged knee ligaments in a clash with Dean Saunders in September, an injury which would eventually end his career?

13. **Whose late goal at Elland Road saved Leeds' long unbeaten home record?**

14. Which club were top of the League at the end of September?

15. **Against which club did Bryan Robson make his Premiership debut?**

1. **Arsenal** 2. Nottingham Forest v Liverpool 3. **Coventry and Norwich** 4. Dion Dublin 5. **Gordon Durie** 6. Eric Cantona 7. **Nottingham Forest** 8. Liverpool 9. **Mark Wright** 10. Dion Dublin 11. **Simon Tracey** 12. Paul Elliott 13. **Steve Hodge** 14. Norwich 15. **Middlesbrough**

 **Quiz 2**   **The Premiership 1992-93**

16. Which player scored his 200th league goal in a 4-1 win over Middlesbrough in November?

17. Whose hat-trick gave Norwich victory over Oldham and a place at the top of the Premiership in November?

18. Which manager was banned from the touchline after three offences in three months?

19. Which club ended Arsenal's run of six straight wins in November?

20. How many points clear were Norwich in December?

21. Which player was accused of throwing a punch at David Howells in December?

22. Against which team did Liverpool suffer their worst defeat in 16 years in December?

23. Norwich suffered their first home defeat in December against which team?

24. Who hit his first QPR hat-trick in December against Everton?

25. In which month did Manchester United hit the top of the Premiership for the first time?

26. Which striker scored two hat-tricks in five days in January?

27. Which club took over at the head of the Premiership with a 5-1 drubbing of Middlesbrough in January?

28. Which club put a ban on players leaving while they are still in the running for silverware?

29. Which player's penalty ended Liverpool's run of seven games without a win in January?

30. Which player was sent off during Arsenal's 1-0 defeat at the hands of Liverpool in January?

16. Ian Rush **17. Mark Robins** 18. Joe Kinnear 19. **Leeds** 20. Eight 21. **Ian Wright** 22. Coventry 23. **Ipswich** 24. Andy Sinton 25. **January** 26. Brian Deane **27. Aston Villa** 28. Norwich City 29. **John Barnes** 30. Nigel Winterburn

 **The Premiership
1992-93**

31. **Which keeper was sent off for the second time in six weeks for handling outside his box in February?**

32. Who were the reigning champions who were just outside the relegation zone in February?

33. **Which player got a hostile reception when Manchester United travelled to Elland Road in February?**

34. Which manager was sacked by Chelsea in February?

35. **Which company signed a deal to sponsor the Premiership in February?**

36. Who scored two goals in five minutes for Manchester United as they recovered from being 1-0 down against Southampton in February?

37. **Whose hat-trick helped Tottenham to a 5-0 trouncing of Leeds in February?**

38. Which team climbed off the bottom of the Premiership with victory over Middlesbrough in February?

39. **Which makeshift striker scored for the seventh consecutive game for Sheffield Wednesday in February?**

40. Which player was given a £20,000 fine in February for backing 'Soccer's Hard Men' video?

41. **Whose late goal kept Aston Villa two points clear of Manchester United in February?**

42. Which player was ruled out of an Arsenal game in February after needing 29 stitches from a fall down the stairs?

43. **Which relegation-threatened side put six past Spurs in March, their worst defeat in 15 years?**

44. For which Liverpool player did Aston Villa offer £3.5m in March?

45. **Which club did Manchester United beat 2-1 in March to put them back top of the Premiership?**

43. **Sheffield United** 44. John Barnes 45. **Liverpool**
39. **Paul Warhurst** 40. Vinnie Jones 41. **Dwight Yorke** 42. Tony Adams
35. **Bass** 36. Ryan Giggs 37. **Teddy Sheringham** 38. Nottingham Forest
31. **Neville Southall** 32. Leeds United 33. **Eric Cantona** 34. Ian Porterfield

 Quiz 2

**The Premiership
1992-93**

46. Manchester United were rocked by defeat from which club, bottom of the Premiership, in March?

47. **What was the score in the top-of-the-table clash between Manchester United and Aston Villa in March?**

48. Which team halted Norwich's revival in March with a 3-0 win?

49. **Which team went five points clear of the relegation zone with a win over Sheffield United in March?**

50. Which manager was sent off in March for allegedly swearing at a linesman?

51. **Which player was given the red card as he was being stretchered off after a clash with Viv Anderson in March?**

52. Which QPR striker broke his leg twice in three months at the beginning of 1993?

53. **Which Manchester United player was fined £1,000 in March for spitting at fans?**

54. Which team did Oldham beat 6-2 in April to leap out of the relegation zone?

55. **Which club were bottom of the Premiership at the start of April?**

56. Which Forest defender was sent off at home to Blackburn in April?

57. **Which team ended Norwich's title hopes in April with a 5-1 mauling?**

58. On which away ground were Crystal Palace beaten 4-0 in April, compounding their relegation problems?

59. **Two late headers from which player against Sheffield Wednesday put Manchester United back on the top of the Premiership in April?**

60. Whose hat-trick for QPR in April kept Nottingham Forest at the bottom of the table?

46. Oldham 47. 1-1 48. Wimbledon 49. **Crystal Palace** 50. Graeme Souness 51. **John Fashanu** 52. Gary Penrice 53. **Eric Cantona** 54. Wimbledon 55. **Middlesbrough** 56. Gary Charles 57. **Tottenham Hotspur** 58. Selhurst Park 59. **Steve Bruce** 60. Les Ferdinand

 Quiz 2   **The Premiership**
1992-93

61. **Who scored Manchester United's only goal against Ipswich in April to keep them top of the League?**

62. Who scored his first Aston Villa goal for a year when they beat Arsenal in April?

63. **Who scored a rare hat-trick for Sheffield Wednesday when they beat Southampton 5-2 on Easter Monday?**

64. Who scored a hat-trick for Norwich in April against Leeds to keep the embers of a title challenge alive?

65. **Which Coventry player's dismissal was revoked in April after referee Rodger Gilford watched the video?**

66. Which ex-Villa player scored his first hat-trick for Liverpool in their 4-0 win over Coventry in April?

67. **Which two rival clubs played out a 3-1 result which ended the title hopes of one team and helped the other out of relegation trouble in April?**

68. How many points clear were Manchester United with only two games left?

69. **Which Villa player was arrested for disorderly behaviour in April after an incident at an Essex nightclub?**

70. Brian Clough announced his retirement in April, after how many years in charge of Nottingham Forest?

71. **Against which team was Brian Clough's last home game in May?**

72. Which team were relegated with one remaining game, despite winning 3-2 at Hillsborough in their penultimate game?

73. **Which player was voted Footballer of the Year in May?**

74. Which team beat Villa 1-0 to give Manchester United the title?

75. **Manchester United's title put manager Alex Ferguson in the record books. Why?**

England and Scotland
Waddle 74. Oldham 75. He became the first manager to win Leagues in
69. Dean Saunders 70. 18 71. Sheffield United 72. Middlesbrough 73. Chris
65. Mick Quinn 66. Mark Walters 67. Ipswich and Norwich 68. Four
61. Denis Irwin 62. Tony Daley 63. Chris Bart-Williams 64. Chris Sutton

Quiz 2 — The Premiership 1992-93

76. Who did Manchester United beat 3-1 to celebrate becoming champions?

77. **How many Liverpool players were sent off during the season?**

78. Who did Oldham beat 3-2 to keep alive their hopes of survival in May?

79. **What was the score in the cup final rehearsal in May?**

80. Who scored a hat-trick for Southampton in their 4-3 defeat at Oldham on the last day of the season?

81. **Which old boy scored the opening goal against Crystal Palace on the last day of the season, condemning them to relegation?**

82. Against which team did Norwich draw 3-3 to give them third place on the last day of the season?

83. **Which club was the last to play Liverpool in front of the Kop before the stand was made all-seater?**

84. Which player scored his 300th goal for his club on the last day of the season?

85. **Which team finished the season without an away win?**

86. What is the final gap at the top of the Premiership between Manchester United and Aston Villa?

87. **Which player was attacked by the crowd on the final day of the season when Manchester United played Wimbledon?**

88. Who was the leading scorer for the season?

89. **Which player was Blackburn's leading scorer for the season?**

90. In which position did Liverpool end a season in which they were criticised for their tactics?

---

76. Blackburn 77. **Six** 78. Liverpool 79. **Sheffield Wednesday 1 Arsenal 0**
80. Matthew Le Tissier 81. **Ian Wright** 82. Middlesbrough 83. **Tottenham
Hotspur** 84. Ian Rush 85. **Leeds** 86. Ten points 87. **Vinnie Jones** 88. Teddy
Sheringham 89. **Mike Newell** 90. Sixty

 Quiz 3   The Charity Shield

1. **Which goalkeeper scored in the 1967 Charity Shield?**

2. Which goalkeeper was beaten by Jennings' huge kick?

3. **Which teams were involved in that game and how did it finish?**

4. What is the highest number of goals scored in a season's competition?

5. **When was it?**

6. When was the first Charity Shield match played at Wembley?

7. **Which teams were involved?**

8. In 1974, two players were sent-off in the Charity Shield. Who were they?

9. **What was so special about that moment?**

10. Who won that ill-tempered match?

11. **When was the first ever Charity Shield?**

12. What was the result?

13. **No Charity Shield has ever finished goalless. True or false?**

14. Why was the 1950 Charity Shield completely different from the other years?

15. **Which club has appeared in the most consecutive Charity Shield's?**

15. **Everton**
United drew 0-0 in 1977 14. A World Cup XI met the Canadian Touring Team
QPR 4-0 in a replay after a 1-1 draw 13. **False - Liverpool and Manchester**
competition 10. Liverpool - on penalties 11. **1908** 12. Manchester United beat
Billy Bremner 9. **It was the first time that a sending-off had occured in the**
Swindon Town 8-4 6. 1974 7. **Liverpool and Leeds** 8. Kevin Keegan and
The score was 3-3. 4. 12 5. **In 1911, when Manchester United beat**
1. **Pat Jennings** 2. Alex Stepney 3. **Tottenham and Manchester United.**

Quiz 3

The Charity Shield

16. What was their record?

17. Which team has won most Charity Shield matches?

18. Who scored a hat-trick for Leeds United in the 1992 Charity Shield?

19. Who scored the only goal in the 1995 Charity Shield between Everton and Blackburn?

20. How many Charity Shield contests have been settled by a penalty shoot-out?

21. How many times has the Charity Shield been shared?

22. When was the last year it was shared?

23. Who was involved?

24. Who scored an overhead kick for Manchester United in the 1994 Charity Shield?

25. When was the first time the trophy was shared?

26. Who were the two teams?

27. What was so different about the Charity Shield matches in 1913 and from 1923 to 1926?

28. Derby County have never won the Charity Shield. True or false?

29. Who were the first London club to win the Charity Shield?

30. What has been the biggest winning margin in Charity Shield's?

16. Four - between 1984 and 1987 17. **Manchester United** 18. Eric Cantona 19. **Vinny Samways** 20. Two - in 1974 and 1993 21. **Eleven** 22. 1991 23. **Arsenal and Tottenham** 24. Paul Ince 25. **1949** 26. Portsmouth and Wolves 27. **A team of amateurs played professionals each year** 28. False - they won it in 1975 29. **Tottenham - in 1921** 30. Five goals - in 1913, 1925, 1968 and 1978

Quiz 4   **Referees**

1. **Which referee was in charge for the 1966 FA Cup final and the 1974 World Cup Final?**

2. Who refereed the 1996 FA Cup final?

3. **Who was the referee for the 1997 Chelsea vs Leicester FA Cup quarter final, decided by a controversial penalty decision?**

4. Who was the referee that sent off five players in the Chesterfield/Plymouth match in the 1996-97 season?

5. **How many Premier League referees were there in the 1996-97 season?**

6. How many 1996-97 English referees are on the FIFA list?

7. **How many referees are on the National List, used in all four English Divisions?**

8. Who was the referee for the 1995 FA Cup final?

9. **Who was in charge for the 1990 World Cup final?**

10. Which referee sent off Kevin Moran in the 1985 FA Cup final?

11. **What was the monstrous name of the Austrian referee that was in charge for two World Cup quali-fiers in 1934 and 1937?**

12. Who was England's only referee in the 1990 World Cup Finals?

13. **Which English referee was in charge for the Third Place Play-Off in Mexico 86?**

14. Who was the Northern Irish referee in the 1986 and 1990 World Cups?

15. **Who was the Scottish referee in the 1982 World Cup Finals?**

1. **Jack Taylor** 2. Dermot Gallacher 3. **Mike Reed** 4. Andrew D'Urso 5. 19
6. 8 7. 69 8. Gerald Ashby 9. **Mr Codesal (Mexico)** 10. Peter Willis
11. **Herr Frankenstein** 12. George Courtney 13. **George Courtney**
14. Mr Snoddy 15. **Mr Valentine**

 **Quiz 4**   **Referees**

16. Who was the English referee at the 1982 World Cup Finals?

17. **Who was the referee that refused to allow Brazil's injury time winner in their 1978 World Cup match against Sweden?**

18. Who refereed the 1994 World Cup Final?

19. **Who was the English referee that was in charge for the Third Place Play Play Off in the 1966 World Cup Finals?**

20. Which World Cup Final did England's Mr Ling referee?

21. **Who was the referee for the 1994 FA Cup final?**

22. Who refereed the 1995-96 League Cup final?

23. **Who was the high profile referee that retired after his match at Crystal Palace in April 1995?**

24. Who was the referee for England's semi-final in Euro 96?

25. **Who was the Scottish referee for the France/Czech Republic semi-final in Euro 96?**

26. Who refereed the Euro 96 final?

27. **What nationality was the referee for England's 4-1 win over Holland in Euro 96?**

28. Who refereed the 1994-95 Coca Cola Cup final?

29. **Who refereed the 1995 Chairty Shield when Everton beat Blackburn1-0?**

30. How much does a referee earn for a 1996-97 Premiership match?

16. Mr White 17. **Clive Thomas** 18. Sandor Puhl 19. **Mr Dagnall** 20. 1954
21. **David Elleray** 22. Robbie Hart 23. **Philip Don** 24. Sandor Puhl
25. **Mr L Mottram** 26. Pierluigi Pairetto 27. **Austrian** 28. Philip Don
29. **Dermot Gallacher** 30. #350

 Quiz **5** The Carling Premiership 1993-94

1. **Who scored a hat-trick on the opening day of the season in the game between Arsenal and Coventry?**

2. Who scored a rare brace when Liverpool met Sheffield Wednesday on the opening day of the season?

3. **Which two future teammates scored when Manchester United drew 1-1 with Newcastle United in August?**

4. Who scored a hat-trick for Everton in August as they beat Sheffield United 4-2?

5. **Which club brought to an end Liverpool's run of four wins at the start of the season?**

6. Against which club did Swindon win their first point of the season?

7. **Who sat at the top of the Premiership after five games?**

8. Which £750,000 signing from Oldham scored four goals in his first five games at his new club?

9. **Which new signing scored a brace for Manchester United when they beat Sheffield United in August?**

10. How many goals did Swindon concede in their first four matches?

11. **Who scored Sheffield Wednesday's first goal of the season, in their fifth game?**

12. Who was sent off for the first time in his career when Coventry beat Liverpool in September?

13. **Who hit a hat-trick for Arsenal when they beat Ipswich 4-0 in September?**

14. Which two players scored three goals in two minutes for Tottenham when they beat Oldham 5-0 in September?

15. **Which two Liverpool players had a heated argument during their derby game with Everton in September?**

Quiz 5

The Carling Premiership 1993-94

16. Whose goal decided the top-of-the-table clash between Liverpool and Arsenal in September?

17. **Which striker, who would later gain fame at a London club, scored four goals for Norwich at Everton in September?**

18. Which Dutchman was sent off within 24 minutes of his West Ham debut in September?

19. **Who scored the first of many goals for Liverpool in their 2-1 victory over Oldham in October?**

20. Just 3,039 turned up to watch Wimbledon on Boxing Day in 1993. Who were they playing?

21. **Which Leeds striker finished with 17 goals in 1993-94?**

22. Which striker went missing when he complained he was homesick for his friends and family in London?

23. **Which team had scored just once in six Premiership games going into November?**

24. Which club recorded six successive League defeats, their worst run since 1941, to leave them in the bottom three in November?

25. **Which two internationals scored braces in the Manchester derby in November?**

26. Which Ipswich player celebrated his 600th appearance for the club in a 2-2 draw with Swindon in November?

27. **Which Hammer scored in their 2-0 win over Oldham in November at the grand old age of 35?**

28. Who scored his first Premiership hat-trick for QPR in their win at Goodison Park in November?

29. **Which striker made it 15 goals in 16 League games when he hit a hat-trick against Liverpool in November?**

30. Which team did Swindon beat for thier first win of the season in November?

---

16. Eric Cantona 17. **Efan Ekoku** 18. Jeroen Boere 19. **Robbie Fowler**
20. Everton 21. **Rod Wallace** 22. Andy Cole 23. **Arsenal** 24. Chelsea
25. **Niall Quinn and Eric Cantona** 26. John Wark 27. **Alvin Martin**
28. Bradley Allen 29. **Andy Cole** 30. QPR

Quiz 5

The Carling Premiership 1993-94

31. Which player clashed with John Fashanu and fractured his cheekbone in November?

32. Who did David Seaman foul to receive the red card when Arsenal met West Ham in November?

33. Which Leeds striker scored his fourth goal in five games when they beat Manchester City 3-2 in December?

34. Which team did Coventry beat in December for Phil Neal's first victory as manager?

35. What was the score in the North London derby at Highbury in December?

36. By how many points were Manchester United leading on December 7?

37. Who scored a well-taken own goal to salvage a point for Sheffield Wednesday at Aston Villa in December?

38. Which two QPR players were sent off when they were beaten 3-2 by Liverpool in December?

39. Which Liverpool defender scored four minutes from the whistle to save them from a home defeat against lowly Swindon in December?

40. How many years separate the birthdates of Robbie Fowler and Mickey Hazard, two scorers in the Tottenham v Liverpool game in December?

41. Who scored the own goal which started Sheffield Wednesday's five-goal rout over West Ham in December?

42. Which club was only one point ahead of bottom-placed Swindon in December?

43. Who scored a hat-trick for Arsenal in their 4-0 win at Swindon in December?

44. Who scored for Liverpool against Wimbledon in December, a year before joining the Reds?

45. Who scored a rare brace for Swindon as they recorded a 3-3 draw at Sheffield Wednesday?

Maskell

41. Mike Marsh 42. Chelsea 43. **Kevin Campbell** 44. John Scales 45. **Craig**
15 37. **Shaun Teale** 38. Simon Barker and Les Ferdinand 39. **Mark Wright** 40. 15
31. **Gary Mabbutt** 32. Trevor Morley 33. **Brian Deane** 34. Arsenal 35. 1-1 36.

 **Quiz 5**   The Carling
Premiership 1993-94

46. Which Southampton player was sent off for elbowing Norwich's Ruel Fox on New Year's Day?

47. **Who were Manchester City leading 2-0 when play was abandoned on New Year's Day?**

48. Which Chelsea player scored his first senior goal when they beat Everton 4-2 on New Years' Day?

49. **Who scored a brace for Liverpool when they clawed their way back from 3-0 down against Manchester United in January?**

50. Which Owl scored his 12th goal of the season to silence Tottenham in January?

51. **Who scored a hat-trick for Everton when they recorded a rare victory, a 6-2 win over Swindon in January?**

52. With which team did Wimbledon have a on-pitch brawl with in January?

53. **Who was stunned by a 2-1 defeat at Swindon in January?**

54. In January a minute's silence was observed at all grounds after the death of which legendary figure?

55. **Which two players had both scored 23 Premiership goals by January 23?**

56. Who headed home the equaliser for West Ham against Norwich in January, only seconds after coming on as a substitute?

57. **Which much-touted striker scored his only goal for Everton in a 4-2 victory over Chelsea in February?**

58. Who hit a hat-trick for Swindon when they beat Coventry in February?

59. **When Villa put five past Swindon in February, who netted a hat-trick?**

60. Who was Newcastle captain for the day when they were beaten 4-2 by Wimbledon at Selhurst Park?

 **Quiz 5** The Carling
Premiership 1993-94

61. Southampton's hat-trick man when they beat Liverpool 4-2 in February was which international?

62. Which Blackburn defender scored their only goal when they triumphed over Newcastle in February?

63. Who scored Norwich's late equaliser to deny Swindon their fifth win of the season in February?

64. Who did John Polston wrestle to the ground to receive his red card when Norwich drew with Blackburn in February?

65. Who returned from injury to complete a hat-trick as Newcastle met Coventry in February?

66. Whose goal gave Arsenal their first victory in six League games when they played Blackburn in February?

67. Which Swindon player ensured that his team were rooted to the bottom when he scored an own goal in their game at Maine Road in February?

68. Which Spurs defender brought down Gavin Peacock to give Chelsea a last-minute penalty and equaliser in February?

69. Who saved two penalties when Aston Villa and Spurs met in February?

70. Manchester United's first home defeat in 17 months was inflicted by which team?

71. Whose injury-time equaliser salvaged a point for Tottenham when they played Sheffield United in February?

72. How many goals did Newcastle score when they faced bottom-placed Swindon in February?

73. Who was second in the Premiership at the start of March?

74. Who missed two months of action with a broken leg but returned to score in the Merseyside derby in March?

75. Which Chelsea player scored for both teams when they met Liverpool in March?

 **Quiz 5** The Carling Premiership 1993-94

76. Which two players were on the scoresheet when Arsenal beat Southampton 4-0 at the Dell in March?

77. **Which Manchester United player scored an own goal when they travelled to Highbury in March?**

78. Which father and son met when Everton played Tottenham in March?

79. **Who beat Southampton in March to climb out of the relegation spot and leave the Saints in their place?**

80. Who scored a goal on his debut for Manchester City, after being signed two minutes before the transfer deadline?

81. **Which Norwegian international scored a brace at Anfield to give Sheffield United hope of avoiding relegation?**

82. Who scored the goals in Blackburn's top-of-the-table clash with Manchester United in April?

83. **Which two McCarthys scored for Oldham when they beat QPR in March?**

84. How many goals were scored when Norwich met Southampton in April?

85. **Who beat Blackburn to prevent them going top of the table in April?**

86. Whose late equaliser for QPR left Blackburn two points behind Manchester United with two games to play?

87. **Who scored two goals for Sheffield United as they beat Newcastle in April, climbing out of the relegation zone?**

88. Who beat Blackburn to end their last hopes of winning the Premiership?

89. **Who scored the goal which ensured Everton's survival in the last game of the season?**

90. Who beat Sheffield United to condemn them to relegation in their last game of the season?

Quiz 6 The European Championship

1. **In which year was the first final held?**

2. The USSR were awarded a walkover into the semi-finals in the 1960 championships. Why?

3. **Which stadium hosted the first final, attracting only 17,966 spectators?**

4. How many teams entered the first championships?

5. **Which Dane was the top scorer in the 1964 Championship with 11 goals?**

6. Which was the first tournament entered by England?

7. **Why did Greece refuse to play Albania in 1964, giving the Albanians a walkover into the second round?**

8. In which city did England play their first European game v France?

9. **The home leg v France in 1962 was which English manager's last game in charge?**

10. Which manager took over the reins for the second leg, which England lost 5-2?

THE AMAZING...
FOOTBALLING MINNOW!

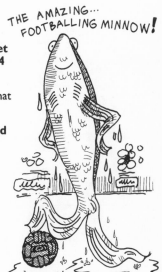

11. **Which team did Northern Ireland upset to go into the second round of the 1964 competition?**

12. Which future N.Ireland manager scored in that game?

13. **Which legendary Soviet goalkeeper and European Footballer of the Year saved a penalty to help them beat Italy in the 1964 championships?**

14. Which footballing minnow put Holland out of the 1964 competition, despite electing to play both legs in Holland?

15. **Which Swede played his 80th international in the second round tie they eventually lost to the Soviets?**

 Quiz 6 — The European Championship

16. A crowd of over 100,000 saw Spain beat which country in the 1964 final?

17. **Which legendary Italian topped the scoring charts for the 1968 championships?**

18. Which player scored the winning goal for Republic of Ireland v Czechoslovakia in the 1968 qualifying competition, only days after breaking through to the Fulham first team?

19. **Which future Wimbledon manager played in that campaign for the Republic of Ireland?**

20. Which team did West Germany meet in the game billed as the 'Match of the Year' in the 1968 qualifying competition?

21. **Which country held West Germany to a 0-0 draw in 1968 to ensure that the World Cup finalists did not qualify for the European quarter-finals?**

22. Which Celtic veteran made his international debut at the age of 36 at Wembley v England in Scotland's qualifying game for the 1968 championship?

23. **Which Northern Ireland player put paid to Scotland's hopes of qualifying for the 1968 tournament?**

24. The biggest-ever European Championship crowd of 134,000 were attracted to which venue?

25. **Which English player limped off with a broken toe v Scotland, but came back on to score in the qualifying for the 1968 tournament?**

26. By which unusual method did Italy progress to the 1968 final?

27. **Who became the first English player to be sent off in an international when he was red-carded in the 1968 semi-final?**

28. Who were England's two scorers when they beat the Soviet Union in the 1968 third-place play-off?

29. **Which team won the 1968 championships in front of a home crowd?**

30. Which German topped the 1972 scoring charts with 11, and was the undoubted star of the tournament?

16. Soviet Union 17. **Luigi Riva** 18. Turloch O'Connor 19. **Joe Kinnear** 20. Czechoslavakia 21. **Albania** 22. Ronnie Simpson 23. **George Best** 24. Hampden Park (Scotland v England in 1968) 25. **Jackie Charlton** 26. They beat the Soviet Union on the toss of a coin 27. **Alan Mullery** 28. Bobby Charlton and Geoff Hurst 29. **Italy** 30. Gerd Muller

 Quiz 6   The European Championship

31. **Which country's World Cup squad was hit by a series of bans for alleged 'commercial activities', leaving them with a decimated 1972 European Championship team?**

32. Who scored England's equaliser at Wembley v Switzerland to help them into the 1972 finals?

33. **Which British team lost all their away games and won all their home games while trying to qualify for the 1972 finals?**

34. Who was the goalkeeper who helped West Germany scrape into the 1972 quarter-finals after only drawing in Turkey?

35. **Who scored the only English goal in their 1972 quarter-final defeat by West Germany?**

36. Which country hosted the final stages of the 1972 tournament?

37. **Who reached their third final in four attempts in 1972, losing to West Germany?**

38. Which Irish player topped the scoring charts for the 1976 European Championships, although his country failed to qualify for the quarter-finals?

39. **Which manager was in charge of England's campaign to qualify for the 1976 finals?**

40. Who scored all five goals when England beat Cyprus at Wembley while trying to qualify for the 1976 European Championships?

41. **Which England player scored against Czechoslovakia in a game which ended 2-1 and effectively ended their chances of qualifying for the 1976 competition?**

42. Who were the only team to beat Wales in their qualification for the 1976 quarter-finals?

43. **Who was the Welsh manager who led them to their first European quarter-final?**

44. Which 34-year-old Wrexham player was the Welsh hero when he scored the winner against Austria to ensure their qualification for the 1976 quarter-finals?

45. **Who was the Scottish keeper for the 1976 campaign, which ended at the group stages?**

 **Quiz 6**   The European
Championship

46. Who was Ireland's player-manager for their 1976 campaign, which also ended at the group stages?

47. **When the Republic of Ireland travelled to Russia in 1975 which club side was playing as the Soviet national team?**

48. Which team embarrassed East Germany with a 2-1 win, winning their first game in the history of the competition in the group stages of the 1976 competition?

49. **The quarter-final between Wales and Yugoslavia in 1976 was almost abandoned. Why?**

50. The 1976 final was the first to be decided by penalties. Who were the two teams involved?

51. **Who was the only player to miss in the 1976 penalty shoot-out?**

52. Which English player top-scored in the 1980 campaign with seven goals?

53. **Which country was chosen to host the 1980 finals?**

54. What was the final result in the first-ever meeting between the Republic and Northern Ireland in the qualifying for the 1980 championships?

55. **Who were the only team to take a point from England in the 1980 qualifying stage?**

56. Which England player was substituted in their game v Bulgaria in 1979 after scoring and then clashing with Grancharov?

57. **Who scored from the penalty spot to give Scotland a win over Norway in the 1980 qualifying tournament?**

58. Who scored Scotland's only goal when they were trounced 3-1 by Belgium in the 1980 group stages?

59. **Which country was the surprise package of the 1980 qualifying tournament, reaching the finals despite failing to win away from home?**

60. Which Welsh player was sent off against Turkey in 1979 after breaking the cheekbone of Mustapha I, who was duly taken off to be replaced by Mustapha II?

46. Johnny Giles 47. **Dynamo Kiev** 48. Iceland 49. **The Yugoslav keeper Maric was hit by a beer can thrown by a Welsh fan** 50. Czechoslovakia and West Germany 51. **Uli Hoeness** 52. Kevin Keegan 53. **Italy** 54. 0-0 55. **Republic of Ireland** 56. Peter Barnes 57. **Archie Gemmill** 58. John Robertson 59. **Greece** 60. Byron Stevenson

 **Quiz 6**

The European Championship

61. **Who was the unlikely hat-trick hero when West Germany beat Holland in the 1980 finals?**

62. Who were England's opponents in the 1980 finals when the Italian police used tear gas to disperse rioting fans?

63. **Who had a 'goal' disallowed in that 1-1 draw?**

64. Who scored the only goal for Italy in their victory over England in the 1980 tournament?

65. **Whose ineffective tackle allowed Graziani to cross for the goal?**

66. Who scored a brace in the 1980 final to give West Germany victory?

67. **Who were their opponents?**

68. Which French genius was the star of the 1984 tournament and finished as top scorer?

69. **Which country hosted the 1984 finals?**

70. Which West Ham player scored for Belgium in their 1983 qualifying game against East Germany?

71. **Who scored Scotland's two goals when they beat East Germany for their only victory of the group stages for the 1984 tournament?**

72. Who scored England's two goals in the opening game of their 1984 qualifying campaign against Denmark?

73. **Who scored the last-minute equaliser for Denmark to make the score 2-2?**

74. Which team did England beat 3-0 for Bobby Robson's first victory as manager?

75. **Who scored a hat-trick in his first appearance on the England starting line-up when they beat Luxembourg 9-0 at Wembley in 1983?**

 Quiz 6   **The European Championship**

76. Who handled the ball in England's crunch tie with Denmark at Wembley in Dec 1983, giving away a penalty?

77. Who stepped up to score the penalty and put an end to England's hopes of qualifying?

78. Wales could have qualified for the 1984 finals had they beaten Yugoslavia in Cardiff. Who scored the Welsh goal in the 1-1 draw?

79. Which Northern Ireland player scored the only goal in their historic home victory over West Germany in 1982?

80. Which Northern Ireland player won his 100th cap against Austria in a European Championship game in 1983?

81. Which Manchester United player scored his first international goal in the same game?

82. Which team qualified for the 1984 finals with a 12-1 win over Malta, prompting claims of match-fixing as they had to win by 11 clear goals?

83. Which team failed to qualify for the finals because of that freak result?

84. Which future Charlton Athletic player broke his leg in the opening game of the 1984 finals?

85. Which French defender headbutted Jesper Olsen, getting himself sent off and suspended for the next three games?

86. Which 18-year-old Belgian orchestrated their victory over Yugoslavia in the 1984 finals?

87. Platini scored two hat-tricks in the 1984 finals. Which teams were on the receiving end of his stunning displays?

88. Which veteran Portuguese striker scored on his record 65th international appearance v Romania, taking them through to the 1984 semi-finals?

89. Whose 119th-minute cross set up Platini for the semi-final winner over Portugal in 1984?

90. Who was the Spanish goalkeeper and captain who dropped the ball over the line from a Platini free-kick in the final?

89. **Jean Tigana** 90. Luis Arconada

85. **Manuel Amoros** 86. Enzo Scifo 87. **Belgium and Yugoslavia** 88. Nene

Jennings 81. **Norman Whiteside** 82. Spain 83. **Holland** 84. Allan Simonsen

76. Phil Neal 77. **Allan Simonsen** 78. Robbie James 79. **Norman Whiteside** 80. Pat

 Quiz 6 — The European Championship

91. **Which country was selected as the venue for the 1988 finals?**

92. Who were the only team to take a point from England in their qualification for the 1988 finals?

93. **How many goals did Gary Lineker score in England's six qualifying games?**

94. How many goals did England put past Turkey at Wembley in 1987?

95. **Which two players scored the only goals of Northern Ireland's unsuccessful qualifying campaign for the 1988 finals?**

96. The 8-0 victory by Holland over Cyprus in the 1988 qualifying competition was declared void. Why?

97. **Which Welsh player was refused permission to play against Denmark in the 1988 qualifying by his Italian bosses?**

98. Who scored the winning goal for Wales in that game in Cardiff?

99. **Which veteran Republic of Ireland defender was controversially picked for their 1988 qualifying game v Scotland and silenced the critics with a winning goal?**

100. Which Scottish player ensured the Republic of Ireland's qualification for the 1988 finals when his late goal took both points against Bulgaria?

101. **Which English referee took control of the opening match of the 1988 finals when Italy drew with West Germany?**

102. Which Italian scored his first international goal in that game?

103. **Who was the Italian goalkeeper whose extra steps were penalised, leading to the West German equaliser?**

104. Which Spaniard's clearly offside goal helped them to victory over Denmark in their first match of the 1988 finals?

105. **Which future Premiership stars scored for West Germany and Italy respectively in that 1988 tournament?**

Burragueno **105.** Jurgen Klinsmann and Gianluca Vialli
101. Keith Hackett 102. Robert Mancini **103. Walter Zenga** 104. Emilio
97. Ian Rush 98. Mark Hughes **99. Mark Lawrenson** 100. Gary Mackay
Dutch fans. The game was replayed behind closed doors and Holland won 4-0
Jimmy Quinn 96. The Cypriot keper was injured by a smokebomb thrown by
91. West Germany 92. Turkey 93. **Five** 94. Eight 95. **Colin Clarke and**

 **Quiz 6** The European Championship

106. Which German scored his first and second international goals in their win over Spain in the 1988 finals?

107. Who was the Danish goalkeeper who had a nightmare game against Italy in 1988, gifting them a 2-0 victory when they only required a draw to qualify for the semi-finals?

108. Who was the manager of West Germany in 1988?

109. Whose goal gave the Republic of Ireland victory over England in their clash in the 1988 finals?

110. Who was the England keeper beaten by that goal?

111. That game almost turned around because of a timely England substitution. Who replaced Neil Webb?

112. When Holland and England met in the 1988 finals, which Dutch striker scored a hat-trick to end England's semi-final hopes?

113. Which player scored the only England goal in that game?

114. Who was Ireland's manager who almost took them into the 1988 semi-finals?

115. Whose superb volley gave the Republic the lead in their game v the Soviet Union in 1988?

116. What was the result in the game between the Soviet Union and England which sealed England's nightmare 1988 tournament?

117. Ireland needed only a draw against Holland to reach the semi-finals. Which Dutch player came on as a substitute to score a late goal and spoil the party?

118. Who presented Peter Shilton with a bouquet of flowers for his 100th cap in the 1988 finals?

119. Holland met West Germany in the 1988 semi-finals. When was the last time that Holland had beaten the Germans?

120. Which German player suffered stomach pains in the warm-up to that Holland semi-final and so had to be replaced for that game?

Quiz 6 — The European Championship

121. **Who tripped Klinsmann to give West Germany a penalty in their semi-final?**

122. Who stepped up to score the semi-final penalty for West Germany in the 1988 finals?

123. **Which German player tripped Marco Van Basten to give Holland a penalty?**

124. Who was the German keeper, later to play in the Premiership, who was beaten by Ronald Koeman's penalty?

125. **Whose pass set up Van Basten for his winner against West Germany in the 1988 semi-finals?**

126. How many Soviet players had been booked going into their semi-final clash with Italy in 1988?

127. **Who scored the Soviet Union's second goal to send them into the 1988 final?**

128. Who scored the first Dutch goal in the 1988 finals between Holland and the Soviet Union?

129. **Whose cross set up Van Basten for the 1988 final's second goal?**

130. In which city was the 1988 final held?

131. **Who was the manager of the winning Dutch team?**

132. Which Danish player featured in the 1988 tournament at the age of 38?

133. **Which French striker finished the 1992 tournament as the top scorer in the campaign with 11 goals?**

134. Which country was selected as hosts for the 1992 finals?

135. **Which team were delayed en route to their qualifying game in Reykjavik in 1990, held at Heathrow for alleged shoplifting offences?**

121. **Frank Rijkaard** 122. Lothar Matthaus 123. **Jurgen Kohler** 124. Eike Immel
125. **Jan Wouters** 126. Seven 127. **Oleg Protasov** 128. Ruud Gullit
129. **Arnold Muhren** 130. Munich 131. **Rinus Michels** 132. Morten Olsen
133. **Jean-Pierre Papin** 134. Sweden 135. **Albania**

 **Quiz 6**   **The European Championship**

136. Which ex-Nottingham Forest player helped Iceland to a historic qualifying win over Spain?

137. Which Scottish player scored the winner against Romania at Hampden Park to begin their successful qualifying campaign for the 1992 tournament?

138. What was the score when Scotland met Bulgaria in Sofia while trying to qualify for the 1992 championships?

139. Which player was penalised for handling the ball in his own area when the Scots travelled to Romania for their qualifier?

140. How many goals did Scotland score in their two ties with San Marino in the 1992 qualification campaign?

141. Which team qualified for the 1992 tournament ahead of Italy?

142. Which country did the Faroe Islands beat in their first ever European Championship game?

143. Brian Laudrup pulled out of the Danish international team after disagreements with their manager. Who was he?

144. The Danes finished second in their qualifying group but made it to the finals. Why?

145. What score was Northern Ireland's home fixture against the Faroe Islands?

146. Who scored his first international goal for two years when Wales met Belgium at Cardiff Arms Park for their qualifier in 1990?

147. Which Welsh player was sent off against Luxembourg in the same qualifying series?

148. Who was the scorer when Wales pulled off a magnificent victory over Germany in 1991?

149. Who were the only team to take a point from Holland in their qualification for the 1992 championships?

150. Who was the England manager when they began their campaign to qualify for the 1992 tournament?

---

136. Toddy Orlygsson 137. **Ally McCoist** 138. 1-1 139. **Gordon Durie** 140. Six 141. **Soviet Union** 142. Austria 143. **Richard Moller-Nielsen** 144. Yugoslavia disqualified because of civil war 145. 1-1 146. Ian Rush 147. **Clayton Blackmore** 148. Ian Rush 149. **Finland** 150. Grahan Taylor

 Quiz **6**   **The European Championship**

151. Who scored an Irish hat-trick when they demolished Turkey in 1990?

152. Which controversial figure was dropped for England's visit to the Republic of Ireland in their qualifying game?

153. Who scored the two goals when England met the Republic at Wembley?

154. Whose scrambled goal gave England the points in Turkey to leave them favourites to qualify for 1992?

155. Who scored the goal 13 minutes from the final whistle to earn England a draw against Poland and seal their qualification for the 1992 finals?

156. Who was the French goalkeeper who kept them in the opening game of the 1992 finals against Sweden?

157. Which English player was drafted in at right-back against Denmark because of injuries?

158. Who replaced him late in the game and twice came close to scoring?

159. Which Danish player, later to play in England, beat Chris Woods but hit the post in that game?

160. Which French player headbutted Stuart Pearce in their 1992 Championship game?

161. Which English player cleared off the line from an Angloma header in the France v England clash in 1992?

162. Which Swedish player scored their only goal as they beat Denmark in the group stages of the 1992 championships?

163. Who scored England's only goal of the 1992 finals?

164. Who chipped the deciding penalty in the shoot-out to win the 1976 finals for Czechoslovakia?

165. Who replaced Gary Lineker when Graham Taylor substituted him in their final 1992 game against Sweden?

Quiz 6 — The European Championship

166. In which minute did Brolin score the winner in that game?

167. **Who scored the winner for Denmark against France, sealing their move into the 1992 semi-finals?**

168. Which future Premiership star scored the only goal when Holland met Scotland in the group stages of the 1992 finals?

169. **Which German played on until half-time against the CIS despite suffering a broken arm after 20 minutes in 1992?**

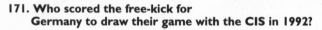

170. Whose last-minute 'fall' earned Germany a free-kick and the equaliser against the CIS in the 1992 finals?

171. **Who scored the free-kick for Germany to draw their game with the CIS in 1992?**

172. Who was the Scotland manager who guided them in the 1992 finals?

173. **Who scored Germany's first goal in their 2-0 win over Scotland in 1992?**

174. Which Scottish defender deflected Stefan Effenberg's cross into his own net for the second German goal in 1992?

175. **Which German player came on as a substitute against Scotland in 1992 but went off five minutes later after clashing heads with Stuart McCall?**

176. Which future Premiership keeper played in the 1992 finals for the CIS?

177. **What was the score in the 1992 clash between Holland and Germany?**

178. Who scored his first international goal in Scotland's 3-0 win over the CIS in 1992?

179. **Who was brought down for a penalty in Scotland's 3-0 victory over the CIS in 1992?**

180. Who was Germany's keeper in their semi-final tie with Sweden in 1992?

166. 82nd 167. **Johnny Elstrup** 168. Dennis Bergkamp 169. **Rudi Voller** 170. Jurgen Klinsmann 171. **Thomas Hassler** 172. Andy Roxburgh 173. **Karl Heinz Riedle** 174. Maurice Malpas 175. **Stefan Reuter** 176. Dmitri Kharine 177. 3-1 178. Brian McClair 179. **Pat Nevin** 180. Bodo Illgner

 ## Quiz 6 — The European Championship

181. Which lofty striker scored Sweden's final goal of the 1992 championships?

182. Who scored a brace for Germany in their semi-final clash with Sweden in 1992?

183. Who scored a brace for Denmark in their semi-final game against Holland in 1992?

184. Which Danish player suffered an horrific knee injury in their clash with Holland in the 1992 semi-finals?

185. Who scored Holland's 85th-minute equaliser in their semi-final with Denmark in 1992?

186. In the penalty shoot-out to decide the semi-final between Holland and Denmark in 1992, who was the only man to miss?

187. In which city was the final of the 1992 championships held?

188. Which future Premiership player scored in the 1992 final between Denmark and Germany?

189. Which was the only team not to play a qualifying game for the 1996 Championship?

190. Which two Premiership players scored in Romania's win over Azerbaijan in the qualifying tournament for Euro 96?

191. Which three countries reached the finals for the first time in 1996?

192. Which player topped the scoring charts for the European qualifying rounds with 12 goals?

193. Who were the only nation to beat Italy in their qualification for the 1996 Championship?

194. In which English city did Holland play the Republic of Ireland for the final place in Euro 96?

195. Who scored the winner when Northern Ireland beat Austria in Vienna in the qualification stages of Euro 96?

---

181. Kennet Andersson 182. Karl Heinz Riedle **183. Henrik Larsen** 184. Henrik Andersen **185. Frank Rijkaard** 186. Marco Van Basten **187. Gothenburg** 188. John Jensen **189. England** 190. Dan Petrescu and Florin Raducioiu **191. Turkey, Switzerland and Croatia** 192. Davor Suker **193. Croatia** 194. Liverpool **195. Phil Gray**

 **Quiz 6** The European Championship

196. Who scored for the Welsh in Dusseldorf when thay pulled off a draw against Germany in their unsuccessful qualifying campaign for Euro 96?

197. Which two players topped the Scottish scoring charts in their qualifying campaign for Euro 96?

198. Who scored the opening goal of Euro 96?

199. Which Swiss player equalised with a penalty against England in 1996?

200. Who provided the pass for England's opening goal of Euro 96?

201. Who captained the England team for their first game of Euro 96?

202. Which three Glasgow Rangers' players scored goals in the 1996 championships?

203. At which ground did Scotland eke out a draw with Holland in the 1996 tournament?

204. Holland appealed for a penalty in their Euro 96 tie with Scotland, claiming handball. Which player was accused?

205. Which player was judged to have fouled Gordon Durie to earn Scotland their penalty against England in 1996?

206. Whose penalty did David Seaman save in the 1996 clash between England and Scotland?

207. Which Scottish defender did Paul Gascoigne beat for the second goal of their 2-0 victory in 1996?

208. Which player came on at half-time as a substitute for Stuart Pearce against Scotland in 1996 but was later replaced by Sol Campbell when he picked up an injury?

209. Who came on to score the only Dutch goal against England in 1996, sealing their move through to the quarter-finals and knocking out Scotland?

210. Alan Shearer scored two goals against Holland in Euro 96. Who scored the other two in their 4-1 victory?

196. Dean Saunders. **197. John Collins and Scott Booth** 198. Alan Shearer **199. Kublilay Turkyilmaz** 200. Paul Ince **201. Tony Adams** 202. Brian Laudrup, Ally McCoist and Paul Gascoigne **203. Villa Park** 204. John Collins **205. Tony Adams** 206. Gary McAllister **207. Colin Hendry** 208. Jamie Redknapp **209. Patrick Kluivert** 210. **Teddy** Sheringham

 **Quiz 6**   The European Championship

211. **Who scored Scotland's only goal of the 1996 championships?**

212. Which two players were sent off in the 1996 game between Spain and Bulgaria?

213. **At which ground did France beat Romania 1-0 in Euro 96?**

214. Who was the only man to score for Bulgaria in the 1996 championships?

215. **What was the final score between France and Spain when they met in Euro 96?**

216. Who scored Spain's winner against Romania to take them through to the 1996 quarter-finals?

217. **Who was Germany's impressive full-back who scored against the Czech Republic in the group stages of Euro 96?**

218. Who netted a brace for Italy against Russia in Euro 96, but was dropped from the starting line-up for the next game?

219. **Who was the Italian manager whose tactical mistakes saw his team fail to qualify for the 1996 quarter-finals?**

220. Which two teams did not win a single point in the 1996 championships?

221. **What was the score in the 1996 tie between Croatia and Portugal?**

222. Which England player was booked in their quarter-final clash with Spain in 1996, ruling him out of the semi-finals?

223. **Which Spaniard's penalty hit the bar in their quarter-final clash with England in 1996?**

224. Whose penalty did David Seaman save in England's quarter-final clash in 1996?

225. **Who was the French goalkeeper who saved a penalty to take his team through to the 1996 semi-finals?**

211. **Ally McCoist** 212. Juan Antonio Pizzi and Petar Hubchev 213. **St. James' Park** 214. Hristo Stoichkov 215. 1-1 216. Guillermo Amor 217. **Christian Ziege** 218. Pierluigi Casiraghi 219. **Arrigo Sacchi** 220. Turkey and Romania 221. **Croatia 0 Portugal 3** 222. Gary Neville 223. **Fernando Hierro** 224. Miguel Nadal 225. **Bernard Lama**

 **Quiz 6**   The European
Championship

226. Which Croat player, who would later become familiar to Premiership spectators, was sent off in their quarter-final against Germany in 1996?

227. Which future Premiership player handled the ball to give Germany a penalty in their 1996 quarter-final against Croatia?

228. Who scored the Czech Republic's winner against Portugal in the 1996 quarter-finals?

229. Which English referee took part in Euro 96?

230. Who scored Germany's equaliser in their Euro 96 semi-final with England?

231. Which English player hit the post in their 1996 semi-final defeat at the hands of Germany?

232. Who was the German keeper who saved Gareth Southgate's penalty in the 1996 semi-final penalty shoot-out?

233. Who converted Germany's final penalty to take them through to the 1996 final?

234. Which French player's penalty was saved in the 1996 shoot-out against the Czech Republic?

235. Who scored the deciding penalty in the semi-final tie between the Czech Republic and France in 1996?

236. What was the attendance for the Euro 96 final at Wembley?

237. Who brought down Patrick Berger in the 1996 final for the Czech penalty?

238. Which German striker scored twice in the Euro 96 final?

239. Which team finished the 1996 tournament top of the Fair Play charts?

240. Which two countries have been chosen as hosts for the 2000 European Championships?

226. Igor Stimac 227. **Nikola Jerkan** 228. Karel Poborsky 229. **David Elleray** 230. Stefan Kuntz 231. **Darren Anderton** 232. Andreas Kopke 233. **Andreas Moller** 234. Reynald Pedros 235. **Miroslav Kadlec** 236. 73,611 237. **Matthias Sammer** 238. Oliver Bierhoff 239. **England** 240. Holland and Belgium

Quiz 7 — F. A. Cup

1. **Who won the first FA Cup in 1871-72?**

2. Where was that game played?

3. **Who beat Derby County 6-0 to record the biggest FA Cup Final win?**

4. Which player has scored the most FA Cup goals this century?

5. **Who has made the most FA Cup appearances?**

6. Who is the youngest player to play in an FA Cup Final at Wembley?

7. **Name the youngest scorer in an FA Cup Final.**

8. Who is the oldest scorer in an FA Cup Final?

9. **Who is the youngest FA Cup Final captain?**

10. Who became the oldest player in the FA Cup, almost 20 years after scoring the winning goal for Manchester City in the Final?

11. **Who is the oldest player to play in an FA Cup Final?**

12. Who holds the record for most FA Cup wins?

13. **Who were the last team outside the top division to play in the FA Cup Final?**

14. Which was the only club to be relegated from the top flight after appearing in an FA Cup Final during the 1980's?

15. **Which team appeared in three successive finals in the 1990's?**

1. **The Wanderers** 2. The Kennington Oval 3. **Bury** 4. Ian Rush (Chester, Liverpool) 5. **Ian Callaghan (Liverpool, Swansea, Crewe), 88 matches** 6. Paul Allen (West Ham United, 1980), 17 yrs 256 days 7. **Norman Whiteside (Manchester United, 1983), 18 yrs 19 days** 8. Bert Turner (Charlton Athletic, 1946), 36 yrs 312 days 9. **David Nish (Leicester City, 1969), 21 yrs 7mths** 10. Billy Meredith, 49yrs 8mths 11. **Walter Hampson (Newcastle, 1924), 41 yrs 8mths** 12. Manchester United, nine 13. **Sunderland (1992)** 14. Brighton (1983) 15. **Manchester United (1994, 1995, 1996)**

Quiz 7 — F. A. Cup

16. Which club lost successive Finals in the 1980's?

17. **Which two players have made the most Finals appearances at Wembley (including replays)?**

18. Which Sunderland player tied the record for most loser's medals in 1992?

19. **Who was a winner with different clubs in successive 1970's Finals?**

20. Who played for QPR in the 1982 Final against Tottenham and then for Tottenham in the 1987 Final?

21. **Who scored for different teams in two of the first three Finals of the 1990's?**

22. Who became the only on-loan player to play in the Final, winning with Manchester United in 1990?

23. **Which father and son have both appeared in Final's with Tottenham?**

24. Which Chile international played for Newcastle in the 1951 Final and scored the winning goal for them in the 1952 Final?

25. **Which Belgian-born player made four Final appearances in six years?**

26. Who was the first American to play in a Final?

27. **Name the last three managers to have won the Cup as player and manager of the same club?**

28. Who is the youngest manager of a Cup Final winning team?

29. **Who is the only foreigner to captain his club to a Final win?**

30. Who has scored the most goals in FA Cup Finals?

 **F. A. Cup**

31. Who scored the second fastest FA Cup Final goal at Wembley in 1955?

32. Which Manchester United player made two substitute appearances in Finals while still a teenager?

33. Who is the youngest goalkeeper to play in an FA Cup Final?

34. Who are the only non-English club to win the FA Cup?

35. Who was the last player to score in every round of the FA Cup in the same season?

36. Since the Football League was formed, only one non-league club have won the Cup. Who are they?

37. Who were the last non-league team to beat a side from the top flight?

38. Which six teams have won the FA Cup and League Championship double?

39. Who was the last team to be runners-up in the FA Cup and League Championship in the same year?

40. Which Scottish club reached two FA Cup Finals?

41. Which club entered the 1992-93 FA Cup but went into liquidation before playing a match?

42. When was the last all-London FA Cup Final?

43. When was the first all-Merseyside FA Cup Final?

44. Which two teams played in the first semi-final to be staged at Wembley?

45. Who became the first player to miss a penalty in the Final?

---

31. Jackie Milburn (Newcastle United, 45 seconds) 32. David McCreery (Manchester United, 1976,1977) **33. Peter Shilton (Leicester City, 1969) 34.** Cardiff City (1927) **35. Peter Osgood (Chelsea, 1970) 36.** Tottenham Hotspur of the Southern League (1901) **37. Sutton United (v Coventry, 1989)** **38.** Preston North End (1889), Aston Villa (1897), Tottenham (1961), Arsenal (1971), Liverpool (1986), Manchester United (1994,1996) **39. Everton (1986) 40.** Queen's Park (1884,1885) **41. Maidstone United** 42. 1982 (Tottenham v QPR) **43.** 1986 **(Liverpool v Everton) 44.** Arsenal v Tottenham, 1991 **45. Charlie Wallace (Aston Villa, 1913)**

 **Quiz 7**   **F. A. Cup**

46. Which two international strikers have had their penalty kicks saved in Wembley Cup Finals?

47. And which two goalkeepers saved the kicks?

48. Which goalkeeper broke his neck in the 1956 Cup Final, but carried on playing to get a winners medal?

49. Which club has made the most semi-final appearances?

50. Who was the first player to be sent-off in the Final?

51. Who was the referee?

52. Who was the last man to be sent-off in an FA Cup semi-final?

53. Which four Nationwide League sides have reached three FA Cup semi-finals, and lost all of them?

54. Which two teams contested the lowest-attended semi-final in 1988?

55. Which ground has staged the most FA Cup semi-finals?

56. Which Chelsea player was refused a winners medal in 1970 because he was wearing a Leeds shirt he had exchanged after the whistle and an official believed he played for Leeds?

57. Which striker scored a hat-trick against West Bromwich for non-league Woking in 1991?

58. Which Cup winners are the only club to have beaten top-flight teams in every round?

59. Which Cup Final song reached number three in the charts in 1988?

60. Who were Hereford's scorers when the Southern League side beat Newcastle United 2-1 in a third round replay in 1972?

---

46. Liverpool's John Aldridge (1988), Tottenham's Gary Lineker (1991) **47.** Dave Beasant (Wimbledon, 1988), Mark Crossley (Nott'm. Forest, 1991) **48.** Bert Trautmann (Manchester) **49.** Everton **50.** Kevin Moran (Manchester United, 1985) **51.** Peter Willis **52.** Lee Dixon (Arsenal, 1993) **53.** Millwall, Norwich City, Stoke City, Oldham Athletic **54.** Luton v Wimbledon **55.** Villa Park (45) **56.** David Webb **57.** Tim Buzaglio **58.** Manchester United (1948) **59.** Liverpool's "Anfield Rap" **60.** Ronnie Radford, Ricky George

Quiz 7 — F. A. Cup

61. Who was the scorer when Sunderland beat Leeds in the 1973 Cup Final?

62. Which Wimbledon goalkeeper saved Peter Lorimer's penalty in the fourth round draw with Leeds in 1975?

63. Who played for Manchester United in the Cup Final of 1979 against Arsenal, and then scored against the Londoners for Wrexham in 1992?

64. Which was the first club to win the Cup on three occasions?

65. Who was the first player to score a hat-trick in a Wembley FA Cup Final in 1953?

66. Who became the first player to score in successive FA Cup Finals at Wembley?

67. Who was the first substitute to appear in a Cup Final?

68. Who was the first substitute to score in the Final?

69. Which two substitutes scored twice when they came on in the 1989 Final?

70. Who were the last team to win the Cup with eleven English players?

71. When was the first FA Cup Final played at Wembley?

72. Who was the first person to win the Cup as player and manager of the same club?

73. Which two teams played in the first Wembley FA Cup Final that went to a replay?

74. What was the first Cup Final replay to be played at Wembley?

75. Which was the first Cup Final to produce gate receipts of £1million?

---

61. **Ian Porterfield** 62. Dickie Guy 63. **Mickey Thomas** 64. The Wanderers (1872,1873,1876) 65. **Stan Mortensen (Blackpool)** 66. Bobby Johnstone (Manchester City, 1955,1956) 67. **Derek Clarke (West Bromwich Albion, 1968)** 68. Eddie Kelly (Arsenal, 1971) 69. **Stuart McCall (Everton), Ian Rush (Liverpool)** 70. West Ham (1975) 71. **1923** 72. Stan Seymour (Newcastle, 1924 (player), 1961,1952 (manager) 73. **Chelsea and Leeds, 1970** 74. 1981, Tottenham v Manchester City 75. **1985, Manchester United v Everton**

 **Quiz 7**   F. A. Cup

76. Which two teams contested the first FA Cup tie to be decided on penalties in 1991?

77. **Which two teams became the first Cup Final sides to have the players' names on the back of their shirts?**

78. Who was the first black player to captain a Cup Final side?

79. **And which other black player captained the same side in the replay?**

80. Who was the first Premiership side to win the Cup?

81. **Who scored in Liverpool's 1992 FA Cup Final success and came on as a substitute in the 1996 Final?**

82. Who scored in the Manchester United v Brighton Final in 1983 and then played in the 1987 Final for Tottenham?

83. **Which Wigan player was carried off on a stretcher after 20 minutes of a 1965 first round replay against Doncaster Rovers but returned to the field to score a hat-trick?**

84. Who are the last non-league team to reach the Final?

85. **How many Final appearances have Bristol City made?**

86. Which team won the FA Cup in 1911, only eight years after forming?

87. **When was the last FA Cup Final played outside London?**

88. When was the last time both semi-finals were played at Wembley?

89. **Who were the first winners of the Littlewoods-sponsored FA Cup?**

90. What was the name of the white horse that pushed the crowds back in Wembley's first Cup Final?

Quiz 7 — F. A. Cup

91. Which Nationwide League club are the only founder member of the Football League not to have won the FA Cup?

92. Who were the first Football League club to win the FA Cup in 1889?

93. William Townley was the first player to score a hat-trick in the Cup Final in 1890. But who did he play for?

94. Who became the first non-league team to reach the Final?

95. Who scored the first FA Cup Final goal at Wembley?

96. Which club had to apply for re-election to the Football League, just seven years after winning the Cup?

97. When was the first all-Lancashire FA Cup Final?

98. What year did the Cup Final teams first wear numbers on their shirts?

99. Which two Manchester City players won FA Cup medals in 1934, but were later in the Munich air crash of 1958?

100. Name the referee of the 1934 Final who later became president of FIFA?

101. Which former Liverpool manager played in Preston's 1938 FA Cup winning team?

102. Which team has reached four FA Cup Finals, and have lost all of them?

103. Portsmouth kept the Cup for seven years, but only reached the Final once. How come?

104. Which London club played in successive Finals in the 1940's?

105. Which team came from 3-1 down to beat Bolton 4-3 in the 1953 Final?

91. **Stoke City** 92. Preston North End 93. **Blackburn Rovers** 94. Southampton, 1900 95. **David Jack (Bolton, 1923)** 96. Cardiff City 97. **1926 (Bolton v Manchester City)** 98. 1933 99. **Frank Swift and Sir Matt Busby** 100. Sir Stanley Rous 101. **Bill Shankly** 102. Leicester City 103. **They won in 1939, but the competition was suspended beacues of the Second World War** 104. Charlton Athletic 105. **Blackpool**

Quiz 7   F. A. Cup

106. How many loser's medals did Sir Stanley Matthews collect?

107. Which team scored 37 goals on their way to winning the Cup?

108. Which team won the Cup in the 1940's without playing a home tie?

109. Which non-league side failed to get into the first round just once between 1949 and 1972?

110. Who won the Cup three times in five years in the 1950's?

111. How many FA Cup Final appearances did George Best make?

112. How long did West Ham have to wait to make their second appearance in the Cup Final?

113. Which teams contested a third round tie that went to four replays in 1955?

114. Which goalkeeper broke his jaw after only six minutes in the 1957 Cup Final, but returned later as an outfield player?

115. When was the last of Bolton's FA Cup wins?

116. Who played in goal for Leicester City in the 1961 Cup Final against Tottenham?

117. Who were the last team to win successive FA Cup Finals?

118. Who scored the 100th Cup Final goal at Wembley?

119. Which two sides faced each other in three successive FA Cup ties each year between 1961 and 1963?

120. How many days did it take to play all the third round matches in 1963?

WHEN WAS THAT?

BOLTON WIN F.A. CUP

Daily Blurb

---

106. Two **107. Derby County, 1946** 108. Manchester United **109. Hereford United** 110. Newcastle United, 1951,1952,1955 **111. None** 112. 41 years **113. Stoke City, Derby County** 114. Ray Wood **115. 1958** 116. Gordon Banks **117. Tottenham 1981,1982** 118. Jimmy Robson, Burnley 1962 **119. Tottenham and Burnley** 120. 66 days

Quiz 7   F. A. Cup

121. **Wembley stadium was refurbished for the 1966 World Cup Finals. But which two teams played the first FA Cup Final in the re-built stadium?**

122. Which FA Cup Final scorer's father played with Sir Matt Busby in the Finals of 1933 and 1934?

123. **Which two Manchester United players won the FA Cup in 1963, having been in the losing United sides of 1957 and 1958?**

124. How many Midlands teams won the Cup betwen 1961 and 1997?

125. **Who were the last team to come back from two goals down to win a Cup Final?**

126. Which player, who did not have his name in the official programme, scored twice in the 1966 Final?

127. **Which two former England goalkeepers played in losing Cup Finals for the same club in the 1960's?**

128. Which teams played in the Centenary Final?

129. **Who scored a last-minute penalty to give Arsenal a draw in the 1971 semi-final against Stoke?**

130. Who played in goal for Tottenham in the 1981 Cup Final?

131. **Which player was on the losing side in successive Finals before winning with Leeds in 1972?**

132. Who were the first holders of the Cup to lose a Final at Wembley?

133. **Which Cup Final was played on April 11th to help the England players prepare for the World Cup Finals?**

134. Who scored twice when Colchester United beat Leeds in the fifth round in 1971?

135. **Which team had their names on the back of their tracksuits before the 1961 Cup Final?**

121. **Leicester City and Manchester United,** 1963 122. David Herd. His father was Alec Herd 123. **Bobby Charlton and Bill Foulkes** 124. Two. West Bromwich Albion (1968), Coventry (1987) 125. **Everton,** 1966 126. Mike Trebilcock 127. **Gordon Banks and Peter Shilton** 128. Leeds and Arsenal 129. Peter Storey 130. Milija Aleksic 131. **Allan Clarke, Leicester City (1969),** Leeds (1970) 132. Arsenal (1972) 133. 1970 134. Ray Crawford 135. **Leicester City**

 Quiz 7   F. A. Cup

136. Which two-time FA Cup loser with Leicester City won the Cup with Arsenal in 1971?

137. Who is the highest-capped England player never to have won an FA Cup Final winners medal?

138. Which team appeared in three Finals in four years during the 1970's?

139. How many internationals were in Sunderland's Cup-winning side of 1973?

140. Who were the last team outside the top flight to win the Cup?

141. How many FA Cup matches did Fulham play in the 1974-75 season?

142. Which two former FA Cup winners were in the Fulham side in the 1975 Final?

143. Which FA Cup Final manager scored the winning goal for non-league Yeovil when they beat Sunderland in 1948?

144. Who was the first player to captain English and Scottish FA Cup winning teams?

145. Who lost an FA Cup Final as player in 1954, and as manager in 1967 and 1976 before winning the trophy with Manchester United?

146. Which Final-winning manager was an unused sub for West Ham in the 1975 Final?

147. Who scored Arsenal's late winner in the 1979 Final against Manchester United?

148. Who captained his side to three FA Cup triumphs at Wembley?

149. Who had to taken off suffering with 'sunstroke and emotion' after scoring an FA Cup Final winner?

150. Who scored Southampton's winning goal in the 1976 Final?

136. Frank McLintock 137. **Peter Shilton** 138. Leeds (1970,1972,1973) 139. **None** 140. West Ham, 1980 141. 12 142. Bobby Moore and Alan Mullery 143. **Alec Stock** 144. Martin Buchan (Aberdeen 1970) Manchester United (1977) 145. **Tommy Docherty** 146. Bobby Gould 147. **Alan Sunderland** 148. Bryan Robson (1983,1985,1990) 149. **Roger Osborne (Ipswich, 1978)** 150. Bobby Stokes

 **Quiz 7**   F. A. Cup

151. How many games did it take Arsenal to beat Liverpool in the FA Cup semi-final of 1980?

152. Who is the only player to play in five post-war FA Cup Finals for the same team?

153. Who was the Manchester City captain in their 1969 Cup success who later went on to become their manager?

154. Who scored both goals in the 1981 FA Cup Final?

155. Which club played in five FA Cup Finals from 1971 to 1980?

156. When Brighton reached the Cup Final in 1983 they beat Liverpool in the fifth round with a goal from a former Liverpool Cup Final goalscorer. Who was it?

157. Roy Dwight played for Nottingham Forest in the 1959 Final. His nephew was at Wembley for the 1984 Final. Who is he?

158. Who scored two Cup Final goals in three years in the 1980's?

159. Because of the Hillsborough disaster in 1989 the semi-final between Liverpool and Nottingham Forest was replayed at another ground. Where?

160. Which teams contested the 100th Cup Final?

161. Who is the only goalkeeper to captain his team in the Cup Final?

162. What was wrong with Tottenham's shirts in the 1987 Final?

163. Who played in six Cup Finals in Scotland before playing, and scoring, in the 1983 FA Cup Final?

164. Who scored for Coventry in the 1987 Final against the same club he had faced in another Final?

165. Who played for only the first two minutes of the 1982 Final for QPR before limping off injured?

165. Clive Allen

sors name on their shirts, some didn't. 164. Dave Bennett
Tottenham 161. **Dave Beasant (Wimbledon, 1988)** 162. Some had the spon-
John 158. Norman Whiteside 159. **Old Trafford** 160. Manchester City and
City) 155. **Arsenal** 156. Jimmy Case 157. **Reg Dwight, now known as Elton**
151. **Four** 152. Pat Rice 153. **Tony Book** 154. Tommy Hutchinson (Manchester

 **Quiz 7** F. A. Cup

166. Who made his last appearance for Tottenham in the 1987 Final?

167. **Who captained Brighton in the 1983 Cup Final instead of suspended Steve Foster?**

168. Which former Cup winner managed Crystal Palace to the Final in 1990?

169. **Who scored an own goal in the 1991 Final?**

170. Who became the first side to win a semi-final on penalties?

171. **Who beat Cup holders Liverpool in a third round replay at Anfield in 1993?**

172. Who scored Arsenal's winner in the semi-final against Tottenham in 1993?

173. **Who invented the FA Cup?**

174. Who was the first man to captain a winning side in successive Finals?

175. **Who is the last Scotsman to captain an FA Cup winning side?**

176. Which Russian goalkeeper played in a Cup Final?

177. **Which Danish international played in the 1986,1988 and 1992 FA Cup Finals?**

178. Which striker played in the 1983 Final and later went on to become a football commentator for Spanish television?

179. **Which two brothers played in the 1977 Final?**

180. Who scored with a 20-yard volley in the 1981 Final replay?

 **Quiz 7**   F. A. Cup

181. **Which former Real Madrid and Marseille star played for Wimbledon in the 1988 Cup Final?**

182. Who was the first Dutchman to play in an FA Cup Final?

183. **Who scored Manchester United's winner in the 1990 FA Cup Final replay?**

184. Who was the last club to lose in the Final, but succeed the following year?

185. **Who is the last player-manager to play in the Final?**

186. Who scored Arsenal's last minute winner in the 1993 Final replay?

187. **Apart from Ian Wright, who scored Crystal Palace's other goal in the 1990 Final?**

188. Who scored for both clubs in the 1987 Final?

189. **Who captained West Ham to FA Cup wins in 1975 and 1980?**

190. Which two players played in the 1968 Cup Final and then went on to win the FA Cup as managers of the same team?

191. **When did Luton Town last play in the FA Cup Final?**

192. Which two teams played out a 4-6 third round match in 1948?

193. **Who scored Crystal Palace's winning goal in their 4-3 semi-final win over Liverpool in 1990?**

194. Which two Everton strikers scored twice in a 4-4 fifth round replay against Liverpool in 1991?

195. **Which Cup Final featured two pairs of brothers on the field?**

---

181. **Laurie Cunningham** 182. Arnold Muhren (Manchester United, 1983) 183. **Lee Martin** 184. Manchester United (1995, 1996) 185. **Glenn Hoddle (Chelsea, 1994)** 186. Andy Linighan 187. **Gary O'Reilly** 188. Gary Mabbutt 189. **Billy Bonds** 190. Howard Kendall and Joe Royle 191. 1959 192. Aston Villa and Manchester United 193. **Alan Pardew** 194. Graeme Sharp, Tony Cottee 195. 1876

 **Quiz 7**   **F. A. Cup**

196. Has there ever been an FA Cup semi-final played outside England?

197. Which club's 4-0 victory at Brighton in 1973 was the biggest away win for a non-league side?

198. Who scored after just 45 seconds on his senior debut in an FA Cup tie in January 1953?

199. Which club played successive away ties in different rounds in the same season but on the same ground?

200. Which club reached a Cup Final after losing a game in the competition in the same season?

201. Who became the first player to play in the FA Cup for two different clubs in the same season?

202. Which Premiership team reached their first FA Cup semi-final in 1997?

203. Who were the last third division team, before Chesterfield in 1997, to reach the semi-finals?

204. Which team beat six Division One sides to FA Cup victory?

205. Who was refused a Cup winners medal from the royal box, and had it presented on the pitch after the official ceremony?

206. Which team collected a £30 clothing voucher as a bonus for winning the Cup?

207. Which Cup Final was dubbed "the Friendly Final"?

208. What was significant about J.F. Mitchell, who played in the 1922 Final for Preston?

209. When was the first FA Cup Final televised?

210. Which famous cricketer has a brother who played in the 1983 Final?

Hove Albion

196. Yes, In Edinburgh in 1885 **197. Walton and Hersham** 198. Albert Taylor (Luton Town) **199. Preston North End. They played Manchester City and Manchester United at Maine Road** 200. Charlton Athletic They lost to Fulham in 1946 but the ties that season was played over two legs **201. Jimmy Scoular in 1946 (Gosport and Portsmouth)** 202. Middlesbrough **203. Plymouth Argyle** 204. Manchester United (1948) **205. Kevin Moran (Manchester United, 1985)** 206. Everton (1933) **207. Liverpool v Everton (1986)** 208. He wore glasses on the pitch **209. 1938** 210. Mike Gatting, His brother, Steve, played for Brighton and

 **Quiz 7**   F. A. Cup

211. Which team took the FA Cup on their tour of South Africa in 1952?

212. Who asked for a transfer just an hour before the 1960 Final?

213. Which wine-bar waiter played in the 1987 semi-final?

214. Who scored for Oldham in the 1994 semi-final against Manchester United?

215. How many players did Mansfield Town have booked in their third round tie against Crystal Palace in 1963?

216. Which English club have played FA Cup ties in all three other home countries, against Linfield, Queen's Park and Cardiff City?

217. Who went 16 matches without a win in the competition, from February 1952 to March 1963?

218. The official record attendance for an FA Cup tie is 126,047. What year?

219. Which team reached two successive Finals without being drawn at home?

220. Which three England World Cup winners have never played in an FA Cup Final?

221. Which England player played his last game for his club in an FA Cup Final, and was stretchered off after only 16 minutes?

222. Who scored for Sutton United in their 2-1 third round victory over Coventry in 1989?

223. Who beat Sutton 8-0 in the following round?

224. Who was sent-off in Manchester United's semi-final replay against Crystal Palace in 1995?

225. Who was sent-off for West Ham in the 1991 semi-final against Nottingham Forest?

---

211. **Newcastle United** 212. Derek Dougan (Blackburn Rovers) 213. **Watford's Gary Plumley** 214. Neil Pointon 215. **Ten** 216. Nottingham Forest 217. **Leeds United** 218. 1923 219. **Arsenal (1971,1972)** 220. Nobby Stiles, George Cohen, Martin Peters 221. **Paul Gascoigne (Tottenham, 1991)** 222. Tony Rains, Matt Hanlon 223. **Norwich City** 224. Roy Keane 225. **Tony Gale**

Quiz 7 — F. A. Cup

226. Who scored Arsenal's consolation goal in their 3-1 semi-final defeat against Tottenham in 1991?

227. Which Footballer of the Year captained his side to victory in the 1964 Final?

228. Which goalkeeper replaced Gary Sprake for Leeds' 1970 Final replay?

229. Who scored both of West Ham's goals in the 1975 Final?

230. Who scored the winning goal for York City against Arsenal in 1985, and scored in the Cup Final two years later?

231. Which non-league team celebrated scoring goals by waddling along the ground like ducks?

232. Who did Arsenal beat 3-0 in the semi-final of 1978?

233. Which London club won in their first FA Cup Final in the 1980's?

234. Who became the first player this century to play in three FA Cup Finals against the same club?

235. How many goal-less FA Cup Finals have there been at Wembley?

236. Name the last two players to be voted Footballer of the Year and captain an FA Cup winning side?

237. What have Sir Stanley Matthews, Harry Johnston, Nat Lofthouse, Tom Finney, Don Revie, Syd Owen, Jimmy Adamson, Bobby Collins, Billy Bremner, Alan Mullery, Emlyn Hughes, Neville Southall, Gary Lineker, Clive Allen, John Barnes and Chris Waddle all got in common?

238. Which man made more than 500 appearances for Coventry and was the club's managing director when they won the Cup in 1987?

239. Which player lost two front teeth after colliding with a team-mate in the 1981 Final?

240. Who beat Hyde FC 26-0 in 1887 for the biggest win in FA Cup history?

---

226. Alan Smith **227. Bobby Moore (West Ham)** 228. David Harvey **229. Alan Taylor** 230. Keith Houchen **231. Aylesbury United** 232. Leyton Orient **233. Wimbledon (1988)** 234. Paul Bracewell - against Liverpool **235. None** 236. Steve Perryman (1982) Eric Cantona (1996) **237. They were named Footballer of the Year but lost in the Cup Final in the same year** 238. George Curtis **239. Graham Roberts (Tottenham)** 240. Preston North End

 **Quiz 7**   F. A. Cup

241. Who scored Chelsea's goal in the 1996 semi-final at Villa Park?

242. Which of the Neville brothers came on as a sub in the 1996 FA Cup Final?

243. Who scored Everton's winner in the 1995 Final?

244. Which two England goalkeepers played in the 1993 Final?

245. Who finished a 20-year association with Arsenal by winning his second FA Cup winners medal?

246. Who scored Manchester United's second goal in a 3-0 fourth round win at Reading in 1996?

247. Liverpool conceded only one goal on their way to the 1996 Final. Who scored against them?

248. Up to the 1997 Final, which Premiership club hasn't beaten Manchester United in the FA Cup for 76 years?

249. Who scored Wimbledon's winner in their 1988 semi-final against Luton?

250. Which two teams met twice in four years in FA Cup semi-finals in the 1990's?

251. Who held Brighton to a 2-2 draw in the first round in 1995?

252. Who did Fulham beat 7-0 in the first round in 1995?

253. By what scoreline did Oxford United beat Dorchester in the first round of 1995?

254. How many goals were scored in the 1995-96 first round tie between Shrewsbury and Marine?

255. Name the last Fourth Division club to reach the quarter-finals.

---

241. Ruud Gullit 242. Gary Neville **243. Paul Rideout** 244. David Seaman (Arsenal) and Chris Woods (Sheffield Wednesday) **245. David O'Leary** 246. Paul Parker **247. Charlton Athletic** 248. Liverpool **249. Dennis Wise** 250. Manchester United and Oldham (1990,1994) **251.** Canvey Island 252. Swansea **253.** 9-1 254. 13 (Shrewsbury won 11-2) **255. Cambridge United**

Quiz 7 — F. A. Cup

256. What year was it?

257. Who has made three appearances in the Final for Tottenham and one for Chelsea in the space of 13 years?

258. Tony Philliskirk scored five goals in a first round tie against Kingstonian in 1992, but does not have it officially recognised because the game was abandoned. Who was he playing for?

259. Which former president of the FA appeared in nine of the first 12 FA Cup Finals?

260. Which three former Liverpool players have all won three Cup winners' medals with the club?

261. What was the amazing feat of all 12 Manchester United players who played in the 1985 Final?

262. Only once in the competition's history have all the quarter-finals been won by the away teams. In which season?

263. Has there ever been an FA Cup Final where the top division was not represented?

264. Which club, in 1994-95, was originally banned from the competition but re-admitted on appeal?

265. Who scored Chesterfield's only goal in their 1996-97 quarter-final win over Wrexham?

266. Which Premiership club beat Blackburn in the fourth round of the 1996-97 season?

267. Who scored a last-minute own goal to send the fifth round tie between Leicester and Chelsea to a replay in 1996-97?

268. Who defeated Leeds at Elland Road to win a place in the 1996-97 quarter-finals?

269. Chelsea came back from 2-0 down at half-time to beat Liverpool in the 1996-97 fourth round. Who scored twice for the Londoners?

270. Which Hull City striker scored six goals in a first round replay against Whitby Town in the 1996-97 season?

 Quiz 8   **Milestones of Football**

1. **Who was the first 'Footballer of the Year'?**

2. Who was the first 'Manager of the Year' in 1966?

3. **Which was the first game to be broadcast on 'Match of the Day'?**

4. Who were the first team to achieve the 'double'?

5. **Who was the first man to hit 60 League goals in a season?**

6. Who was the first player in British football to score a 'golden goal'?

7. **Which club were the first to concede and score 100 League goals in one season?**

8. Who was the first player to notch up a century of England appearances?

9. **Who was the first player to notch up a century of Scotland appearances?**

10. Who was the first player to notch up a century of Northern Ireland appearances?

11. **Where was the first indoor World Cup game?**

12. Who were England's opponents for the first all-seated football international at Wembley?

13. **Who was the first black player to win a full England cap?**

14. Who was the first black player to captain England at full international level?

15. **Who was the first man to play in and then manage League Championship-winning teams?**

1. **Stanley Matthews** 2. Jock Stein 3. **Liverpool 3 Arsenal 2 (1964)**
4. Preston (1889) 5. **Dixie Dean (1927-28)** 6. Iain Dunn (Huddersfield)
7. **Manchester City** 8. Billy Wright 9. **Kenny Dalglish** 10. Pat Jennings
11. **Seattle (USA v Canada in 1976)** 12. Yugoslavia 13. **Viv Anderson**
14. Paul Ince 15. **Ted Drake**

 Quiz 8   Milestones of Football

16. Which club was first to be relegated from the Football League in 1923?

17. **In what year were the Division Three North and South replaced by Divisions Three and Four?**

18. In which year was the Premier League created?

19. **Who was the first player to reach 1000 League appearances when he played for Leyton Orient in 1996?**

20. Which Manchester City keeper became the first to play in all four divisions in one season in 1986/87?

21. **Who were the first club to take the FA Cup out of England?**

22. Who is the only man to score a hat-trick in a post-war FA Cup final?

23. **In what year was the hymn 'Abide With Me' introduced as part of the FA Cup Final build-up?**

24. Who was the first guest of honour at the FA Cup final of 1923?

25. **Who was the first player sent off playing for England?**

26. In what year did Walter Winterbottom become the first official manager of England?

27. **Who was the first manager to win the League Championship with two different clubs when he led both Huddersfield and Arsenal to the title?**

28. Who was the first man to become a player-manager in the top flight when he took over QPR in 1968?

29. **In which year was the first FA Cup final at Wembley Stadium?**

30. In which year was the first Wembley game played under floodlights?

16. Stalybridge Celtic 17. 1957 18. 1992 19. **Peter Shilton** 20. Eric Nixon
21. **Cardiff City in 1927** 22. Stan Mortensen 23. 1927 24. King George V
25. **Alan Mullery** 26. 1946 27. **Herbert Chapman** 28. Les Allen 29. 1923
30. 1955

 **Quiz 8**　　　　Milestones of Football

31. Who scored the first 'golden goal' which decided a major international tournament?

32. In which year was the first penalty scored in a first-class match?

33. Which club was the first in competitive British football to win a game through a penalty shoot-out?

34. Who became the first player to miss an FA Cup final penalty at Wembley when he failed to convert in 1988?

35. Who was the first player to score 200 goals in the Scottish Premier League?

36. Who were the first British club to play in Europe?

37. When did the Scottish First Division become the Premier League?

38. In which year were the first shinguards used?

39. In which year was professionalism in the game legalised?

40. In which year did the white ball come into official use?

41. In which year were substitutes introduced into Football League matches?

42. The 'three points for a win' system was intro-duced by the Football League in which year?

43. When was the 'professional foul' made a sending-off offence?

44. When was the 'backpass' rule put into operation?

45. In which year was the numbering of Football League shirts made compulsory?

THE LATEST THING

31. Oliver Bierhoff (Euro 96 final) 32. 1891 **33. Manchester United (Watney Cup semi-final v Hull in 1970) 34.** John Aldridge **35. Ally McCoist 36.** Hibernian in 1955/56 **37.** 1975 **38.** 1874 **39.** 1885 **40.** 1951 **41.** 1965 **42.** 1981 **43.** 1990 **44.** 1992 **45.** 1939

 **Quiz 8**   **Milestones of Football**

46. Two substitutes were permitted in League games from which year?

47. **Who was the first substitute to score in an FA Cup final?**

48. In which year was the ceiling for footballers' earnings abolished?

49. **Who was the first British footballer to earn £100 a week?**

50. Who became the first sponsors of the Football League in 1983?

51. **Which club was the first to install an artificial pitch, in 1981?**

52. Which year saw the end of artificial turf pitches in the First Division?

53. **According to the original Taylor Report, when were all Premier League and First Division stadia required to become all-seater?**

54. When was the FA's School of Excellence at Lilleshall opened?

55. **Leyton Orient player Terry Howard hit the headlines when he lost his job in Feb 1995. Why?**

56. Which was the first football match to be televised in its entirety?

57. **What was introduced in Jan 1963 after a spell of particularly bad weather?**

58. Who were the first Olympic Games football champions in 1908?

59. **In which year was the first football code of laws compiled?**

60. The foundation of the Football Association occurred in which year?

46. 1987 47. **Eddie Kelly (Arsenal v Liverpool, 1971)** 48. 1961 49. **Johnny Haynes** 50. Canon 51. **QPR** 52. 1991 53. **August 1994** 54. 1984 55. **First recorded instance of a player being sacked at half-time.** 56. Arsenal 3 Everton 2 (August 1936) 57. **Pools Panel** 58. Great Britain 59. **1848** 60. 1863

 Quiz 8   Milestones of Football

61. Who did England play in the first official international in 1872?

62. The referee's job was made a little easier with what 1878 introduction?

63. In which year were goal nets introduced?

64. Which country did England play in the first Wembley international?

65. In 1935 trials were held for which innovation in football discipline?

66. Which was the first club to complete a hat-trick of consecutive League titles?

67. In which year was the first live television transmission of an FA Cup Final?

68. Who were the first foreign team to beat England in a full international at Wembley?

69. The last Football League Christmas Day programme was completed in which year?

70. The system of loan transfers was introduced in which year?

71. A decision by the PFA in 1978 precipitated which introduction into English football?

72. A European ban on all English clubs was introduced in which year?

73. Who, in 1986, became the first club to ban visiting supporters?

74. The system of play-off matches for promotion and relegation was introduced in which year?

75. Which English club was the last to revert to grass from artificial pitches?

 **Quiz 9**   **The Commentators**

1. **Which television sports presenter made his TV debut covering a John Conteh fight in 1979?**

2. Which politician took over from Danny Baker as the presenter of Radio Five Live's Six-O-Six programme?

IT'S HIS FIRST TIME...!

3. **Which television sports presenter hosted a holiday programme?**

4. Which former Tottenham and Manchester United player now works for the BBC?

5. **Which former England international is the main summariser for the BBC?**

6. Who hosts ITV's sports programme 'Do I Not Like That'?

7. **Which two Premiership managers worked for the BBC during Euro '96?**

8. Which former England international now has his own show on BBC Radio Five Live?

9. **Whose has commentated on football for the BBC since 1971?**

10. Who commentated on his first World Cup Final in 1994?

11. **Which former Liverpool and Scotland striker works for ITV Sport?**

12. Which former Newcastle manager is a regular summariser on ITV?

13. **Who is the former Luton and Leicester manager who works for BBC?**

14. Which former England international worked on the BBC's coverage of Newcastle's 1996-97 Uefa Cup campaign?

15. **Which two former internationals had a long-running Saturday luchtime show on ITV?**

---

1. Desmond Lynam 2. David Mellor **3. Desmond Lynam** 4. Garth Crooks **5. Trevor Brooking** 6. Richard Littlejohn **7. Ruud Gullit and David Pleat** 8. Gary Lineker **9. John Motson** 10. Barry Davies **11. Ian St John** 12. Kevin Keegan **13. David Pleat** 14. Chris Waddle **15. Ian St John and Jimmy Greaves**

 **Quiz 9**   **The Commentators**

16. What was the show called?

17. **Who hosts Channel Four's Football Italia?**

18. Which former commentator also works on Football Italia?

19. **Which former BBC commentator now works for satellite channel Eurosport?**

20. Which former England international works for ITV, Channel Four and Sky Sports?

21. **Who is Sky Sports' main football commentator?**

22. Who took over from Desmond Lynam as the presenter of BBC's Grandstand?

23. **Who is the host of Grandstand's Football Focus?**

24. Who is Channel Four's main commentator for Football Italia?

25. **Which former Scotland striker appears on Channel Four's Football Italia?**

26. Who was the original host of Radio Five Live's 'Six-O-Six' programme?

27. **Who is Sky Sports' top football presenter?**

28. Who is Sky Sports' main summariser, and also has a column in The Express newspaper?

29. **Which sports presenter turned down the chance to stand-in for Terry Wogan on his chat-show?**

30. Name the former Watford striker who appears on Channel Four's Football Italia?

16. 'Saint and Greavsie' 17. **Gary Richardson** 18. Kenneth Wolstenholme
19. **Archie McPherson** 20. Ray Wilkins 21. **Martin Tyler** 22. Steve Rider
23. **Gary Lineker** 24. Peter Brackley 25. **Joe Jordan** 26. Danny Baker
27. **Richard Keys** 28. Andy Gray 29. **Desmon Lynam** 30. Luther Blissett

 **Quiz 9**   **The Commentators**

31. Which international manager worked for ITV during Euro '96?

32. Who presents BBC's Sport on Friday programme?

33. Which woman personality presents Sky's Goals on Sunday programme?

34. Which former Page Three model hosts a sports programme on Channel Five?

35. Which former Pisa defender works on Channel Four's Football Italia?

36. Which former footballer is a team captain in BBC's television quiz 'They Think It's All Over'?

37. Which television commentator's middle name is Baden?

38. Which television commentator was a director at Gillingham from 1977 to 1985?

39. Which comedian presented the nostalgia football show 'There's Only One Brian Moore'?

40. Which football pundit is a former head of sport at London Weekend Television?

41. Which international manager worked for the BBC in the 1994 World Cup?

42. Which former Brighton and Liverpool striker moved to Spain and became a commentator after his playing days?

43. Which former England captain works for BBC Radio Five Live?

44. Fantasy Football League's 'Statto' also commentates for Eurosport. What is his real name?

45. In which year did Bob Wilson defect from BBC to ITV?

31. **Glenn Hoddle** 32. Helen Rollason 33. **Anna Walker** 34. Gail McKenna 35. **Paul Elliott** 36. Gary Lineker 37. **Brian Moore** 38. Brian Moore 39. **Bob Mills** 40. Jimmy Hill 41. **Terry Venables** 42. Michael Robinson 43. **Jimmy Armfield** 44. Angus Loughran 45. 1994

 **Quiz 10** The Carling Premiership 1994-95

1. **The first goal of the season comes at Highbury, where Arsenal are playing Manchester City. Who is the scorer?**

2. Which German scores his first Premiership goal at Sheffield Wednesday on the first day of the season?

3. **Which team do Liverpool beat 6-1 on the opening day of the season?**

4. In the draw between Newcastle and Leicester City in August which player suffers a cheek-bone fracture?

5. **Which £5m player scores his first for Blackburn in August against Leicester City?**

6. Which German scores a brace in Manchester City's 4-0 win over Everton in August?

7. **Which team went top after three games and three victories?**

8. Who scores a four-and-a-half minute hat-trick for Liverpool when they beat Arsenal 3-0 in August?

9. **Which club went top of the Premiership for a day in August?**

10. Which team begins the season with the prospect of having six points deducted?

11. **Which captain is sent off in Wimbledon's 2-1 win over Leicester in September?**

12. Which player scores seven goals in his first six games in the Premiership?

13. **Who scores Arsenal's own goal in Newcastle's 3-2 win in September?**

14. **Which ex-Tottenham player scores the winner as Ipswich pull off a shock victory over Manchester United in September?**

15. **Who hit a hat-trick for Liverpool as they trounce Sheffield Wednesday in September?**

1. **Kevin Campbell** 2. Jurgen Klinsmann 3. **Crystal Palace** 4. Peter Beardsley 5. **Chris Sutton** 6. Uwe Rosler 7. **Newcastle United** 8. Robbie Fowler 9. **Nottingham Forest** 10. Tottenham Hotspur 11. **Vinnie Jones** 12. Jurgen Klinsmann 13. **Martin Keown** 14. Steve Sedgeley 15. **Steve McManaman**

Quiz 10 — The Carling Premiership 1994-95

16. Which player scores his 100th goal for Arsenal in October?

17. **Who is sent off when Blackburn meet Manchester United in October?**

18. Who are the only club in Britain without a win after 12 games?

19. **Which club ends Newcastle's unbeaten run at the end of October?**

20. Which club ends Nottingham Forest's unbeaten run on the same day?

21. **Which foreigner's goal at Villa Park in November lifts Manchester United to third in the table?**

22. Which three managers get the sack at the beginning of November?

23. **Which player scores a hat-trick in November as Manchester United's set their biggest derby win in history?**

24. At White Hart Lane in November Tottenham fight back against Aston Villa from 3-0 down only to lose to a last-minute winner. Who scored that goal?

25. **Which on-loan striker scores for Everton in their first win of the season in the Liverpool derby?**

26. Who scores a hat-trick as Blackburn go top in November after a 4-0 win over QPR?

27. **Who scores a hat-trick for Tottenham as they produce a 4-2 win at home to Newcastle in December?**

28. Which two strikers net a brace in Manchester United's 3-2 win over QPR in December?

29. **Which team are the first of the season to beat Manchester United at Old Trafford when they win 2-1 in December?**

30. Which team set a club record seven games without a goal in a goalless draw at home to Tottenham in December?

---

16. Ian Wright 17. **Henning Berg** 18. Everton 19. **Manchester United** 20. Blackburn 21. **Andrei Kanchelskis** 22. Ossie Ardiles, Mike Walker and Ron Atkinson 23. **Andrei Kanchelskis** 24. Dean Saunders 25. **Duncan Ferguson** 26. Alan Shearer 27. **Teddy Sheringham** 28. Les Ferdinand and Paul Scholes 29. **Nottingham Forest** 30. Everton

Quiz 10 — The Carling Premiership 1994-95

31. **Which Sheffield Wednesday new boy scores twice on his debut at Everton on Boxing Day?**

32. In Manchester United's Boxing Day clash with Chelsea, who scores the winner in their 3-2 victory?

33. **Who scores his first goal in his 98th match for Arsenal in December?**

34. Blackburn achieve a six-point lead in the Premiership at the start of January with a hat-trick from which player against West Ham?

35. **The North London derby at White Hart Lane ends 1-0. Who is sent off for Arsenal?**

36. Ipswich record their first-ever win at Anfield thanks to a goal from which player?

37. **Which Manchester United player scores but is then stretchered off when they play Newcastle in January?**

38. The battle of the top two clubs, Manchester United and Blackburn, is resolved with a goal from which player in January?

39. **Which two Hammers are dismissed when they meet Sheffield Wednesday in January?**

40. Which South African international scores two goals as Leeds beat QPR 4-0 in January?

41. **Which goalkeeper is sent off after only two minutes in a game against Leeds in February?**

42. In February, which Everton player is sent off on his debut?

43. **Which Manchester United player scores his first goal for the club in a 1-0 victory over Aston Villa in February?**

44. What was the scoreline when Blackburn are beaten by Tottenham in February, losing the chance of stretching their lead to five points?

45. **Who hits a hat-trick as Aston Villa put seven past Wimbledon in February?**

---

31. **Guy Whittingham** 32. Brian McClair 33. **John Jensen** 34. Alan Shearer 35. **Stefan Schwarz** 36. Adam Tanner 37. **Mark Hughes** 38. Eric Cantona 39. **Alvin Martin and Tim Breacker** 40. Phil Masinga 41. **Tim Flowers** 42. Earl Barrett 43. **Andy Cole** 44. 3-1 45. **Tommy Johnson**

Quiz 10 — The Carling Premiership 1994-95

46. Which Arsenal player breaks a leg in the 1-1 draw with Leicester in February?

47. **Which goalkeeper is sent off when Blackburn beat Sheffield Wednesday 3-1 in February to reclaim their place at the top of the league.**

48. Who scores his first goal for Arsenal when they beat Nottingham Forest in February?

49. **Which club scores three goals in the last 13 minutes at Villa Park in February to take themselves off the bottom of the table?**

50. Who scores his first goal for Leeds in February when they beat Everton 1-0 at home?

51. **A goal from which player gives Everton an unexpected win at home to Manchester United in February?**

52. How many goals do Manchester United put past Ipswich in March to establish a Premiership record?

53. **Which player scores five goals in that game?**

54. Which two Everton men are sent off when the Toffeemen squander a two-goal lead at Leicester in March?

55. **Joe Kinnear is ordered from the bench in a game against Manchester United in March when which player is sent off?**

56. Which Coventry player scores a hat-trick as they beat Liverpool 3-2 in March?

57. **Against which club does Alan Shearer score his 100th league goal in March?**

58. Which player scores an own goal as Liverpool beat Manchester United 2-0 in March?

59. **Which two Nottingham Forest players score six goals in two games to lift their club to fourth in March?**

60. Which team beat Sheffield Wednesday 7-1 to give the Owls their biggest-ever home defeat in April?

---

46. Ian Selley **47. Kevin Pressman** 48. Chris Kiwomya **49. Leicester City** 50. Tony Yeboah **51. Duncan Ferguson** 52. Nine 53. Nine **54. Andy Cole** 54. Vinny Samways and Duncan Ferguson **55. Alan Kimble** 56. Peter Ndlovu **57. Chelsea** 58. Steve Bruce **59. Bryan Roy and Stan Collymore** 60. Nottingham Forest

Quiz 10 — The Carling Premiership 1994-95

61. **Who scores the winner for Southampton in their seven-goal thriller with Tottenham in April?**

62. What is the biggest points lead which Blackburn attain over Manchester United?

63. **Whose Leeds hat-trick condemns Ipswich to the bottom of the table in April and confimed relegation a week later?**

64. Whose late Tottenham equaliser denies Crystal Palace three vital points in April?

65. **Whose last-minute equaliser for Leeds against Blackburn helps Manchester United to cut the gap to six points with five games remaining?**

66. Which team brings an end to Newcastle's 15-month unbeaten run at St James' Park?

67. **Who scores the winner for Manchester City when they beat Blackburn in April?**

68. Who beats Leicester 2-0 in April to condemn the Foxes to relegation?

69. **Blackburn beat Palace 2-1 in April to restore their eight-point lead. Neither Shearer or Sutton scores, but who does?**

70. Who scores his 28th goal of the season in the North London derby at Highbury in April?

71. **After defeat against which club do angry Norwich fans protest, leading to 13 arrests, in April?**

72. Which team beats Blackburn 2-0 at the end of April to keep the championship race alive?

73. **Who scores a brace for Manchester United on May 1 in their win over Coventry to close the gap to five points?**

74. Whose last-minute goal for Leeds gave them a win over Norwich which relegates the Canaries?

75. **A goal from which player gives Manchester United a win over Sheffield Wednesday, closing the gap at the top?**

---

61. Jim Magilton 62. Eight points 63. Tony Yeboah 64. Jurgen Klinsmann 65. Brian Deane 66. Leeds United 67. Paul Walsh 68. Liverpool 69. Jeff Kenna and Kevin Gallacher 70. Jurgen Klinsmann 71. Liverpool 72. West Ham 73. Andy Cole 74. Carlton Palmer 75. David May

Quiz 10 — The Carling Premiership 1994-95

76. Who do Blackburn beat to restore their five-point lead at the top?

77. **Who scores the penalty to give Manchester United a victory at home to Southampton and a gap of only two points with one game to play?**

78. Who beats Blackburn on the last day of the season?

79. **Who scores the West Ham goal which ultimately denies Manchester United the title?**

80. Which team beats Crystal Palace on the last day of the season to condemn the Eagles to relegation?

81. **Which team finishes one positition above the relegation places?**

82. Which team finishes in third behind Blackburn and Manchester United?

83. **What is the final points gap between the top two teams?**

84. Which two players were sent off in the game between QPR and Manchester United in August, the first dismissals of the Premiership season?

85. **How many managers lose their jobs throughout the season?**

86. Which Crystal Palace player receives a ban after testing positive for cannabis?

87. **Which referee revokes his decision to send off Alvin Martin in West Ham's game with Sheffield Wednesday?**

88. Which club are hit by allegations of 'bungs' in their transfer dealings with Scandinavian clubs?

89. **Which player retires but then returns at the age of 38 when his team face possible relegation?**

90. At which unlikely venue did Jurgen Klinsmann announce that he will play only one season in England?

76. Newcastle United 77. **Denis Irwin** 78. Liverpool 79. **Michael Hughes** 80. Newcastle United 81. **Aston Villa** 82. Nottingham Forest 83. **One point** 84. Clive Wilson and Paul Parker 85. **12** 86. Chris Armstrong 87. **Paul Danson** 88. Arsenal 89. **Gordon Strachan** 90. The Comedy Café

 **Quiz 11** Foreign Players In England

1. **Who became the most expensive foreign player in the Premiership when he cost Arsenal £7.5m in June 1995?**

2. Which Belgian international played a season with Sheffield Wednesday in 1995-96?

3. **At one time Middlesbrough had three Brazilians in their squad. Can you name them?**

4. Which midfielder was shortlighted as PFA Young Player of the Year in his first season in England?

5. **Which former Middlesbrough striker played in the 1994 World Cup Finals?**

6. Which foreign striker is nicknamed 'The White Feather'?

7. **For how much did Swedish midfielder Tomas Brolin join Leeds for?**

8. Which club did he sign from?

9. **Who were the two Argentinians that arrived at Tottenham after the 1978 World Cup Final?**

10. Which two Italian clubs did Chelsea's Ruud Gullit play for?

11. **Which two European strikers were part of Tottenham manager Ossie Ardiles' Fab Five?**

12. Who was the Romanian midfielder at Tottenham during 1994-95?

13. **How many of Norway's 1994 World Cup squad were playing their football in England at the time of the Finals?**

14. Patrick Vieira is just one one of three French players to play at Arsenal in 1996-97. Name the other two.

15. **Which foreign player broke Aston Villa's transfer record when he signed for £3.5m in June 1995?**

Garde and Nicolas Anelka 15. **Savo Milosevic**
14. Remi
11. **Jürgen Klinsmann and Ilie Dumitrescu** 12. Gica Popescu 13. 10
8. Parma 9. **Ossie Ardiles and Ricky Villa** 10. AC Milan, Sampdoria
4. Patrick Vieira 5. **Jan-Aage Fjortoft** 6. Fabrizio Ravanelli 7. **£4.5m**
1. **Dennis Bergkamp** 2. Marc Degryse 3. **Juninho, Emerson, Branco**

Quiz 11 — Foreign Players In England

16. Who moved to England just four days after lifting the European Cup for Juventus?

17. **Australian Mark Bosnich was at another Premiership club before Aston Villa. What club was it?**

18. Where did Blackburn buy Lars Bohinen from?

19. **Which Zimbabwean played for Coventry in 1996-97?**

20. How much did Gianfranco Zola cost Chelsea when he moved from Parma?

21. **Which Blackburn player played in a 1996 European Cup semi-final?**

22. What nationality is Chelsea goalkeeper Frode Grodas?

23. **Name the former clubs of Chelsea's Dan Petrescu?**

24. Where did Middlesbrough buy Mikkel Beck from?

25. **What nationality is Sasa Curcic?**

26. Name the Aston Villa defender from Portugal?

27. **Dwight Yorke plays for which country?**

28. Where did Blackburn buy Henning Berg from?

29. **Who was Chelsea's Danish defender in the 1994 FA Cup Final?**

30. Derby had a Danish defender in 1996-97. Who is he?

Quiz 11 — Foreign Players In England

31. Which Chelsea player formerly played for Bayern Munich?

32. Which Russian winger joined Everton for £5million in August 1995?

33. Which USA '94 star joined Tottenham from Steaua Bucharest for £2.6million?

34. Who cost Arsenal £1.75million when he joined them in 1994 from Benfica?

35. Marc Hottiger played for Everton in 1996-97. Which other English club had he previously played for?

36. Name the two players who joined Sheffield Wednesday from RS Belgrade in 1995.

37. How much did Chelsea pay for Italian international Roberto Di Matteo?

38. And from which club did they buy him from?

39. Which Czech Republic star joined Manchester United from Slavia Prague in 1996?

40. How much did he cost?

41. Which two South Africans played for Leeds United in 1995-96?

42. From which club did Leeds buy Tony Yeboah from?

43. Which midfielder did Coventry buy from Benfica?

44. Which Croation defender joined Derby in 1995?

45. From which club did he come from?

31. **Erland Johnsen** 32. Andrei Kanchelskis 33. **Ilie Dumitrescu** 34. Stefan Schwarz 35. **Newcastle** 36. Darko Kovacevic and Dejan Stefanovic 37. **£4.9m** 38. Lazio 39. **Karel Poborsky** 40. £3.5m 41. **Lucas Radebe and Philomen Masinga** 42. Eintracht Frankfurt 43. **Marques Isaias** 44. Igor Stimac 45. **Hadjuk Split**

Quiz 11 — Foreign Players In England

46. Another Croation international joined Derby in 1996. Name him.

47. **From which club did Everton buy Daniel Amokachi in 1994?**

48. What country does Amokachi represent?

49. **Which Norwegian international defender did Liverpool buy from Rosenborg?**

50. Name the Dutch goalkeeper who signed for Manchester United in 1996.

51. **From which club did he come from?**

52. Ronnie Johnsen joined Manchester United in 1996. Where from?

53. **Phillipe Albert joined Newcastle in 1994. From which club?**

54. And how much did he cost Newcastle?

55. **Which foreigner won consecutive championships with different English clubs?**

56. Who were Manchester United playing on the night of Eric Cantona's infamous "kung-fu kick"?

57. **Jordi Cruyff joined Manchester United from which club?**

58. Name the Manchester United star who joined them from Norwegian side Molde?

59. **Which Swedish winger has played for two Premiership sides?**

60. Which Italian side did he play for before joining Arsenal?

Quiz 11 — Foreign Players In England

61. **Where did Newcastle buy Colombian international Faustino Asprilla from?**

62. And how much did he cost?

63. **David Ginola came to Tyneside from which French side?**

64. Name the Croatian player who joined Nottingham Forest from Spanish side Real Ovieda?

65. **Who became the first Italian to play in the Premiership?**

66. From which club did Nottingham Forest buy him from?

67. **Another player joined Forest from Serie A in 1994. Who was he?**

68. How much did he cost?

69. **From which club did Aston Villa buy midfielder Sasa Curcic from?**

70. How much did they pay for him?

71. **Who was the first foreigner to captain a side in the FA Cup Final?**

72. Which World Cup star did West Ham buy from Espanol for £2.4million?

73. **Newcastle had a Czech Republic player in their 1996-97 squad. Who is he?**

74. Which Frenchman joined Chelsea in 1996?

75. **Which foreign player scored the Premiership's first hat-trick of the 96-97 season?**

61. **Parma** 62. £6.7m 63. **Paris St Germain** 64. Nikola Jerkan 65. **Andrea Silenzi** 66. Torino 67. **Brian Roy** 68. £2.5m 69. **Bolton** 70. £4m 71. **Eric Cantona** 72. Florin Raducioiu 73. **Pavel Srnicek** 74. Franck Leboeuf 75. **Fabrizio Ravanelli**

 Quiz 11 Foreign Players In England

76. Against which team did Fabrizio Ravanelli score his first Premiership goal?

77. **Which two English clubs has defender Ken Monkou played for?**

78. Which country did he come from?

79. **Name the Israeli international who plays for Totenham.**

80. Name the Icelandic international who played for Bolton in 1996-97?

81. **For which other English club has he played for?**

82. Which Croatian defender joined West Ham from German club Karlsruhe in 1995?

83. **Name the Danish defender who played in Euro '96 and played for West Ham in 1996-97?**

84. Who joined West Ham from AC Milan in the summer of 1996?

85. **Which Manchester United players former clubs are Hvidovre and Brondby?**

86. Which Premiership player scored in the Euro 96 final?

87. **Name the Australian who joined West Ham from West Adelaide.**

88. Name the Norwegian who played for Wimbledon in 1996-97.

89. **Which country does Liverpool goalkeeper Michael Stensgaard come from?**

90. How much did Jurgen Klinsmann cost Tottenham?

Quiz 11 — Foreign Players In England

91. Against which club did Klinsmann score his first Premiership goal?

92. Which Wimbledon midfielder was signed from Rosenberg?

93. Name the American goalkeeper who signed for Luton Town from West Ham in 1995.

94. Which Dutch defender moved to Sheffield United from Man.City in 1995?

95. Name the former Liverpool player who became player-manager of Swansea City in 1995-96.

96. Sheffield Wednesday paid £275,000 for a Dutch winger in 1996. Who was he?

97. From which club did he sign from?

98. Name the Dutch midfielder who has played for both Bolton and WBA?

99. From which country did Manchester City sign Mikhail Kavelashvili in March 1996?

100. How much did they pay for him?

101. Jorge Cadette joined Celtic in March '96. From which club?

102. What was the fee?

103. Name the two Swedish midfielders who joined Bolton in the summer of 1996.

104. Which Serie A player joined Glasgow Rangers in July 1996?

105. Name the only member of Portugals' Euro '96 squad to play in the 1996-97 Premiership.

Quiz 11 — Foreign Players In England

106. Which Danish international joined Tottenham for a fee of £1.65million?

107. From which club did he sign?

108. Name the Bolivian international who left the Premiership to join Washington DC

109. Name the Zimbabwe international who joined Plymouth in August 1996.

110. Which Belgium player joined Coventry for a fee of £1million in August 1996?

111. From which club did Tottenham sign Norwegian goalkeeper Espen Baardsen?

112. Which Liverpool star helped the Czech Republic qualify for Euro '96 with four goals in qualifying?

113. Which Manchester United star is nicknamed "the express train"?

114. Which Danish defender returned home after two unsuccessful seasons at Liverpool under Graeme Souness?

115. Name the Everton star who was part of the Danish Euro '96 squad.

116. Which Russsian international played for Chelsea in 1996-97?

117. Name the Swiss International who cost Tottenham £3.75million.

118. From which club did he sign?

119. Which Manchester United player is known as "The Milkman"?

120. Name the former Torino player who joined Grimsby in August 1996.

106. Allan Neilsen **107. Brondby** 108. Jaime Moreno **109. Bruce Grobbelaar** 110. Regis Genaux **111. San Francisco Blackhawks** 112. Patrik Berger **113. Karel Poborsky** 114. Torben Piechnik **115. Claus Thomsen** 116. Dmitri Kharine **117. Ramon Vega** 118. Cagliari **119. Peter Schmeichel** 120. Ivano Bonetti

 Quiz 11 Foreign Players In England

121. **Which former Serie A star left Glasgow Rangers in the summer of 1996?**

122. Name the French midfielder who joined Arsenal from AC Milan in August 1995?

123. **Which American player has played for Milwall and Leicester?**

124. Who did Egil Ostenstadt sign for in October '96?

125. **Name the Israeli midfielder who also joined Southampton in the same month.**

126. Name the Aston Villa player who scored a hat-trick in the World Cup Qualifying win against the Faroe Islands.

127. **Which Blackburn player scored Greece's only goal in the 2-1 defeat by Demark in a World Cup Qualifying game in October '96?**

128. Name the Croatian defender who helped Croatia to a 4-1 victory over Bosnia in the same month.

129. **Which former West Ham player scored two goals in Ajax's 4-1 Champions League game against Rangers in 1996?**

130. Name the two foreigners who scored five of Southampton's goals in their 6-3 victory against Manchester United.

131. **Which Dutch international scored a hat-trick against Wales in the 7-1 World Cup Qualifying win?**

132. From which club did Southampton sign defender Ulrich Van Gobbel?

133. **Name the former Inter Milan player who played for Sheffield Wednesday in 1996-97?**

134. Tottenham added to their Scandanavian contingent when they signed who from Norwegian side Rosenberg in November '96?

135. **How much did he cost?**

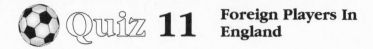

Quiz 11 — Foreign Players In England

136. Name the Norwegian defender who has played for both Leeds and Oldham.

137. **Which Ukrainian joined Coventry for a fee of £800,000 in January 1997?**

138. Who did Middlesbrough sign from Inter Milan during 1996-97?

139. **How much did Middlesbrough pay for him?**

140. At the same time Middlesbrough signed a player from Slaven Bratislava. Who was he?

141. **In February 1997, Blackburn signed a striker from Odense. Who?**

142. Name the goalkeeper who left Bradford to join Middlesbrough.

143. **Name the Dutch striker who joined Nottingham Forest for £4.5million in March '97.**

144. From which club did he sign?

145. **Name the two Costa Rican players who joined Derby in March '97.**

146. Name the former Spurs striker who was part of Belgium's 1986 World Cup squad that finished fourth.

147. **Name the Brazilian striker that Newcastle bought from Fluminense.**

148. Name the Argentinian World Cup winner who had an FA Cup Final song named after him.

149. **Which former Manchester United midfielder was part of the Danish World Cup side that reached the second round of the 1986 tournament?**

150. Name the former Tottenham goalkeeper that played in the 1994 World Cup Finals for Norway.

THE ULTIMATE FACT AND QUIZ BOOK

 **Quiz 11**   Foreign Players In England

151. **Name the Arsenal player who became renowned for his poor goalscoring record.**

152. From what club did he sign from?

153. **Name the Estonian goalkeeper who joined Derby in 1997?**

154. Which Premiership striker scored the winning goal that dented England's 1998 World Cup hopes?

155. **Which two foreigners scored the goals against Stockport that effectively put Middlesbrough into the Coca-Cola Cup Final in 1997?**

156. Name the Dutch defender that scored his first Premiership goal for Leeds v Everton in March 1997.

157. **Name the Norwegian midfielder that joined Nottingham Forest in 1993.**

158. Name the ex-Tottenham player that scored four goals for Romania in a World Cup qualifying game v Liechtenstein.

159. **Which Finnish international had a spell at Bolton?**

160. Who is the only foreigner to have captained a winning FA Cup Final side?

161. **Who was the first foreigner to play in an FA Cup Final?**

162. Which foreigner has made the most FA Cup Final appearances?

163. **Name the two Belgium born players that played in FA Cup Finals during the 1980's.**

164. Name the former Czeckoslovakian manager of Aston Villa.

165. **From which club did Arsene Wenger leave to manage Arsenal?**

151. John Jensen 152. Brondby 153. Mart Poom 154. Gianfranco Zola 155. Mikkel Beck and Fabrizio Ravanelli 156. Robert Molenaar 157. Alf-Inge Haaland 158. Gica Popescu 159. Mixu Paatelainen 160. Eric Cantona 161. Alfred Goodwin (India - 1872) 162. Bruce Grobbelaar (4) 163. Nico Claesen and Pat Van den Hauwe 164. Jozef Venglos 165. Grampus Eight

Quiz 11 — Foreign Players In England

166. What nationality is Lionel Perez, Sunderland's goalkeeper in 1996-97?

167. Name Sunderland's Polish defender in the 1996-97 season.

168. Which Real Zaragoza player scored the wonder goal that defeated Arsenal in the 1994 Cup-Winners' Cup Final?

169. Which Premiership side did he previously play for?

170. Name the Portuguese player who played for West Ham in 1996-97.

171. For which country does Georgiou Kinkladze play for?

172. From which club did Manchester City sign him from?

173. Although he has played for England, where was Matthew Le Tissier born?

174. Which Swedish international did Sheffield Wednesday buy from PSV Eindhoven for £2million in 1994?

175. Who did Liverpool sign from Rosenberg during the winter of 1996?

176. For which two Premiership clubs has Hans Segers played for?

177. In 1993 Sheffield United signed a Norwegian international for £400,000. Who was he?

178. Name the Bulgarian goalkeeper that appeared for Reading in the 96-97 season.

179. From which club did Arsenal sign French 17 year old Nicolas Anelka?

180. Who scored the winning goal for Tottenham in the 1981 FA Cup Final replay v Manchester City?

Quiz 11 — Foreign Players In England

181. **Which Bulgarian played for Aberdeen in the 1996-97 season?**

182. Which Danish striker, who played in Euro '96, moved to Rangers in March 1996 for £1.5m?

183. **Who did Everton sell Andrei Kanchelskis to in 1997?**

184. Which World Cup goalscorer played for Rangers in the 1995-96 season?

185. **Which Danish striker was voted Scottish Player of the Year in 1995?**

186. Which German striker played for Celtic in the 1996-97 season?

187. **Can you name his Italian strike partner?**

188. Who was George Graham's last signing at Arsenal?

189. **Where did Graham sign him from?**

190. Who have Blackburn signed rom Halmstad?

191. **Who is the Dutchman who played for Derby in 1996-97?**

192. What nationality is Leicester's Pontus Kaamark?

193. **Who was W.B.A Canadian striker in the 1996-97 season?**

194. Which German defender played for Manchester City in the 1995-96 season?

195. **Which American goalkeeper has played in the Premiership for a London club?**

---

181. **Iian Kiriakov** 182. Erik Bo Andersen 183. **Fiorentina** 184. Oleg Salenko
185. **Brian Laudrup** 186. Andreas Thom 187. **Paulo Di Canio** 188. Glenn
Helder 189. **Vitesse Arnhem** 190. Niklas Gudmundsson 191. **Robin Van der
Laan** 192. Swedish 193. **Paul Peschisolido** 194. Michael Frontzeck
195. **Juergen Sommer**

Quiz 12   The World Club Cup

1. **AC Milan played in the 1993 World Club Cup, despite finishing runners-up in the European Cup. Why?**

2. Who were the first British club to play in the World Club Cup?

3. **Who scored the winning goal for Celtic in their first leg match against Racing Club of Argentina in 1967?**

4. Who didn't play in Celtic's away leg in 1967 after being hit by a stone in the pre-match warm-up?

5. **The 1967 match went to a replay after a 2-2 aggregate score. The replay was a brutal which Celtic lost 1-0. How many players were sent-off in the game?**

6. Who was the Manchester United player sent-off in the 1968 first leg against Estudiantes?

7. **What was the score in that game?**

8. Another United player was sent-off in the return leg at Old Trafford. Who?

9. **What was the score in the second leg between United and Estudiantes in 1968?**

10. Who scored United's goal?

11. **Which United player had a 'goal' disallowed in the final minute of the 1968 match?**

12. Who were the first British club to win the World Club Cup?

13. **Which Premiership manager played for Nottingham Forest in the 1980 Final against Nacional?**

14. Why did European Cup runners-up Malmo play in the 1979 Final?

15. **Where was the 1980 Final played?**

---

1. **Marseille were stripped of European Cup because of match-fixing**
2. Celtic 3. **Billy McNeill** 4. Ron Simpson 5. **Five** 6. Nobby Stiles 7. 1-0 to
Estudiantes 8. George Best 9. 1-1 10. Willie Morgan 11. **Brian Kidd** 12. No
British club has won it 13. **Martin O'Neill** 14. Forest declined to take part
15. Tokyo

Quiz 12   The World Club Cup

16. Which famous Brazilian played for Flamenco against Liverpool in the 1981 Final?

17. **What was the score in the 1981 Final?**

18. Who was Liverpool's goalkeeper in that game?

19. **Two of Liverpool's players in the 1981 Final became management colleagues in 1997. Who are they?**

20. Kenny Dalglish played in the 1981 Final for Liverpool. Which other player in that game went on to become a manager at Anfield?

21. **Who did Aston Villa lose to in the 1983 Final?**

22. Which goalkeeper won one cap for England and played for Aston Villa in the 1981 Final?

23. **Liverpool did not take part in the 1977 Final against Boca Juniors. Who took their place?**

24. How many appearances have four-time European Champions, Liverpool, made in the World Club Cup?

25. **Which Argentinian played for Independiente against Liverpool in 1984 and later went on to score in the 1986 World Cup Final?**

26. Who were the last British side to compete in the World Club Cup?

27. **What year was it?**

28. Which Danish international played in Liverpool's 1984 defeat?

29. **Which former England striker played for Nottingham Forest in the 1980 Final?**

30. Which Aston Villa player played in the 1982 Final, and was still playing for the club in 1994?

16. Zico 17. 3-0 to Flamenco 18. Bruce Grobbelaar 19. Kenny Dalglish and Terry McDermott 20. Graeme Souness 21. Penarol of Uruguay 22. Jimmy Rimmer 23. Borussia Moenchengladbach 24. Two 25. Jorge Burruchaga 26. Liverpool 27. 1984 28. Jan Molby 29. Trevor Francis 30. Gordon Cowans

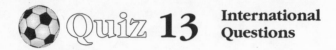

Quiz 13 International Questions

1. **What was the score between England and Germany when they met in America in 1993?**

2. Who scored for England in that game?

3. **Who was in goal for the disastrous 2-0 World Cup Qualifying defeat in Norway in 1992?**

4. Who scored a stunning free-kick for England against Holland at Wembley in the same year?

5. **Who got a brace of goals for England against Turkey in 1992?**

6. What was the score in England's friendly against Brazil in May 1992?

7. **Which two England players made their full international debuts in the 1-0 win in Hungary in 1991?**

8. Which striker scored on his England debut against France in Feburary 1992?

9. **Who were England's opponents at Wembley in September 1991 for the first defeat of Graham Taylors's reign?**

10. Who made his England debut against USSR in May 1991 as a substitute?

11. **Who returned to the England side for the European Championship Qualifier against Ireland in Dublin in 1990?**

12. Which North African country did England play in their last friendly prior to the 1990 World Cup?

13. **Who defeated England at Wembley in May 1990?**

14. Who scored twice against Czechoslovakia in March 1990 at Wembley?

15. **Who scored for England against Yugoslavia at Wembley earlier that same year?**

Quiz 13 International Questions

16. Who were England's opponents for three successive goalless draws in 1989?

17. **Who came on to score on his England debut at Hampden Park in 1989?**

18. Which Middle Eastern country gained a 1-1 draw with England in 1988?

19. **Who did Paul Gascoigne make his England debut against?**

20. Which South American country drew 1-1 with England in May 1988?

21. **Who were beaten 8-0 at Wembley in October 1987?**

22. Which Premiership manager made his last full international appearance against West Germany in September 1987?

23. **Who scored all four goals in England's win over Spain in Madrid in 1987?**

24. Which nation beat England 1-0 in September 1987?

25. **Who scored two goals in England's win over Mexico in a friendly prior to the 1986 World Cup Finals?**

26. Which current manager ended his international career against Scotland at Wembley in 1986?

27. **Who scored in England's 3-0 win over West Germany in 1985?**

28. Who did Gary Lineker score his first international goal against?

29. **Which goalkeeper made his debut in that same game?**

30. Which two players shared the goals in England's 4-1 win over Finland in 1982?

16. Sweden, Poland and Italy 17. **Steve Bull** 18. Saudi Arabia 19. **Denmark** 20. Colombia 21. **Turkey** 22. Peter Reid 23. **Gary Lineker** 24. Sweden 25. **Mark Hateley** 26. Trevor Francis 27. **Kerry Dixon (2) and Bryan Robson** 28. Republic of Ireland 29. **Gary Bailey** 30. Bryan Robson and Paul Mariner

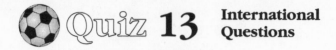

Quiz 13 — International Questions

31. **Which former West Ham winger made his only two England appearances in 1982?**

32. Against whom did Bryan Robson make his England debut in 1980?

33. **Which side crushed England 4-1 in the 1979/80 season?**

34. Who scored for England in the 4-3 defeat in Austria in 1979?

35. **Who scored the England goals in the 2-0 win over Italy at Wembley in 1977?**

36. Which player scored for England against Finland in October 1976?

37. **What was the score when England beat Scotland in May 1975?**

38. Which country were beaten 7-0 by England at Wembley in 1973?

39. **Which country became the first to win at Wembley in six years when they won 3-1 in a European Championship Qualifier in April 1972?**

40. Who were beaten 6-1 by England in a 1966 World Cup warm up game?

41. **Who scored four goals in that game?**

42. Who beat England 5-1 in 1964?

43. **Who did England beat 10-0 in 1964?**

44. Which players scored four and three goals respectively in that game?

45. **Who left Wembley in 1963 having been thrashed 8-3?**

31. **Alan Devonshire** 32. Switzerland 33. **Wales** 34. Ray Wilkins, Kevin Keegan and Steve Coppell 35. **Kevin Keegan and Trevor Brooking.** 36. Joe Royle 37. **5-1** 38. Austria 39. **West Germany** 40. Norway 41. **Jimmy Greaves** 42. Brazil 43. **USA** 44. Roger Hunt and Fred Pickering 45. **Northern Ireland**

Quiz 13 — International Questions

46. Jimmy Greaves scored four goals in that game but who notched a hat-trick?

47. **Which side did England also put eight past in that same year?**

48. Which goalkeeper conceded five in a European Championship Qualifier in Paris in 1963?

49. **Who scored in the famous 9-3 Wembley win over Scotland in 1961?**

50. Who did England also score nine and eight goals respectively against that year?

51. **Which side beat England 5-0 in a warm up game for the 1958 World Cup finals?**

52. In what year did Bobby Charlton make his England debut?

53. **Which former England coach also played in that game?**

54. Against which South American country did Bobby Moore make his debut?

55. **Which home nation were beaten 10-0 by England on their ground in 1947?**

56. Who did England lose to in the first friendly after the disastrous 1992 European Championship?

57. **What was the score when England beat a Milla-less Cameroon at Wembley in Feburary 1991?**

58. **How many goals did England manage during three friendlies with Australia in June 1983?**

59. **Which country beat England 4-1 in May 1959?**

60. Who did England play in their first game after the 1966 World Cup?

---

46. Terry Paine 47. **Switzerland** 48. Ron Springett 49. **Bobby Robson, Jimmy Greaves (3), Bobby Smith (2), Johnny Haynes (2), and Bryan Douglas** 50. Luxembourg and Mexico 51. **Yugoslavia** 52. 1958 53. **Don Howe** 54. Peru 55. **Portugal** 56. Spain 57. **2-0** 58. Two 59. **Peru** 60. Northern Ireland

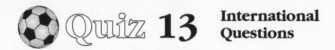

Quiz 13 — International Questions

61. **What was the score in the famous England-Hungary game at Wembley in 1953?**

62. In the return game in Budapest the following year how many goals did Hungary put past the hapless England defence?

63. **Which former England manager scored twice in the 5-1 win in Denmark in 1955?**

64. Who was the first substitute to be used by England?

65. **Who were the only country to keep a clean sheet against England between May 1955 and May 1958?**

66. Which England player grabbed four goals in the 7-2 win over Scotland in April 1955?

67. **Who scored for England in the 3-1 win over West Germany in Berlin in 1956?**

68. Which players scored twice in England's 7-0 rout of Austria in 1973?

69. **Which England player scored twice in the 5-1 win over Scotland in 1975?**

70. Who scored the only goal in Budapest in May 1992?

71. **Which player scored on his debut in the World Cup Qualifier in Turkey in May 1991?**

72. Who played in goal for England against Brazil in 1978?

73. **Who scored twice for England in the 3-0 win over Czechoslovakia in 1974?**

74. Which Chairman scored in the 1-1 draw with Wales in April 1970?

75. **Against which nation did Peter Shilton make his England debut?**

---

61. 6-3 to Hungary 62. Seven **63. Don Revie 64.** James Mullen (of Wolves)
65. Sweden 66. Denis Wilshaw **67. Johnny Haynes, Duncan Edwards and Colin Grainger 68.** Mike Channon and Allan Clarke **69. Gerry Francis 70.** Neil Webb **71. Dennis Wise 72.** Joe Corrigan **73. Colin Bell 74.** Francis Lee
75. East Germany

 **Quiz 13** International Questions

76. Which country defeated England 1-0 at Wembley in May 1972?

77. **Which England players scored twice in the 5-2 win over Belguim in 1947?**

78. Who scored four goals for England in the 9-2 victory over Northern Ireland in 1949?

79. **Which England midfielder scored twice in the 4-0 win at home to Norway in September 1980?**

80. Who came on as a substitute to grab the equaliser away to lowly Iceland in his only England appearance in June 1982?

81. **Who scored twice for England in the impressive 3-1 win over World Champions Argentina in May 1980?**

82. Who plundered all five England goals in the win over Cyprus in April 1975?

83. **Who scored the goals in the 2-2 draw with Argentina in May 1974?**

84. From which Scandanavian country did England beat 5-1 in 1956?

85. **Which England defender made his debut in the 1-0 win away to Holland in 1969?**

86. Who scored the only goal of that game?

87. **Which former Ipswich player scored his only England goal in the 5-1 win over Scotland in 1975?**

88. Which ground staged England's 1995 Umbro Cup match against Sweden?

89. **Who scored his first England goal in that game?**

90. Which country conceded five goals at Wembley in May 1994?

Quiz 13 — International Questions

91. Which nation defeated Scotland at Hampden in March 1994?

92. Who scored the goals in Scotland's 2-1 win against Austria in April 1994?

93. Who scored the Scottish goal in the 1-1 draw with Switzerland in the World Cup Qualifier in September 1993?

94. Which Premiership player grabbed the consolation goal in Scotland's 3-1 defeat in Rome the following month?

95. Which country did Scotland beat 6-1 in September 1984?

96. Which East European country did Scotland beat in Glasgow in March 1986?

97. Which nation did Scotland beat 7-2 in 1929?

98. Which Middle Eastern country embarrassed Scotland 3-1 in their only ever meeting, at Hampden in 1990?

99. What was the score in the inaugural game with the 'Auld Enemy'?

100. Who scored for Scotland in the 1-1 draw with Russia at Hampden in 1994?

101. Against which country did Denis Law make his Scottish debut?

102. Who scored Scotland's winnner against England in November 1964?

103. Who scored Scotland's goal against Spain in Valencia in 1975?

104. Which striker scored the Scotland goal in the draw with Belguim in 1983?

105. Where did Wales and Scotland meet in their 1977 World Cup Play-Off game?

91. Holland 92. Tosh McKinlay and Billy McGinlay 93. **John Collins** 94. Kevin Gallacher 95. **Yugoslavia** 96. Romania 97. **Norway** 98. Egypt 99. 0-0 100. Scott Booth 101. **Holland** 102. Alan Gilzean 103. **Joe Jordan** 104. Charlie Nicholas 105. **Anfield**

 **Quiz 13** International Questions

106. What was the result of that game?

107. Who scored a hat-trick for Wales in their 1957 World Cup Qualifier against East Germany?

108. Which country beat Northern Ireland 8-2 in the 1950 British Championship?

109. Which nation beat Northern Ireland for qualification to the 1978 World Cup Finals?

110. Which two countries did Northern Irleand beat in that group?

111. Who is Northern Ireland's most capped player?

112. Which Republic of Ireland player was sent-off against Macedonia in a 1998 World Cup qualifyer?

113. Name the three England players of the early 1990's who started their careers at Crewe?

114. Which striker won two caps for England, but played only 18 minutes?

115. Which England international was once loaned out to Aldershot early in his career?

116. Who was the last British player to be voted European Footballer of the Year?

117. When Matthias Sammer made his debut for Germany, it was his 24th cap. How come?

118. Who, in 1993, became the first black player to captain England?

119. In one of soccer's biggest tragedy's which national team was killed in a plane crash en-route to a 1993 World Cup qualifyer?

120. Who was named new England captain after Euro 96?

---

106. 2-0 to Scotland **107. Palmer** 108. Scotland **109. Holland** 110. Iceland and Belgium **111. Pat Jennings** 112. Jason McAteer **113. David Platt, Geoff Thomas and Rob Jones** 114. Kevin Hector **115. Teddy Sheringham** 116. Kevin Kegan **117. He had made 23 appearances for East Germany before the two countries united** 118. Paul Ince **119. Zambia** 120. Alan Shearer

Quiz 14 — Scottish League And Cup

1. **Who scored Rangers' winning goal in the 1971 Scottish League Cup Final?**

2. What was the score recorded in the 1984 Scottish Cup, which remains a British record this century?

3. **Who was Scotland's Player of the Year in 1996?**

4. Which team beat Celtic 3-1 in the 1970 Scottish Cup Final?

5. **Which Scottish club signed Norwich City's Kevin Drinkell for £500,000 at the start of the 1987-88 season?**

6. Who was voted Scotland's Young Player of the Year in 1981?

7. **Which two teams shared the Division One title in the first season in 1891?**

8. Who won the first Scottish Premier Division in 1976?

9. **Who was voted Player of the Year by the Scottish Football Writers in 1974?**

10. Which former Chelsea star was voted Second Division Player of the Year by the SFA in 1982?

11. **Which Dutchman was voted Premier Division Player of the Year by the SFA in 1989?**

12. Who was the first player since 1972 to score a hat-trick in the Scottish FA Cup Final in 1996?

13. **Where were both Scottish FA Cup semi-finals played in 1996?**

14. Who did Celtic beat in the 1995 Scottish FA Cup Final?

15. **Who won six of the first nine Scottish FA Cup Finals?**

1. **Derek Johnstone** 2. Stirling Albion 20 Selkirk 0 in 1984 3. **Paul Gascoigne** 4. Aberdeen 5. **Rangers** 6. Charlie Nicholas 7. **Dumbarton and Rangers** 8. Rangers 9. **The Scotland World Cup Squad** 10. Pat Nevin 11. **Theo Snelders** 12. Gordon Durie 13. **Hampden Park** 14. Airdrieonians 15. **Queen's Park**

Quiz 14 — Scottish League And Cup

16. When was the first Rangers-Celtic Scottish FA Cup Final?

17. Who won?

18. Why was the FA Cup withheld in 1909?

19. Which team won the FA Cup four times in five seasons in the early 1980's?

20. Who was voted Scottish Manager of the Year in 1990?

21. Before the end of the 1996-97 season, who was the last Scottish player to be voted Player of the Year by the SFA?

22. What year was it?

23. What was the highest score in the Scottish FA Cup, and still a British record?

24. What year was it in?

25. On that same day Dundee Harp beat which team 35-0 in the Cup?

26. 11 goals were scored in the Premier Division game between Celtic and Hamilton in January 1987. What was the score-line?

27. How many goals did Celtic score when the two teams met again in November 1988?

28. Which Scottish team holds the British record score this century?

29. Nine players scored that day. Which player got seven goals?

30. Which Dundee United striker scored five times in the Premier Division against Morton in November 1984?

Quiz 14 Scottish League and Cup

31. Which Ayr player set a British record of 66 League goals in one season in 1927-28?

32. When Arbroath beat Bon Accord in the 1885 Scottish Cup, how many goals did John Petrie score?

33. Who is the Scottish League's top scorer with 410 goals?

34. Which player scored 338 League goals in a career that started at St Mirren and finished at Clapton Orient?

35. Which club did Gerry Baker score 10 goals against for St Mirren in the 1960 Scottish Cup first round?

36. Which team scored 142 goals in just 34 League games in the 1937-38 season?

37. Which team conceded just 19 goals in 36 Premier Division games in 1990?

38. Who scored the fastest goal in Scottish Cup history for Aberdeen in 1982?

39. How many seconds was it?

40. Which former Motherwell striker, later to play for Liverpool, scored the fastest hat-trick in Scottish history in 1959?

41. Which Scottish goalkeeper scored for Hibernian in 1988?

42. Who did he score against?

43. Which other goalkeeper has scored in a League match?

44. Which Danish striker scored in 15 consecutive matches for Dundee United in 1964-65?

45. Which Scottish club went 14 consecutive games without scoring to set a British record?

31. Jimmy Smith 32. 13 33. Jimmy McGrory 34. Dave Halliday 35. Glasgow University 36. Raith Rovers 37. Rangers 38. John Hewitt 39. 9.6 40. Ian St John 41. Andy Goram 42. Morton 43. Ray Charles - for East Fife in 1990 44. Finn Dossing 45. Stirling Albion

Quiz 14 — Scottish League And Cup

46. Which two Scottish teams attracted an attendance of 143,470 in March 1948?

47. **How many people were inside Hampden Park for the 1937 Scottish Cup Final?**

48. 135,826 turned up to watch Celtic play an European Cup semi-final in 1970. Which other British team were they playing?

49. **What is the record attendance for a Scottish League Cup Final?**

50. Which two teams were playing?

51. **Who captained Aberdeen to Scottish Cup glory in 1970, and then led Manchester United to FA Cup glory seven years later?**

52. Four players were sent-off when Rangers faced Celtic in the Scottish Cup quarter-final in 1991. Can you name the players?

53. **Which former Scottish international was sent-off 11 times in Scottish matches?**

54. How many times was he sent-off for Scotland?

55. **Which two Hearts players were suspended by the Scottish FA for fighting each other in a 'friendly' game?**

56. Billy McLafferty was banned for eight-and-a-half months and fined £250 by the Scottish FA. Why?

57. **Which club was he playing for at the time?**

58. Which former Rangers striker was banned for 12 games for violent conduct in a game against Raith in 1994?

59. **Which manager was also chairman of the club at the same time, in 1988?**

60. Which club was he at?

---

46. Rangers and Hibernian 47. 146,433 48. Leeds 49. 107,609 50. Celtic and Rangers 51. **Martin Buchan** 52. Terry Hurlock, Mark Walters and Mark Hateley of Rangers and Peter Grant of Celtic 53. **Willie Johnston** 54. Once 55. **Graeme Hogg and Craig Levein** 56. Because he had failed to turn up to a disciplinary hearing after being sent-off 57. **Stenhousemuir** 58. Duncan Ferguson 59. **Jim McLean** 60. Dundee United

 **Quiz 14** Scottish League And Cup

61. 66 people died when they were trampled near the end of the Rangers-Celtic match in 1971. Where did the tragedy happen

62. Which Celtic goalkeeper died after suffering a fractured skull against Rangers in 1931?

63. How was the 1987 Scottish League Cup Final decided?

64. Who won the game?

65. What was the penalty shoot-out score between Aberdeen and Celtic in the 1990 Scottish Cup Final?

66. Celtic lost the Scottish League Cup Final on penalties. To which side?

67. Which team won every match in the Scottish League in the 1898-99 season?

68. Before the 1997-98 season, how many times have Rangers completed the League and Cup double?

69. Before the 1997-98 season, how many times have Rangers completed the domestic treble?

70. How many trophies did Celtic win in the 1966-67 season?

71. Who were the last club to win the Scottish Cup for three years in succession?

72. When was that?

73. Before the 1997 Final, who are the three players to be sent-off in Scottish Cup Finals?

74. Who holds the record for unbeaten matches in the Scottish League?

75. How many games were they unbeaten?

61. Rangers' Ibrox Park 62. John Thomson **64. Penalties** 64. Rangers, beating Aberdeen 65. 9-8 to Aberdeen 66. Raith Rovers **67. Rangers** 68. 14 **69. Five** 70. Five **71. Aberdeen** 72. 1982-83-84 **73. Jock Buchanan, Roy Aitken and Walter Kidd** 74. Celtic **75. 62 matches**

THE ULTIMATE FACT AND QUIZ BOOK

Quiz 14 — Scottish League And Cup

76. Who became the first player to score 200 goals in the Premier Division?

77. **Which team set a Scottish League record of 40 consecutive home defeats in the 1990's?**

78. Which team collected a total of 67 points out of a possible 72 in the 1963-64 season?

79. **Which Rangers player won nine Scottish Championship medals in 11 years?**

80. Who were the first Scottish club to play in the European Cup?

81. **What season was it?**

82. Which round did they reach?

83. **What season was the first Premier Division played?**

84. Who were the sponsors of the 1996-97 Scottish FA Cup?

85. **What year did the Scottish FA introduce penalty shoot-outs to the Cup Final?**

86. Who provided the shock of the 1995 Scottish Cup by beating Aberdeen 2-0?

87. **Who did Tommy Burns leave to become manager of Celtic?**

88. Which manager was fined £2,000 by the SFA for breach of contract?

89. **When was the Scottish FA formed?**

90. Who became the youngest player in the Scottish League when he played for Queen's Park in 1946?

 **Quiz 14** Scottish League And Cup

91. How old was he?

92. Who remains the oldest player to earn his first cap for Scotland?

93. How old was he - and who did he play against?

94. Which two Scottish sides shared Firhill Park for five years?

95. Which Scottish club play their home games at Hampden Park?

96. Who were the first Scottish club to have an artificial pitch?

97. Which goalkeeper played for Scotland Under-21's in the afternoon and then turned out for Clyde that same evening?

98. Who were the first Scottish club to issue a Stock Exchange share issue?

99. Which two Scottish clubs have won the European Cup-Winners Cup?

100. Which Scottish club beat Eintracht Frankfurt 5-1 in an Uefa Cup first round, second leg, after losing the first leg 3-0?

101. Which clubs did Alex Ferguson play for?

102. How many Scottish League clubs did Alex Ferguson manage before joining Manchester United?

103. Name them.

104. Who was named Scottish Manager of the Year in 1995?

105. Which goalkeeper was named 1981 Player of the Year?

---

91. 15 92. Ronnie Simpson 93. 36 - **against England** 94. Partick Thistle and Clyde
95. Queen's Park 96. Stirling Albion 97. **Scott Howie** 98. Hibernian 99. **Rangers
and Aberdeen** 100. Kilmarnock 101. **Queen's Park, St Johnstone,
Dunfermline, Rangers, Falkirk and Ayr United** 102. Three 103. **East
Stirling, St Mirren and Aberdeen** 104. Jimmy Nicholl (Raith) 105. **Alan Rough**

 Quiz 15 Irish League and Cup

1. **How many times have Moyola Park won the Irish F. A. Cup?**

2. Who were the Irish League champions in 1982?

3. **In the 1995-96 Irish Premier Division, who finished higher, Glenavon or Glentoran?**

4. Waterford were FAI League Champions for three consecutive seasons. Name the years.

5. **Who was the 1996 Irish Premier Division Player of the Year?**

6. Name the 1996 Smirnoff Irish Premier Division Manager of the Year.

7. **In the replay of the 1996 FAI Cup Final, how many players with the surname Geoghegan played in the Shelbourne side?**

8. Which club were relegated from the Irish Premier Division at the end of the 1995 - 96 season?

9. **In the 1995-96 FAI Premier Division, which club had three points deducted for fielding players deemed to be 'illegal' ?**

10. Who scored the winning goal for Glentoran in last year's Irish Cup Final?

11. **The 1996 Bord Gais FAI League Cup Final between Shelbourne and Sligo Rovers was decided on penalties. Who won and what was the score?**

12. Who were the Irish League Champions in 1976?

13. **How many times have Shamrock Rovers completed the FAI League and Cup double ?**

14. Who was the 1995-96 FAI Premier Division's Young Player of the Year?

15. **Who was the 1995-96 Irish Premier Division's top scorer?**

goals

13. **Six** 14. Mick O'Byrne (U.C.D.) 15. **Gary Haylock (Portadown) with 20**
8. Bangor 9. **U.C.D.** 10. Glen Little 11. **Shelbourne, 4-3** 12. Crusaders
5. **Peter Kennedy (Portadown)** 6. Ron McFall (Portadown) 7. **Two**
1. **Once - in 1881** 2. Linfield 3. **Glentoran** 4. 1967-68, 1968-69, 1969-70

Quiz 16 — Welsh League And Cup

1. Which team beat Barry Town on penalties to win the 1996 Welsh Cup?

2. Who won the first Welsh Cup?

3. Who did they beat in the Final?

4. Which team won the Welsh Cup for five consecutive years from 1967?

5. Who did Cardiff City lose the Cup Final to in 1939?

6. Which team appeared in the Cup Final on six occasions in eight years from 1887?

7. When was the last time Aberwystwyth won the Welsh Cup?

8. Which non-league team did Cardiff City beat in the 1992 Cup Final?

9. Cardiff City played in 11 consecutive Cup Finals from 1967. True or False?

10. Who were the Welsh League Champions in 1995?

11. Who did Swansea beat 8-0 in the Welsh Cup quarter-finals in 1995?

12. Bangor City won 12-1 in the fourth round of the 1995 Welsh Cup fourth round. Who were their victims?

13. Shrewsbury lost the 1931 Cup Final 7-0. To who?

14. Which famous non-league side reached the Cup Final twice in the 1980's?

15. Who were the first club to win the Welsh Cup in a penalty shoot-out?

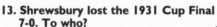

1. Llansantffraid 2. Wrexham 3. Druids 4. Cardiff City 5. South Liverpool 6. Chirk 7. 1900 8. Hednesford 9. True 10. Bangor City 11. Porthmadog 12. Maesteg Park Athletic 13. Wrexham 14. Kidderminster 15. Llansantffraid

Quiz 17 — The Carling Premiership 1995-96

1. **Who broke his leg in the 1-1 draw between Blackburn and Middlesbrough in December?**

2. Who scored after just 12 seconds against Coventry in September 1995?

3. **Who became the youngest Premiership player when he turned out for West Ham at Manchester City on New Year's Day in 1996?**

4. Who scored a hat-trick on the opening day of the season but was still on the losing side?

5. **Who scored Manchester United's consolation goal in a 3-1 defeat at Aston Villa on the opening day of the season?**

6. Why did Manchester United change their grey away kit at half-time at Southampton in the 1995-96 season?

7. **Who scored Leeds' two goals in their win at West Ham?**

8. Who was sent-off for West Ham at Manchester United in 1995-96?

9. **Who scored three goals in the first three games for Manchester United in the 1995-96 season?**

10. Defending champions, Blackburn, lost three of their first four games of the season. Which clubs beat them?

11. **Which former Everton players scored for the club against Southampton in 1995-96?**

12. Which striker scored against his former club for Nottingham Forest in a 1-1 draw in August?

13. **Which two foreign players scored for Coventry in a 2-2 draw at Chelsea in the 1995-96 season?**

14. Which Belgian international scored for Sheffield Wednesday at Wimbledon?

15. **Which veteran striker scored the only goal for Wimbledon against Liverpool in September?**

Quiz 17 — The Carling Premiership 1995-96

16. Which three England internationals scored for Liverpool in their 3-0 win against Blackburn in September 1995?

17. **Who scored his first two goals for Arsenal in a 4-2 win against Southampton?**

18. Robbie Fowler scored four times against Bolton in a 5-2 victory but who scored the other Liverpool goal?

19. **Who crowned his Middlesbrough debut with a goal in the opening day draw at Arsenal?**

20. Eric Cantona capped his return from suspension to score from the penalty spot to equalise for Manchester United in the 2-2 draw against Liverpool. Who scored United's first goal?

21. **Who scored for Chelsea against his former club but lost the match 4-1 in October?**

22. Chris Armstrong scored his first goal for Tottenham against which club?

23. **What was the scoreline when Manchester City played at Liverpool in October?**

24. Manchester City won their first league of the season against Bolton. But what month was it in?

25. **Who beat Nottingham Forest 7-0 in November?**

26. Who scored both Everton goals in the Merseyside derby at Anfield?

27. **Manchester United scored three goals in the first eight minutes in a 4-1 win in November. Against which team?**

28. Who won the North London derby at White Hart Lane?

29. **Who scored a hat-trick but was on the losing side against Shefield Wednesday in December?**

30. Blackburn were beaten 5-0 in December. By who?

16. Jamie Redknapp, Robbie Fowler and Stan Collymore 17. **Dennis Bergkamp**
18. Steve Harkness 19. **Nick Barmby** 20. Nicky Butt 21. **Mark Hughes (v Manchester United)** 22. Everton 23. **6-0 to Liverpool** 24. November
25. **Blackburn** 26. Andrei Kanchelskis 27. **Southampton** 28. Tottenham (2-1)
29. **Coventry's Dion Dublin** 30. Coventry

Quiz 17   The Carling Premiership 1995-96

31. **Who was sent-off for West Ham in their 3-0 defeat at Everton in December?**

32. Who was beaten 6-2 by Sheffield Wednesday in December?

33. **Which player scored five goals in two games against Coventry in the 1995-96 season?**

34. Who scored all four goals for Liverpool when they twice met Manchester United in the season?

35. **Which former Tottenham player scored against his old club in Bolton's 2-2 draw in December?**

36. Who did Leeds beat 3-1 on Christmas Eve?

37. **Who was sent-off in Wimbledon's 2-1 defeat of Chelsea on Boxing Day?**

38. Which two England internationals scored two of the four goals that Tottenham put past Manchester United on New Year's day?

39. **Who scored an injury time winner for Chelsea against QPR in January?**

40. Which two players scored twice when Liverpool beat Leeds 5-0 at Anfield in January?

41. **Who scored Manchester United's only goal in their win at West Ham?**

42. Who scored a hat-trick for Chelsea in a 5-0 victory against Middlesbrough in February?

43. **Which foreign star won the Tottenham-West Ham match with a goal after five minutes?**

44. Who won 4-1 at Middlesbrough in February?

45. **How many goals did Manchester United put past Bolton when they met in February?**

---

31. **Ludek Miklosko** 32. Leeds 33. **Savo Milosevic** 34. Robbie Fowler
35. **Gudni Bergsson** 36. Manchester United 37. **Vinnie Jones** 38. Teddy
Sheringham, Sol Campbell 39. **Paul Furlong** 40. Neil Ruddock and Robbie Fowler
41. **Eric Cantona** 42. Gavin Peacock 43. **Dani** 44. Bolton 45. **Six**

Quiz 17 — The Carling Premiership 1995-96

46. Which two Chelsea players scored when they met Wimbledon in March?

47. **Which team scored three goals in eight minutes against Aston Villa in March?**

48. Who scored twice for Arsenal in their 3-1 victory over Manchester City in March?

49. **Which Dutch international scored both goals in Sheffield Wednesday's 3-2 defeat at Aston Villa?**

50. 50,028 watched the Manchester United-Arsenal match in March. What was the score?

51. **Arsenal beat Newcastle 2-0 in March. Which Scottish defender scored the first goal?**

52. The 4-3 win for Liverpool against Newcastle was dubbed "game of the decade". Who scored Newcastle's three goals?

53. **Who scored the winner in the Manchester derby in April?**

54. Which striker scored twice to help Blackburn beat Newcastle at Ewood Park?

55. **Who scored his first hat-trick for Chelsea in the 4-1 victory over Leeds in April?**

56. Blackburn's 5-1 win at Nottingham Forest included two goals from an England international. Who was it?

57. **Who scored Manchester United's consolation in their 3-1 defeat at Southampton?**

58. What was the result at Goodison Park in the Merseyside derby?

59. **Who scored a hat-trick for Everton in their 5-2 win at Sheffield Wednesday in April?**

60. When Manchester United beat Nottingham Forest 5-0 who scored twice?

 **Quiz 17** The Carling Premiership 1995-96

61. Who scored Newcastle's only goal in a 1-0 win at Leeds?

62. Which England international scored twice at Elland Road in Tottenham's 3-1 win in May?

63. Which two internationals scored in the last ten minutes to give Arsenal a 2-1 win over Bolton on the last day of the season?

64. Who scored a goal on his last appearance for the club when Manchester City and Liverpool drew on the final day of the season?

65. Manchester United won the Premiership title with a 3-0 win at Middlesbrough. Who scored their goals?

66. Which team beat West Ham 3-0 but ended the day relegated?

67. Which team claimed the last Uefa Cup on the final day of the season?

68. Which two teams both had goalless draws on the last day of the season to stave off relegation?

69. Which German made his debut for Manchester City in the opening day draw against Tottenham?

70. Who scored the Goal of the Season?

71. Who scored three goals in the first two games of the season for his new club?

72. Who scored and was later sent-off in Wimbledon's 3-0 win at QPR in August?

73. Who scored the only goal of the game on his debut for Liverpool against Sheffield Wednesday?

74. Who did Bolton beat for their first win in the Premiership?

75. Andrea Silenzi became the first Italian to play in the Premiership when he joined Nottingham Forest. How many league goals did he score in his first season?

---

61. Keith Gillespie 62. Darren Anderton 63. David Platt and Dennis Bergkamp 64. Liverpool's Ian Rush 65. David May, Andy Cole and Ryan Giggs 66. QPR 67. Arsenal 68. Southampton and Coventry 69. Eike Immel 70. Tony Yeboah 71. Les Ferdinand (Newcastle) 72. Dean Holdsworth 73. Stan Collymore 74. Blackburn 75. None

Quiz 17 — The Carling Premiership 1995-96

76. Which Wimbledon player thought he had been sent-off against Liverpool, instead of Vinnie Jones?

77. Who had his sending-off revolked in September?

78. Who scored twice for QPR in a 3-1 win at Leeds in September?

79. Who made his Liverpool debut against Blackburn in September?

80. Who was sent-off for West Ham at Arsenal in September?

81. Who scored against his former club for Newcastle in a 3-2 win in October?

82. Who scored on his debut for Blackburn in a 2-1 win over Southampton in October?

83. Who earned a three-match suspension after stamping on Chelsea's John Spencer's head?

84. Who replaced sent-off Paul Heald as Wimbledon goalkeeper when they lost 6-1 at Newcastle?

85. Who scored a last-minute winner for Newcastle over Liverpool in November?

86. Who made his debut for Middlesbrough in their 1-1 draw against Leeds in November?

87. Who lost their record 25-game unbeaten run with a 7-0 defeat at Blackburn?

88. Who scored a superb goal for Bolton in their 3-2 defeat at Chelsea in November?

89. Who made his Premiership debut at the age of 34 for QPR in December?

90. Which England player was sent-off for Arsenal at Southampton in December?

76. Andy Thorn **77. Vinnie Jones** 78. Daniele Dichio **79. Jason McAteer** 80. Julian Dicks **81. Les Ferdinand** 82. Lars Bohinen **83. Julian Dicks** 84. Vinnie Jones **85. Steve Watson** 86. Juninho **87. Nottingham Forest** 88. Sasa Curcic **89. Mark Hateley** 90. Tony Adams

 **Quiz 18** The World Cup

1. **The United States finished in third place in which World Cup?**

2. Who failed a routine drugs test in the 1994 World Cup and as a result was expelled from the competition?

3. **This Colombian player scored an own goal when playing the United States in the 1994 World Cup. What was his name and what happened when he returned home?**

4. Which two past winners failed to qualify for the 1994 World Cup finals?

5. **Name the three countries to make their World Cup debut in the 1994 finals?**

6. Who was Brazil's captain in the 1970 World Cup?

7. **Which manager recieved a one-match touchline ban and a £10,000 fine from FIFA in the 1994 finals?**

8. In the World Cup campaigns of 1990 and 1994 Ireland have played nine games. How many did they actually win?

9. **The United States played Brazil in the second round of the 1994 World Cup. What was the score?**

10. Who beat USA 7-1 in the 1934 World Cup?

11. **Wales missed out on qualifying for the 1994 World Cup. Who was their manager at the time?**

12. Altogether there were 52 games played in the 1990 World Cup. How many players were sent off?

13. **Which captain has led two losing teams in the World Cup finals?**

14. Which team beat the defending champions Argentina in the opening match of the 1990 World Cup finals?

15. **Who was the top goalscorer of the 1990 World Cup?**

1. **1930 World Cup - Uruguay** 2. Diego Maradona 3. **Andres Escobar** 4. Uruguay and England 5. **Saudi Arabia, Greece and Nigeria** 6. Carlos Alberto 7. **Jack Charlton** 8. Two 9. **Brazil won 1-0** 10. Italy 11. **Terry Yorath** 12. 16 13. **Karl-Heinz Rummenigge** 14. Cameroon 15. **Salvatore Schillaci**

Quiz 18 — The World Cup

16. Who was Cameroon's famous centre-forward in the 1990 finals?

17. **West Germany beat Holland 2-1 in the second round of the 1990 finals. During the game which Dutch player was sent off for spitting?**

18. Dutch manager Leo Beenhakker went on to manage which international team in the 1994 World Cup?

19. **In the 1990 World Cup who won the Fair Play award?**

20. Who became the first man to captain and manage a World Cup winning side?

21. **How many players were there left on the pitch at the end of the 1990 World Cup final?**

22. In 1990 Scotland qualified but once again failed to get past the first phase. How many times had this happened before?

23. **What nationality was the referee in the England v Argentina 'Hand of God' 1986 quarter-final?**

24. Ray Wilkins was sent off when England played Morocco in their second game of the 1986 finals. What for?

25. **Who returned from a two-year suspension to become the top goalscorer in the 1982 World Cup?**

26. In the 1982 semi-final West German keeper Harald Schumacher knocked unconscious which French defender in a now infamous challenge?

27. **After this incident what action did the referee take?**

28. Two Ipswich Town players played a major role in the English 1982 World Cup team. Who were they?

29. **Who captained the French team in the 1982 finals?**

30. How many games did England lose before being eliminated from the 1982 World Cup?

16. Roger Milla 17. **Frank Rijkaard** 18. Saudi Arabia 19. **England** 20. Franz Beckenbauer 21. **20** 22. 7 23. **Tunisian** 24. For throwing the ball at the referee 25. **Paulo Rossi** 26. Patrick Battiston 27. **He awarded West Germany a goal kick** 28. Mick Mills and Paul Mariner 29. **Michel Platini - check** 30. None

Quiz 18 The World Cup

31. How many goals did England conceed before being eliminated from the 1982 World Cup?

32. Northern Ireland progressed to the second phase of the 1982 World Cup. When were the other occasions they have for the finals?

33. Argentina had to beat Peru by four goals to reach the 1978 World Cup final, they won 6-0. Where was the Peruvian goal-keeper Quiroga born?

34. Which Scottish player failed a random drugs test in the 1978 finals and was sent home?

35. What was used for the first time in the 1974 World Cup finals?

36. Which player has appeared in five World Cup tournaments?

37. The fastest goal in a World Cup final was scored by who in 1974?

38. England failed to qualify in 1974 thanks to which team?

39. Name the Dutch captain for the 1974 finals?

40. Who was the top goalscorer in the 1970 World Cup?

41. England, Wales, Scotland and Northern Ireland were not eligible to participate in the first World Cup in Uruguay 1930 – why?

42. England made their World Cup debut in which tournament?

43. In the 1950 World Cup England lost 1-0 to a team of rank outsiders, who were they?

44. What did Brazil get to keep after winning the 1970 World Cup?

45. Who scored the only, goal of the 1990 World Cup final?

31. One 32. 1958 and 1986 33. Argentina 34. Willie Johnstone 35. A new trophy. The FIFA World Cup replaced the old Jules Rimet trophy. 36. The Mexican goalkeeper Antonio Carbajal who appeared in the 1950 World Cup through to the 1966 World Cup. 37. Johan Neeskens 38. Poland 39. Johan Cruyff 40. Gerhard Muller 41. They had withdrawn from FIFA in 1928 42. Brazil in 1950 43. USA 44. Jules Rimet trophy 45. Andreas Brehme

Quiz 18 — The World Cup

46. Who refused to shake hands with the President of FIFA after the 1990 World Cup final?

47. **Which team did Alf Ramsey brand "animals" in the 1966 World Cup?**

48. Who scored England's two goals against Portugal in the 1966 World Cup semi-final?

49. **Which country has withdrawn from the World Cup on four occasions?**

50. In 1966 which team were pelted with rotten fruit on their return from England?

51. **What was the name of the dog who found the stolen Jules Rimet trophy in 1966?**

52. Who was captain of the England 1962 World Cup team?

53. **How old was Pele when he made his World Cup debut for Brazil in 1958?**

54. Who was the first person to score a goal in the World Cup finals?

55. **What was stolen from the Olympic Stadium in Rome on 8 July after the 1990 World Cup?**

56. What was the name of the Italian 1990 World Cup mascot?

57. **What fruit was the 1982 Spanish World Cup mascot based on?**

58. In 1974 West Germany had two children as their World Cup mascots. What were their names?

59. **How many times has the host nation won the World Cup?**

60. Why did Uruguay refuse to defend their World Cup title in Italy in 1934?

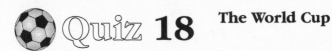

Quiz 18   The World Cup

61. Which team has held the World Cup the longest?

62. In which World Cup was Britain represented by all four Home Countries?

63. Who were the first country to hold both the European Championship and the World Cup at the same time?

64. What has been the highest score in a World Cup finals match?

65. Who holds the individual goal scoring record in a World Cup tournament?

66. Who was the manager of the 1974 Dutch World Cup squad?

67. The 1986 World Cup final was held in which stadium?

68. Who won the Most Exciting Team award at the 1994 World Cup?

69. Who won the Fair Play award at the 1994 World Cup?

70. Which two ex-England players recently backed Japan's failed bid for the 2002 World Cup?

71. How many countries will be playing in the 1998 World Cup?

72. Who called the Polish keeper Jan Tomaszewski a "clown" before the England v Poland 1974 World Cup qualifier?

73. Where did the draw for the 1994 World cup finals take place?

74. Who were the first team to qualify for the 1994 World Cup?

75. What did all the 15 penalties awarded in open play in 1994 have in common?

---

61. Italy. They won it in 1938, then war broke out so they held onto it until 1950. 62. Sweden 1958 **63. West Germany 64.** Hungary 10 El Salavador 1. 1982 **65. Just Fontaine (France) in 1958** 66. Rinus Michels **67. Azteca Stadium** 68. Brazil **69. Brazil 70.** Sir Bobby Charlton and Gary Lineker **71. 32** 72. Brian Clough **73. Ceasars Palace, Las Vegas** 74. Mexico **75. They were all converted**

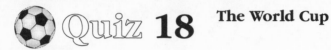 **Quiz 18**   The World Cup

76. In the 1994 World Cup the referees and linesmen's kit came in which three colours?

77. **Up to the 1994 finals, which is the only country to have played in every World Cup tournament?**

78. For the first time in the World Cup finals what was awarded for a win in a group match in 1994?

79. **The 1994 World Cup mascot "Striker" was a dog created by whom?**

80. Who won the Golden Ball award for best player in the 1994 World Cup?

81. **Who said:"I don't know how we do it sometimes." When England reached the 1990 World Cup semi-finals?**

82. Scotland lost 1-0 to which unfancied team in their first match at the 1990 World Cup?

83. **Who is England's top scorer in all World Cup matches?**

84. Scotland's manager resigned after the 1986 finals - who was he?

85. **Who scored in the Republic of Ireland's shock defeat of Italy in the 1994 World Cup?**

86. Who scored the goal in England's shock defeat by the United States in the 1950 World Cup tournament?

87. **Who scored the 1,000th World Cup goal in 1978?**

88. Which was the first black African country to qualify for the World Cup finals?

89. **Why did the English referee Jack Taylor delay the start of the 1974 World Cup final?**

90. In the 1970 World Cup what was Bobby Moore accused of stealing in Bogota, Colombia?

Quiz 18 The World Cup

91. Who are currently the only two players to have scored in more than one World Cup Finals?

92. Who is the oldest player to have won a World Cup winners medal?

93. Which African country have qualified for both World Cup Finals that have been held in Mexico?

94. What could Argentina and Uruguay not agree on before the start of the 1930 World Cup final?

95. Spain entered the 1938 World Cup, why did they not compete?

96. In the 1970 World Cup match between England and Brazil who scored Brazil's winning goal?

97. In 1970 England lost to West Germany in the quarter-finals, but who scored the two English goals?

98. Which World Cup tournament was the first to be televised?

99. Who was the first player to score in every game of a World Cup tournament?

100. Which country was eliminated from the 1974 World Cup on goal difference without losing a game?

101. Who was Argentina's chain-smoking manager in the 1978 World Cup?

102. Who is the youngest player ever to have played in the World Cup?

103. Who was Brazil's philosophical captain in the 1982 World Cup?

104. Alf Ramsey was an England player in which World Cup?

105. What was the average age of the England World Cup winning squad in 1966?

---

91. Pele in 1958 and 1970, Paul Breitner (West Germany) 1974 and 1982. 92. Dino Zoff aged 40 - Italy 93. **Morocco** 94. They couldn't agree on which ball to use **95. Because of the outbreak of the Spanish Civil War.** 96. Jairinho 1970. 100. Scotland **101. Cesar Luis Menotti** 102. Norman Whiteside - **97. Martin Peters and Alan Mullery** 98. Switzerland 1954 99. **Jairinho, Brazil** Northern Ireland **103. Socrates** 104. 1950 World Cup **105. Twenty-six and a half years**

Quiz 18   The World Cup

106. Who were the two reserve goalkeepers in England's 1966 squad?

108. How many goals did Jimmy Greaves score in the 1966 World Cup?

109. Who was awarded the Silver Ball trophy for goals and assists in the 1994 World Cup?

110. Who won the Lev Yashin Goalkeeper Award in the 1994 World Cup?

111. What will be the tournament mascot for the French World Cup in 1988?

112. Who countries will co-host the 2002 World Cup?

113. Which European country did Italy beat in the 1934 semi-final?

114. England failed to qualify in 1974 thanks to a 1-1 draw with Poland at Wembley in October 1973. England had already played them in Poland in June of that same year, what was the score?

115. Which countries did Cameroon beat to reach the World Cup quarter-finals in 1990?

116. Prior to the 1994 World Cup which team had appeared in five tournaments but failed to win a game?

117. How many times have Mexico played in the finals?

118. Who topped England's group in the 1986 tournament?

119. What has been Spain's most successful World Cup?

120. Where did they finish?

120. Fourth

and Colombia 116. Bulgaria **117. Ten** 118. Morocco **119. 1950 in Brazil**
South Korea **113. Austria** 114. Austria 1-4. England lost 2-0 **115. Argentina, Romania**
(Italy) 110. Michel Preud'homme (Belgium) **111. A cockerel.** 112. Japan and
106. Peter Bonetti and Ron Springett. **107. 16** 108. None **109. Roberto Baggio**

 **Quiz 18** The World Cup

121. **Who was the first player banned for drug taking by FIFA in a World Cup?**

122. Who finished top of England's qualifying group in the lead up to the 1990 World Cup?

123. **England drew with the Republic of Ireland in the 1990 World Cup, who scored the goals?**

124. In the 1990 World Cup who replaced David Seaman after he had broken his thumb in training?

125. **Which was the first African country to reach a World Cup quarter-final?**

126. Who presented the Jules Rimet trophy to the Italian captain Combi after his team had won the 1934 World Cup?

127. **In the 1994 qualifiers San Marino lost nine games and drew one. Who was the draw against?**

128. Why did India withdraw from the 1950 World Cup?

129. **Who were the first team to win the World Cup outside of their own continent?**

130. In their opening game of the 1990 World Cup Holland, the favourites, were held to a 1-1 draw, by who?

131. **In the same group the Republic of Ireland also drew 1-1 with Holland, who scored the goals?**

132. Who did Italy beat in the 1934 World Cup Final?

133. **Why were Nigeria disqualified from the 1974 World Cup?**

134. How many players did Brazil use in the 1962 World Cup?

135. **Allan Clarke made his international debut against which team in the 1970 World Cup?**

---

121. Haiti's Ernest Jean-Joseph, 1974. 122. Sweden. 123. Sheedy and Lineker. 124. Dave Beasant. 125. Cameroon 126. Mussolini 127. Turkey 128. FIFA had told them they would not be allowed to play barefoot. 129. Brazil in 1958 130. Egypt 131. Ruud Gullit and Niall Quinn 132. Czechoslovakia 133. After crowd trouble at a home fixture against Ghana which led to the match being abandoned 134. 12 135. Czechoslovakia

 **Quiz 18**   The World Cup

136. Peter Shilton's World Cup finals debut was against which team in 1982?

137. Ex-England manager Bobby Robson played in which World Cup?

138. In which tournament and against which team did Gordon Banks play his last World Cup game?

139. Who missed a late goalscoring chance for England against Brazil in the 1970 finals?

140. Who managed the 1982 World Cup winning Italian team?

141. How long did it take Bryan Robson to score England's first goal in the 1982 tournament against France?

142. Who finished third in the 1982 World Cup?

143. Having successfully qualified for the 1950 World Cup why did the Scottish team refuse to go?

144. What was the nationality of the linesman who awarded England's third goal in the 1966 World Cup final?

145. North Korea beat which team to progress to the quarter-finals in the 1966 World Cup?

146. Which German defender has scored in two World Cup Finals?

147. Which two Dutch brothers played in the 1978 World Cup Final?

148. In the match for third place in the 1970 World Cup who did West Germany beat 1-0?

149. The first penalty to be awarded in a World Cup final was in which tournament?

150. Which Dutch player had his arm bandaged in the 1978 World Cup final against Argentina?

Quiz 18 — The World Cup

151. Who held Scotland to a 1-1 draw in a first round match during the 1978 World Cup?

152. What was unusual about the two goalkeepers in the 1978 World Cup Final?

153. In the 1982 World Cup which team drew all three of their first round matches?

154. In the 1982 World Cup who beat the hosts 1-0 in the first round?

155. Who scored the goal?

156. Which team were threatened with expulsion from the 1986 World Cup tournament for persistant foul-play?

157. Which two teams were in the third place play-off in the 1986 World Cup - and what was the score?

158. What position did Alf Ramsey play in the 1950 World Cup squad?

159. In England's second game in the 1986 World Cup against Morocco, what injury did Bryan Robson sustain?

160. Who qualified for the 1950 World Cup without having to play a single game?

161. Which city hosted the first World Cup final in 1930?

162. Played 6, lost 6, goals for 1, goals against 22 - the worst record in the World Cup finals. Which team is this?

163. Up to the end of the 1994 finals, Brazil have the best record in the World Cup followed by the Germans. Who are third?

164. Who was the eccentric Colombian goalkeeper in the 1990 World Cup?

165. In which World Cup match did Chelsea's Peter Bonnetti earn his seventh and last England cap?

---

151. Iran 152. Jan Jongbloed wore number eight shirt and Ubaldo Fillol wore the number seven. **153. Italy and Cameroon** 154. Northern Ireland **155. Gerry Armstrong** 156. Uruguay **157. Belgium anf France. France won 4-2.** 158. Right-back **159. Shoulder injury** 160. Brazil **161. Montevideo** 162. El Salvador **163. Italy** 164. Rene Higuita **165. The quarter-final against West Germany-1970**

 ## Quiz 18   The World Cup

166. Billy Wright captained England through how many World Cup finals campaigns?

167. Up to 1994, how many finals matches have New Zealand played?

168. Who was the youngest player in the England World Cup final team of 1966?

169. In England's 1970 World Cup quarter-final against West Germany Sir Alf Ramsey made a critical substitution when the German's pulled a goal back, what was it?

170. In the 1978 World Cup, Scotland beat Holland 3-2 in a first round group match. Who scored for the Scots?

171. In the same group which two unfancied teams did the Scots lose to and draw with?

172. Who did the West Germans put six past in a first round group match of the 1978 World Cup?

173. Who was the first player to be sent off in a World Cup final?

174. Which England player announced his retirement after the third place play-off in the 1990 World Cup?

175. Italy, Spain, Holland and Sweden all applied to stage the first World Cup. Why did FIFA ultimately choose Uruguay?

176. In the 1938 World Cup which country received a bye through to the second round due to Germany's invasion of Austria?

177. Who was the Russian goalkeeper in the 1958 World Cup?

178. Why did Gordon Banks miss the 1970 World Cup quarter-final against West Germany?

179. Patented by the Dutch, 'Total Football' made its debut in which World Cup?

180. The Soviet Union failed to qualify for the 1974 World Cup after drawing with Chile 0-0 in Moscow and refusing to play the return leg. Why did the Russians refuse to play in Chile?

---

166. Three 167. **Three** 168. Alan Ball 169. **Bobby Charlton came off for Colin Bell** 170. Archie Gemmill (2, 1 pen) and Kenny Dalglish 171. **Peru and Iran** 172. Mexico 173. **Monzon** 174. Peter Shilton 175. **They were Olympic soccer champions and they promised to underwrite the costs of the competing countries** 176. Sweden 177. **Lev Yashin** 178. Because of food poisoning. 179. **1974** 180. Because the National Stadium in Chile had been used to house prisoners in Chile's Civil War

THE ULTIMATE FACT AND QUIZ BOOK

 **Quiz 18** The World Cup

181. Which country knocked Mexico out of the World Cup in the qualifying stages of 1974?

182. Which Dutchman did the West German Uli Hoeness trip to give Holland a penalty in the 1974 World Cup final?

183. Where and when was the first World Cup held?

184. Which three European countries reached the 1986 semi-finals?

185. Which country became the first to win the World Cup on foreign soil?

186. Who scored Scotland's only goal in the 1986 finals?

187. In which World Cup did England make their first appearance?

188. Which English club ground staged one of the semi-finals in 1966?

189. Who did England beat in the 1966 semi-final?

190. Which Arsenal goalkeeper played for Wales in the 1958 World Cup Finals?

191. Who was sent-off in England's quarter-final against Argentina in 1966?

192. Geoff Hurst scored a hat-trick in the 1966 Final. Who got England's other goal?

193. Who scored Brazil's fourth goal in their win over Italy in the 1970 Final?

194. In which World Cup finals did Zaire made their first appearance?

195. Who was Scotland's top scorer in the 1974 finals?

192. Martin Peters 193. Carlos Alberto 194. 1974 195. Joe Jordan
188. Goodison Park 189. Portugal 190. Jack Kelsey 191. Antonio Rattin
West Germany 185. Italy in 1938 186. Gordon Strachan 187. 1950
181. Haiti 182. Johan Cruyff 183. 1930 in Uruguay 184. Belgium, France and

 Quiz 18   The World Cup

196. What is the highest recorded attendance at a World Cup finals match?

197. Gary Lineker scored a hat-trick in England's last group game in the 1986 finals. Against which country?

198. Lineker scored six of England's seven goals in the 1986 finals. Who got the other one?

199. When Argentina beat England in 1986 which England player was the last to touch the ball before Diego Maradona scored his "hand of God" goal?

200. Which club did Gary Lineker join after the 1986 finals?

201. Who scored Argentina's winning goal in the 1986 Final?

202. Which Chilean goalkeeper feigned injury against Brazil in the qualifying round tie for Italia '90, and was banned from international football for life?

203. Who scored the only goal for Cameroon in the opening game of the 1990 finals against Argentina?

204. How many players did Cameroon finish that game with?

205. Who is the oldest player to score in a World Cup finals match?

206. Who scored England's winning goal against Egypt to help them through to the second round of the 1990 Finals?

207. Who scored the Republic of Ireland's winning penalty in the shoot-out against Romania in the 1990 Finals?

208. Who did Andreas Brehme's shot deflect off to open the scoring for Germany in the 1990 semi-final against England?

209. The opening game of the 1994 finals was played at Soldier Field. What city is the stadium in?

210. How many European teams qualified for the quarter-finals in 1994?

 Quiz **18**   The World Cup

211. Who beat the reigning champions, Germany, in the quarter-finals in 1994?

212. Who scored their goals?

213. Where was the 1994 Final played?

214. Which three Italians missed penalty's in the 1994 Final shoot-out to give Brazil the World Cup?

215. What were England the first to achieve for 32 years in 1966?

216. Who scored West Germany's last-minute equaliser against England in the 1966 Final?

217. Who was the West German goalkeeper in the 1996 Final?

218. Which was the last World Cup Finals that Italy failed to qualify for?

219. Which veteran Italian defender played in the 1982 Final when he was just 18?

220. Who scored Italy's goals in the 1982 Final against West Germany?

221. Who scored the last goal from open play in the 1994 finals?

222. Italy were runners-up in 1994, but where did they finish after the group matches?

223. Holland beat the Republic of Ireland in the second round in 1994. Who got the Dutch's second goal?

224. Italy beat Nigeria 2-1 in the second round of 1994. Who scored both the Italian goals?

225. How many goals did Romario score in the 1994 Finals?

---

211. Bulgaria 212. Hristo Stoitchkov and Yordan Letchkov 213. **Pasadena, California** 214. Daniele Massaro, Franco Baresi and Roberto Baggio 215. **They won the World Cup on their home soil** 216. Wolfgang Weber 217. **Jan Tilkowski** 218. 1958 219. **Guiseppe Bergomi** 220. Paolo Rossi, Allesandro Altobelli and Marco Tardelli 221. **Kennet Andersson** 222. Third 223. **Wim Jonk** 224. Roberto Baggio 225. **Five**

Quiz 18 — The World Cup

226. Who did Brazil beat in the 1962 World Cup Final?

227. **When did New Zealand make their first appearance in the Finals?**

228. Which two British countries reached the quarter-finals of the World Cup in 1958?

229. **Which country finished third in the 1974 World Cup?**

230. Who pipped England for qualification to the 1978 Finals?

231. **How far did Northern Ireland go in the 1982 Finals?**

232. One of Northern Ireland's stars in 1982 was Gerry Armstrong. Which second division club was he playing for at the time?

233. **When was the last time Wales reached the finals?**

234. What round did they reach?

235. **Who scored the goal that knocked them out?**

236. Up to 1994, have Scotland ever got past the first round of the finals?

237. **What is the record number of goals scored by one player in the finals?**

238. Who holds that record?

239. **Who were the joint top scorers in the 1994 World Cup?**

240. Before playing in 1994 when was Norway's last appearance in the World Cup Finals?

226. Czechoslovakia 227. 1982 228. Northern Ireland and Wales 229. **Poland** 230. Italy 231. **Second stage** 232. Watford 233. 1958 234. Quarter-finals 235. **Pele** 236. No 237. 13 238. Just Fontaine of France in the 1958 Finals 239. **Oleg Salenko and Hristo Stoitchkov** 240. 1938

 Quiz **18**   The World Cup

241. Who finished third in the 1990 World Cup Finals?

242. Who beat Bulgaria to finish third in the 1994 World Cup?

243. Who did Argentina beat in a play-off to qualify for the 1994 World Cup Finals?

244. Which two countries qualified ahead of England for the 1994 World Cup Finals?

245. Who missed England's final penalty in the 1990 World Cup semi-final?

246. Who were the first country not to score in a Final?

247. What year was it?

248. Whose goal knocked the U.S.A out of the 1994 World Cup?

249. Which World Cup finals match was the first to be played indoors?

250. Where was that game played?

251. Who succeeded the injured Bryan Robson as England captain in the 1990 World Cup finals?

252. Can you name the other three countries in England's Group One during the 1966 World Cup?

253. All of England's 1966 group games were played at Wembley, except one. Where was that played and who were the two teams?

254. Who is the oldest player to captain a World Cup winning side?

255. Before the start of the 1998 World Cup, who is the last player to score in a Final?

---

254. Italy's Dino Zoff (40) 255. Andreas Brehme

252. Mexico, Uruguay and France 253. White City, Uruguay v France

Switzerland, 1994 250. The Silverdome, Detroit **251. Peter Shilton**

Waddle 246. Argentina **247. 1990** 248. Brazil's Bebeto **249. USA v**

241. **Italy** 242. Sweden **243. Australia** 244. Norway and Holland 245. **Chris**

 **Quiz 18**   The World Cup

256. Who was the first substitute to score in a World Cup?

257. Which five nations boycotted the first World Cup in 1930 because they were passed over as hosts in favour of Uruguay?

258. Who is the oldest player to score World Cup finals goal?

259. What was unique about the West Germany-Italy final in 1970?

260. Which nation was originally selected as hosts for the 1986 finals and why did they withdraw?

261. Why did Roberto Rojas of Chile incur a life ban after a 1990 qualifying match?

262. Which nation played a World Cup match only two days after the country had been devastated by an earthquake?

263. Who was leading scorer in the 1974 World Cup finals?

264. Who is the only man to play in two World Cup winning sides and to win it again as a manager?

265. Which player scored four goals in one match during the 1986 finals?

266. Which nation qualified for five finals series between 1962 and 1986 yet failed to win any of 16 matches?

267. Why was England's match with Brazil in Sweden in 1958 unique?

268. Who was the first player to score at least five goals in two different World Cups?

269. Who has scored a record number of finals goals?

270. Which nation set a record by schedulling finals matches for 17 different stadia?

---

256. Juan Basaguren for Mexico in a 4-0 win over El Salvador on June 7, 1970. 257. Spain, Italy, Sweden, Hungary and Holland 258. Cameroon's Roger Milla. 259. It is the only match in World Cup finals history to produce five extra time goals. 260. Colombia - because of economic difficulties. 261. Goalkeeper Rojas faked injury claiming a flare had hit him causin g the game to be abandoned. 262. Peru - in the 1970 World Cup. 263. Gregorz Lato of Poland with seven goals. 264. Brazil's Mario Zagalo - he played in 1958 and 1962 and was manager in 1970. 265. Emilio Butragueno (Spain) v Denmark in 1986. 266. Bulgaria. 267. It was the first scoreless draw in the finals. 268. Teofilo Cubillas (Peru) in 1970 and 1978. 269. Gerd Muller (West Germany) with 14. 270. Spain (1982).

THE ULTIMATE FACT AND QUIZ BOOK

 Quiz **18**   The World Cup

271. **Which goalkeeper played in a record five World Cups yet appeared on the winning side only once?**

272. Which nation did not qualify for the finals between 1938 and 1974 then reached the next four, finishing third twice?

273. **Who was the first player to score an extra-time goal in a Final?**

274. Which event in World Cup history occurred on March 20, 1966?

275. **Which two pairs of brothers have played in World Cup winning teams?**

276. Who is the only player to represent different nations in a World Cup Final?

277. **Which is the smallest city to host the finals?**

278. Which nation holds the highest goals-per-game average in world cup matches?

279. **Who scored the goal that knocked out Italy in 1966?**

280. Which manager hid in Europe for a month after his team was eliminated from the 1966 World Cup?

281. **Which nation lost 32 successive qualifying matches?**

282. Who refereed the first World Cup Final in 1930?

283. **Who was the first substitute to score three times in a World Cup finals match?**

284. Who finished top scorer in the 1966 finals?

285. **Name the only city to host an entire World Cup finals series.**

---

271. **Antonio Carbajal of Mexico.** 272. Poland. 273. Italy's Angelo Schiavio in 1934. 274. The trophy was stolen from a Westminster exhibition. 275. **Jack and Bobby Charlton (England 1966) and Fritz and Ottmar Walter (W.Germany 1954).** 276. Luis Monti (Argentina 1930 and Italy 1934). 277. **Berne, Switzerland, which had a population of 150,000 in 195.** 278. Turkey with an average of 3.33 goals per game. 279. **Pak Doo Ik of North Korea.** 280. Vicente Feola of Brazil. 281. **Luxembourg.** 282. Jean Langenus of Belgium. 283. **Laszlo Kiss of Hungary v El Salvador, June 1982.** 284. Eusebio (Portugal). 285. **Montevideo, Uruguay, in 1930.**

Quiz 18 The World Cup

286. Which is the only nation to reach the semi-finals four times and have not been beaten?

287. Why were England uncertain whether their 1986 meeting with Portugal would go ahead?

288. Who was sent off after a record 55 seconds of a 1986 World Cup match?

289. Which player scored four goals in a finals match but was still on the losing side?

290. Which nation won 47 of 48 internationals between 1950 and 1956 yet failed to win the World Cup?

291. Which was the first Asian country to play in the World Cup?

292. Which nation's only appearance in the finals resulted in a 6-0 defeat?

293. Whose ripped shorts fell to his ankles seconds after he scored from a penalty in a 1938 semi-final?

294. Which two teams were involved in a 7-3 match in the group stages of the 1958 tournament?

295. Who was the first player to score in an Olympic Final and a World Cup Final ?

296. Who were the first country to win the World Cup in a penalty shoot-out?

297. What year was it?

298. Who missed a penalty in his 100th appearance for his country in the 1978 World Cup Finals?

299. Who was England's goalkeeper when they drew 0-0 with Brazil in the 1958 Finals?

300. Who beat the hosts Argentina in the group stages of the 1978 World Cup Finals?

286. Argentina. **287. The Portuguese players had been on strike in a row over bonuses. 288.** Jose Batista(Uruguay) v Scotland. **289. Ernst Wiilimowski (Poland) against France in 1938. 290.** Hungary. **291. The Dutch East Indies(now Indonesia) who qualified for the 1938 finals. 292.** The Dutch East Indies, crushed by Hungary in 1938. **293. Italy's Giuseppe Meazza. 294.** France and Paraguay. **295. Pedro Cea of Uruguay in 1924 and 1930. 296.** Brazil. **297. 1994 298.** Kazimierz Deyna **299. Colin McDonald 300.** Italy

 **Quiz 18**   The World Cup

301. Who finished ahead of Brazil in the group stages of the 1978 World Cup finals?

302. Which Argentinian scored in the 1990 World Cup semi-final?

303. Who were in West Germany's group in the 1978 World Cup?

304. Who beat Mexico and drew with West Germany in the 1978 finals?

305. Who finished third in the 1978 World Cup?

306. Who conceded 12 goals in their three group matches in the 1978 World Cup?

307. Who scored Argentina's three goals in the 1978 Final?

308. Who scored Holland's consolation goal in the 1978 Final?

319. Which goalkeeper saved two penalties in the 1974 World Cup finals?

310. Who scored for Scotland in three World Cup finals?

311. Who beat West Germany in the group stages of the 1974 World Cup?

312. Who played in three World Cup's for Brazil, scoring nine goals?

313. Who is the only player to score in every game of a World Cup finals series when he scored seven in the 1970 Finals?

314. Paulo Rossi scored a hat-trick when Italy beat Brazil 3-2 in the second stage of the 1982 Finals. Who scored Brazil's two goals?

315. Who did Scotland beat 5-2 in the 1982 World Cup finals?

Quiz 18 — The World Cup

316. Who scored Scotland's goal in their 4-1 defeat to of Brazil in 1982?

317. Which two England strikers both scored two goals in the 1982 finals?

318. Against who did England draw their two games with in the second stage of the 1982 World Cup?

319. Which players came on as substitutes for England in their second stage match against Spain?

320. Who scored West Germany's consolation goal in the 1982 Final?

321. Northern Ireland reached the second stage of the 1982 finals. Who were in Northern Ireland's group in that second stage?

322. Who did Italy beat in the semi-final to reach the 1982 World Cup Final?

323. Who missed the final stages of the 1962 World Cup through injury?

324. Which Frenchman gave his name to the first World Cup trophy?

325. Who captained West Germany to the 1990 World Cup?

326. How much - in Francs - did the original World Cup trophy cost?

327. How many people attended the first World Cup?

328. In the 1934 World Cup Finals, 12 of the competing nations were from Europe. Who were the other four teams present?

329. Who scored England's goal in the third place play-off in 1990?

330. Which two players scored hat-tricks in the 1990 World Cup?

---

316. David Narey 317. **Paul Mariner and Trevor Francis** 318. West Germany and Spain 319. **Kevin Keegan and Trevor Brooking** 320. Paul Breitner 321. **France and Austria** 322. Poland 323. **Pele** 324. Jules Rimet 325. **Lothar Matthaus** 326. 50,000 francs 327. **343,500** 328. Egypt, Argentina, Brazil and USA 329. **David Platt** 330. Thomas Skuhravy and Michel

Quiz 18 — The World Cup

331. Who did Sweden beat 8-0 in the second round of the 1938 Finals – this country's last appearance in the tournament's finals?

332. Who scored Italy's only goal in the 1990 quarter-final against the Republic of Ireland?

333. Who was the England manager in the 1950 Finals?

334. Who did England beat in the second round of the 1986 World Cup Finals?

335. Who were clear favourites to win the 1954 World Cup?

336. What was that team's nickname?

337. Which Brazilian made his first finals appearance in 1958?

338. Who was Northern Ireland's goalkepper inthe 1958 Finals?

339. Who hosted the 1954 World Cup?

340. Who beat South Korea 9-0 in the group stage of the 1954 World Cup?

341. Which countries scored 17 goals in two group matches in the 1954 World Cup?

342. Which two countries played each other twice in the 1954 tournament?

343. Which two nations contested a 7-5 quarter-final in the 1954 Finals?

344. Who beat West Germany 6-3 to finish third in the 1958 World Cup?

345. Which player scored four goals against Denmark in the 1986 finals?

---

331. Cuba 332. Salvatore Schillaci 333. **Walter Winterbottom** 334. Paraguay
335. Hungary 336. "The Magical Magyars" **337. Pelé** 338. Harry Gregg
339. Switzerland 340. Hungary **341. Hungary** 342. West Germany and Hungary
343. Austria and Switzerland. 344. France 345. **Emilio Butragueno**

 Quiz 18   The World Cup

346. Who beat Wales in the quarter-finals of the 1958 Finals?

347. Who was the English referee in the 1974 World Cup Final?

348. What was so unusual about the 1974 World Cup Final?

349. How many British Isles countries reached the 1958 finals?

350. Who was sent-off against Brazil in the 1982 tournament?

351. Who did England lose to in the 1962 quarter-finals?

352. Which two South American countries reached the 1962 quarter-finals?

353. Who replaced Gary Lineker in England's 3-0 defeat of Poland in the 1986 Finals?

354. Who scored Portugal's goal in their 1-0 win over England in 1986?

355. Which Englishmen led Sweden to the 1958 World Cup Final?

356. Who became the first country to win the World Cup four times?

357. Which two teams were involved in the 'Battle of Santiago' in the 1962 World Cup?

358. Who hosted the 1962 World Cup?

359. How many teams competed in the 1950 World Cup Finals?

360. Who did Italy beat in the 1938 World Cup Final?

346. Brazil 347. **Jack Taylor** 348. Two penalties were awarded - the first spot-
kicks in a Final 349. **All four, England, Northern Ireland, Scotland and Wales**
350. Diego Maradona 351. **Brazil** 352. Chile and Brazil 353. **Kerry Dixon**
354. Carlos Manuel 355. **George Raynor** 356. Brazil 357. **Chile and Italy**
358. Chile 359. 13 360. Hungary

 Quiz **18**   The World Cup

361.What was the score in the 1938 Final?

362.Who hosted the 1954 World Cup?

363.Who hosted the 1958 World Cup?

364.The England team were without three important players in the 1958 World Cup Finals, Why?

365.Brazil played Wales in the 1958 Finals, what was the score?

366.What was the average goals per game in the first World Cup tournament in 1930?

367. In what year did FIFA first moot the idea of staging a World Cup?

368. Which three countries made a bid to stage the subsequently aborted 1942 World Cup?

369.In the 1934 World Cup qualifying match between Hungary and Bulgaria, who was the referee?

370. Before travelling to the 1950 World Cup in Brazil where did the England team train?

371. When Northern Ireland qualified for the 1958 finals what did the Irish FA order the team not to do?

372. Which country did FIFA allow back into the World Cup tournament in 1954?

373.Who was Northern Ireland's manager in the 1958 World Cup finals?

374.What was the score in the 1958 World Cup final?

375.Who was the assistant manager of the 1994 Republic of Ireland World Cup squad?

361. 4-2 362. Switzerland **363. Sweden** 364. Roger Byrne, Duncan Edwards and Tommy Taylor had all been killed in the Munich air disaster. **365. 1-0 to Brazil.** 366. 3.9 **367. 1904** 368. Brazil, Argentina and Germany. **369. Herr Frankenstein of Austria.** 370. Ascot **371. Play their group games on a Sunday.** 372. West Germany **373. Peter Doherty** 374. Brazil 5 Sweden 2. **375. Maurice Setters**

Quiz 19   British Players In Foreign Countries

1. **Who was the first professional player to move from an English club to Italy?**

2. Which were the first Italian club to buy a player from England?

3. **Who was the first player to transfer from Scotland to Italy, with a move from Hibernian to Juventus?**

4. Who moved from English football to AC Milan in June 1961?

5. **Who moved from English football to Torino in 1961?**

6. Who moved from Aston Villa to Italy in 1961 for £85,000?

7. **Who was the first person to move from England to Germany?**

8. Who moved from WBA to Real Madrid in 1979?

9. **Which player moved from Manchester City to Werder Bremen in 1979?**

10. How much did Liam Brady cost Juventus when he left Arsenal in 1980?

11. **Trevor Francis moved to which foreign club for £900,000?**

12. Who was the first £1m player to move abroad from a British club?

13. **Which two players moved from English clubs to AEK Athens in 1983?**

14. Which club did Mark Hateley move from when he joined AC Milan?

15. **How much did Ray Wilkins cost AC Milan when he joined them in 1984?**

---

1. **Eddie Firmani** 2. **Sampdoria** 3. **Joe Baker** 4. Jimmy Greaves 5. **Denis Law**
6. Gerry Hitchens 7. **Kevin Keegan** 8. Laurie Cunningham 9. **Dave Watson**
10. Juventus 11. **Sampdoria** 12. Luther Blissett to AC Milan 13. **Trevor Ross**
and **Tommy Langley** 14. Portsmouth 15. **£150,000**

Quiz 19 — British Players In Foreign Countries

16. Which two players moved from Aston Villa to Bari in 1985?

17. How much did Ian Rush cost Juventus when he left Liverpool in 1987?

18. Which Italian club did Paul Elliott join in 1987?

19. How much did David Platt cost when he moved to Bari?

20. How much did Paul Gascoigne cost Lazio when he moved to Italy?

21. How much did Des Walker cost Sampdoria when he joined them in 1992?

22. Who played for AC Milan and Verona from 1981?

23. Which Italian club did amateur centre forward Norman Adcock join in 1945 to become the first ever player to move to play in Europe?

24. Which British export became the French First Division's top scorer in the 1994 season?

25. Which former Arsenal championship winner moved to Stabaeck in Norway?

26. Which two Brits teamed up for the same club in Italy for the 1996-97 season?

27. Which player joined Reggiana in the 1996-97 season from an English club?

28. Ted McMinn moved from Rangers to which Spanish side in 1987?

29. Mick Robinson moved from QPR to which Spanish side in 1987?

30. Which two British internationals moved abroad in May 1986?

Quiz 19 British Players In Foreign Countries

31. **Who moved from Celtic to Nantes in 1987?**

32. Which ex-Manchester United player moved to Kaizer Chiefs in South Africa in January 1988?

33. **How much did Steve Archibald cost Barcelona when he moved from Tottenham?**

34. Which club did Mark McGhee move to from Aberdeen?

35. **Which club did Andy King join from Everton in 1984?**

36. Which club did Raphael Meade join when he left Arsenal?

37. **Which foreign club did John Richards join in 1983?**

38. Who did Peter Barnes join in 1982 when he moved from Leeds?

39. **Who moved from Liverpool to Lucerne in a free transfer in 1983?**

40. Watford's Gerry Armstrong moved to which foreign club in 1983?

41. **How much was the transfer fee when Graeme Souness moved to Sampdoria?**

42. Eric Black joined which French side when he moved from Aberdeen for £200,000 in 1986?

43. **Dale Tempest joined Lokeren from which English club?**

44. Gary Owen moved to which foreign club from WBA in 1986?

45. **Louie Donowa moved from Norwich to which Spanish club in 1986?**

 **Quiz 19**   British Players In
Foreign Countries

46. Tony Woodcock left Arsenal for which German club in 1986?

47. **Sammy McIlroy left Manchester City for which foreign club in 1986?**

48. Tottenham gave Ally Dick a free transfer to which Dutch team in 1986?

49. **Joe Jakub joined which Dutch team for £20,000 in 1986?**

50. Garry Brooke moved to which club when he left Norwich in 1987?

51. **Murdo McLeod joined which German side in 1987?**

52. Which club did Frank Stapleton join on a free transfer to in 1987?

53. **George O'Boyle moved from Linfield to which French club in 1987?**

54. Which foreign club did Tony Sealey join when he left Leicester in 1987?

55. **Dave Swindlehurst joined Anorthosis from which club in 1987?**

56. Ex-Norwich player John Devine moved to which club in September 1987?

57. **Gary Waddock joined which French club in January 1988 after he left QPR?**

58. Which French team signed Ian Wallace when he left Nottingham Forest in 1984?

59. **Bob Latchforrd left Swansea on a free transfer to join which club?**

60. Which team signed Jim Bett when he left Glasgow Rangers in 1983?

Quiz 19 British Players In Foreign Countries

61. Who moved from the Premiership to Malaysia in 1996?

62. Tony Marchi left Tottenham for which foreign side in 1961?

63. John Charles joined which Italian side for #70,000 in 1962?

64. Mick Walsh left QPR for which European team in 1980?

65. How much did Trevor Francis cost Sampdoria when he joined them in 1982?

66. Francois Van Der Elst left West Ham for which side in 1983?

67. Which two Tottenham players from the 1980s moved to France?

68. What are the four Italian teams that Liam Brady played for?

69. Which clubs did David Platt play for in Italy?

70. How many seasons did Denis Law spend in Italy?

71. How many seasons did Trevor Francis spend at Sampdoria?

72. How many games did Jimmy Greaves play in Italy?

73. Who scored 87 goals in six seasons in Italy from 1957-63?

74. Frank Ratcliffe moved from Aldershot to which serie B side for the 1949-50 season, where he scored 18 goals in 27 games?

75. In which season did Ian Rush play in Italy?

61. **Tony Cottee** 62. Lanerossi Vicenza 63. AS Roma 64. Porto 65. £900,000
66. Lokeren 67. Glenn Hoddle and Chris Waddle 68. Juventus, Sampdoria,
Inter Milan, Ascoli 69. Bari, Juventus, Sampdoria 70. 1 (1961-62) 71. 4
72. 10 (with 9 goals) 73. John Charles 74. Alessandria 75. 1987-88

 Quiz 19   **British Players In Foreign Countries**

76. What was the name of the team that Gary Lineker played for in Japan?

77. **Which country did Richard Gough leave Rangers to play in after the 1996-97 season?**

78. Which former Watford striker had a spell at French club Nantes?

79. **Which American team did Rodney Marsh play for?**

80. Which team did Charlton's Mike Flanagan play for in America?

81. **Which former Welsh international had a spell at Vancouver Whitecaps?**

82. With which Turkish team did Les Ferdinand have a loan spell with?

83. **Dean Saunders spent a season at which foreign club before moving back to Nottingham Forest?**

84. Dalian Atkinson moved to which foreign club when he left Aston Villa?

85. **Which Scot played for Borussia Dortmund in the 1996-97 season?**

86. Mo Johnston spent the 1996-97 season playing where?

87. **Chris Woods was playing in which country before playing for Southampton in the 1996-97 season?**

88. How many goals did David Platt score in his first season in Italy?

89. **Who moved to Paris St Germain after three years at AC Milan?**

90. Josiah (Paddy) Sloan moved from Sheffield United to which foreign team for the 1948-49 season?

 Quiz 20   The League Cup

1. In which year did the first final of the League Cup take place?

2. In which year did the first Wembley final take place?

3. Who were the winners of the first League Cup?

4. Who were the Second Division underdogs who reached the 1961 final, and led 2-0 after the first leg?

5. Who scored the winning goal in the first-ever League Cup final?

6. Who was the Spurs manager who refused to let his side take part in the first League Cup?

7. Which Fourth Division side reached the 1962 final?

8. Who put the holders out of the competition in 1962?

9. The 1961 final was completed in which month?

10. Which Villa player was the top scorer in the 1961 competition?

11. Who were the first winners of the League Cup who did not play their football in the top flight?

12. Who holds the all-time scoring record in the League Cup?

13. Which Welsh international scored a brace for Birmingham in the 1963 final?

14. Which club reached the final in 1964 and 1965?

15. Which club, now no longer in the League, reached the fifth round in 1964 only to be beaten 6-0 by West Ham?

15. Workington

11. **Norwich in 1962** 12. Geoff Hurst 13. **Ken Leek** 14. Leicester City
Nicholson 7. **Rochdale** 8. Ipswich 9. **September** 10. Gerry Hitchens
1. **1961** 2. 1967 3. **Aston Villa** 4. Rotherham 5. **Peter McParland** 6. Bill

 **Quiz 20**   **The League Cup**

16. Which future England manager scored a penalty in the 1965 final?

17. **Who was the legendary English goalkeeper who played in both the 1964 and 1965 finals?**

18. Which club reached the final three times in five years between 1966 and 1970?

19. **Which Stoke player scored ten goals in the 1963-64 season?**

20. Which Premiership striker's father was the top scorer in the 1964-65 season while playing for Aston Villa?

21. **Whose brainchild was the League Cup, leading it to be labelled his 'folly'?**

22. In which year was the introduction of a European place for the winners?

23. **Which two clubs were the only teams not to enter the 1967 competition?**

24. Which club won the 1967 competition, but could not qualify for Europe because they were not a First Division club?

25. **Which Leeds full-back scored the only goal of a dour 1968 final?**

26. Which team lost in the final in 1968 and 1969?

27. **Which television commentator played in goals for Arsenal in the 1969 final?**

28. Which Swindon player scored a brace in the 1969 final to shock Arsenal?

29. **Who were the first club to win a place in Europe through the competition?**

30. Which Manchester City stalwart scored a penalty in the 1970 semi-final derby clash?

16. Terry Venables 17. **Gordon Banks** 18. WBA 19. **John Ritchie** 20. Mark Hateley 21. **Alan Hardaker** 22. 1967 23. Liverpool and Everton 24. QPR 25. **Terry Cooper** 26. Arsenal 27. **Bob Wilson** 28. Don Rogers 29. **Arsenal** 30. Francis Lee

Quiz 20 — The League Cup

31. **Which WBA striker scored their only goal in the 1970 final?**

32. In which year did Tottenham reach their first final?

33. **In which year did the Football League reject a £600,000 offer for sponsorship of the competition?**

34. Which Tottenham player was the top scorer in the 1970-71 and 1971-72 campaigns?

35. **Which Stoke keeper saved a penalty in the 1972 semi-final to give them their first visit to Wembley?**

36. How many games did West Ham and Stoke play in the 1972 semi-finals before a winner was finally decided?

37. **Who was the Stoke manager who led his team to glory in 1972?**

38. Which Stoke player, at the age of 35, scored his first goal in 18 months when he hit the winner in the 1972 finals?

39. **Who were the first club to win the trophy twice?**

40. Which England international scored Tottenham's only goal in the 1973 final?

41. **Who was the Wolverhampton hero when he replaced Phil Parkes in goal and pulled off a series of stunning saves to win the 1974 final?**

42. Which Manchester City player caused controversy when he left the field immediately after losing the 1974 final, without collecting his loser's medal?

43. **Which future Watford manager scored the opener for Wolves in the 1974 final?**

44. In which year were there no First Division sides in the semi-finals?

45. **Which Fourth Division side reached the semi-finals in 1975 after beating Leeds and Newcastle United?**

44. 1975 45. Chester City
40. Ralph Coates 41. Gary Pierce 42. Rodney Marsh 43. Kenny Hibbitt
36. Four 37. Tony Waddington 38. George Eastham 39. Tottenham Hotspur
31. Jeff Astle 32. 1971 33. 1971 34. Martin Chivers 35. Gordon Banks

 **Quiz 20**   **The League Cup**

46. Who was the Villa manager who led them to victory in 1975 after two previous final defeats?

47. **Which two England internationals scored Manchester City's goals in the 1976 final victory over Newcastle?**

48. Which Villa player and future manager was the top scorer in the 1976-77 campaign?

49. **Which Welsh international scored a last-minute goal to give Villa a second replay in the 1977 final against Everton?**

50. For how many minutes did Aston Villa and Everton play to decide the 1977 competition?

51. **Which 18-year-old keeper was drafted in to keep goal for Forest against Liverpool in the 1978 final?**

52. Who did Phil Thompson bring down in a profesional foul to give Forest and penalty and eventually victory in the 1978 final?

53. **Which team upset Liverpool in the 1979 championship when they beat the favourites in the second round?**

54. Which bargain basement striker, bought from a local non-League club, scored a brace for Forest in the final against Southampton in 1979?

55. **Which club reached three consecutive finals at the end of the Seventies?**

56. Which fellow First Division side did Arsenal beat 7-0 in the second round of the 1979-80 competition?

57. **Who was the Liverpool keeper who brought down Garry Birtles in the semi-final of the 1979-80 competition?**

58. Which former winners reached the semi-finals in 1980 while still a Third Divison side?

59. **Which Wolves player took advantage of confusion between Peter Shilton and David Needham to score the only goal of the 1980 final?**

60. Who won their first League Cup in 1981?

 Quiz 20   The League Cup

61. Who scored West Ham's only goal in the replay for the 1981 final?

62. Which Liverpool player was the top scorer for the 1980-81 competition?

63. How many consecutive League Cups did Liverpool claim?

64. By what name was the League Cup known between 1982 and 1986?

65. Which Liverpool player scored a brace in the 1982 final, when the Reds beat Tottenham in extra-time?

66. Which former Liverpool keeper was beaten three times by his old club in the 1982 final?

67. Which Liverpool manager led them to victory in 1983 and then retired?

68. When Burnley beat Bury 8-4 in the 1982-83 competition, how many different players scored for Burnley?

69. Who was the Burnley manager sacked by his club on the day of their fifth round victory over Tottenham Hotspur?

70. What was the Wembley crowd when Liverpool met Manchester United in the 1983 final?

71. Which Manchester United player was the competition's top scorer in 1982-83?

72. Who scored the opening goal in the 1983 final, giving Manchester United an early lead?

73. At which ground was the 1984 replay held?

74. Which Third Division side held Liverpool to a draw at Anfield in the 1984 semi-finals?

75. In which year did Liverpool meet Everton at Wembley for the first time in history?

61. **Paul Goddard** 62. Kenny Dalglish 63. **Four** 64. Milk Cup 65. **Ronnie Whelan** 66. Ray Clemence 67. **Bob Paisley** 68. Eight - one of which was a Bury player 69. **Brian Miller** 70. 100,000 71. **Steve Coppell** 72. Norman Whiteside 73. **Maine Road** 74. Walsall 75. 1984

 Quiz 20   The League Cup

76. Which two teams met in a 'derby' game in the 1985 semi-finals?

77. **Which team won the 1985 competition in the same year that they were relegated from the First Division?**

78. Whose own goal gave Norwich victory in 1985?

79. **Who ended Liverpool's amazing run in the competition when they beat them 1-0 in the third round of the 1984-85 competition?**

80. Who played in goal for Norwich in their victory over Sunderland in the 1985 final, winning his second winner's medal?

81. **Who won their first major trophy when they triumphed in the 1986 final?**

82. Which First Division team did Fourth Division Swindon beat in the third round of the 1985-86 competition?

83. **Whose goal for QPR at Loftus Road eventually gave them a place in the 1986 final?**

84. What was the final score when Oxford beat QPR in the 1986 final?

85. **Who began their sponsorship of the League Cup in 1987?**

86. Which First Division team was beaten by Fourth Division Cambridge in the second round of the 1986-87 tournament?

87. **Who were Chelsea beaten by in the third round of the 1986-87 tournament?**

88. Who scored all three goals for Tottenham when they met Arsenal in the 1987 semi-finals?

89. **Who scored a brace for Arsenal in the 1987 final, giving them the cup on their third Wembley visit?**

90. After which final was the League Cup trophy broken?

Quiz 20   The League Cup

91. **Which club lifted their ban on away fans in order to compete in the 1987-88 competition, and went on to win the tournament?**

92. Who were Luton playing in the 1987-88 quarter-finals when crowd trouble broke out?

93. **Who was the replacement keeper who saved a penalty for Luton in the 1988 final?**

94. Who scored a brace for Luton as they won the 1988 cup against Arsenal?

95. **Who took the penalty for Arsenal in the 1988 final that would have given them a two-goal lead?**

96. Which Forest player finished the 1988-89 competition as top scorer?

97. **Which Fourth Division side put First Division Middlesbrough out of the 1988-89 competition?**

98. Which Third Division side reached the 1989 semi-finals only to be beaten by Nottingham Forest in extra-time?

99. **Whose extra-time goal gave Nottingham Forest a place in the 1989 final?**

100. Who did Luton beat in the semi-finals of the 1988-89 competition?

101. **Who scored the goals for Forest in their 3-1 victory over Luton in the 1989 final?**

102. Which scorer in the 1989 final later became a member of the Crazy Gang?

103. **Nottingham Forest's fifth visit to the League Cup final came in which year?**

104. Which Fourth Division side drew 1-1 at Stamford Bridge before winning the second leg in 1989-90?

105. **Who put six goals past West Ham in their semi-final first leg in 1990?**

91. **Luton** 92. Bradford 93. **Andy Dibble** 94. Brian Stein 95. **Nigel Winterburn** 96. Nigel Clough 97. **Tranmere** 98. Bristol City 99. **Garry Parker** 100. West Ham 101. **Nigel Clough and Neil Webb** 102. Mick Harford 103. **1990** 104. Scarborough 105. **Oldham**

 Quiz 20   The League Cup

106. Who scored the only goal of the 1990 final?

107. Who sponsored the League Cup in 1991 and 1992?

108. Who hit a hat-trick for Manchester United when they beat Arsenal in the fourth round of the 1990-91 competition?

109. Which Coventry hat-trick man from the 1990-91 quarter-finals later played for Blackburn?

110. Whose hat-trick for Manchester United in the 1990-91 quarter-finals put out Southampton?

111. Who did Sheffield Wednesday beat in the semi-finals of the 1990-91 tournament?

112. Who scored the only goal of the 1991 final?

113. What was the aggregate score when Sheffield Wednesday beat Chelsea in the 1991 semi-finals?

114. How many of Manchester United's League Cup final team of 1991 were still at the club in 1997?

115. Peterborough United put out which two top-flight teams in the 1991-92 competition?

116. Which Tranmere player was top scorer in the 1991-92 competition?

117. Who scored his 100th goal for Manchester United in the 1992 final?

118. Which Second Division team reached the 1992 semi-finals, only to lose to Manchester United in extra-time?

119. Which teams contested the 1993 FA and League Cup finals?

120. Scarborough beat which Premiership team 3-0 in the second leg of the second round of the 1992-93 tournament?

---

106. Nigel Jemson 107. **Rumbelows** 108. Lee Sharpe 109. **Kevin Gallacher** 110. Mark Hughes 111. **Chelsea** 112. John Sheridan 113. 5-1 114. Three - Irwin, McClair and Pallister. 115. **Wimbledon and Liverpool** 116. John Aldridge 117. **Brian McClair** 118. Middlesbrough 119. **Sheffield Wednesday and Arsenal** 120. Coventry

 **Quiz 20**   The League Cup

121. **Who were the only non-Premiership side in the 1992-93 quarter-finals?**

122. Who scored Arsenal's only goal when they scraped through against Scarborough in the fourth round of the 1992-93 competition?

123. **Who scored a brace for Sheffield Wednesday when they beat Blackburn in the 1992-93 semi-finals?**

124. Who scored Wednesday's goal in the 1993 final, which they eventually lost 2-1?

125. **Who scored Arsenal's equaliser when they beat Sheffield Wednesday in the 1993 final?**

126. Who scored the winner for Arsenal in the 1993 final, but then had his arm broken when Tony Adams dropped him while celebrating?

127. **Who began their sponsorship of the League Cup in the 1992-93 season?**

128. Aston Villa won the trophy in 1994. How many times had they won it before?

129. **Who scored all five goals when Liverpool beat Fulham in the second round (second leg) in 1993-94?**

130. Who scored the Manchester United winner against Portsmouth to give them a semi-final place?

131. **Who were the only non-Premiership side to reach the 1994 semi-finals?**

132. Who did Manchester United beat in the semi-finals of the 1993-94 competition?

133. **What score was the 1994 semi-final first leg between Tranmere and Aston Villa?**

134. Who scored the Villa goal against Tranmere in the second leg of the 1994 semi-final, which took the game to penalties?

135. **Who was the Villa goalkeeper who saved a penalty against Tranmere to give them a 1994 final berth?**

 **Quiz 20**   **The League Cup**

136. Who scored two goals for Villa in the 1994 final against Manchester United?

137. **Which player was shown the red card in the 1994 final?**

138. Who put Leeds out of the competition at the second round stage in 1994/95?

139. **Which two players scored twice when Crystal Palace beat Aston Villa in the fourth round of the 1994/95 competition?**

140. Who scored the Bolton goal which gave them their first semi-final place, in the 1995 tournament?

141. **Who was the leading scorer in the 1994-95 tournament?**

142. Who scored the goal which gave Bolton victory over Swindon in 1994-95, booking their place in the final?

143. **Who scored Liverpool's two goals as they progressed from the 1994-95 semi-finals?**

144. Who did Liverpool beat in the 1994-95 semi-finals?

145. **Which Liverpool star played against the Reds in the 1995 final?**

146. Who scored the goals for Liverpool in the 1995 final?

147. **Whose screamer gave Bolton some consolation in the 1995 final?**

148. What was the final score in the 1995 final between Liverpool and Bolton?

149. **How many appearances have Aston Villa made in the final?**

150. Who were Villa's opponents in the 1996 final?

---

136. Dean Saunders 137. **Andrei Kanchelskis** 138. Mansfield 139. **Chris Armstrong and Gareth Southgate** 140. David Lee 141. **Jan - Aage Fjortoft** 142. John McGinlay 143. **Robbie Fowler** 144. Crystal Palace 145. **Jason McAteer** 146. Steve McManaman 147. **Alan Thompson** 148. 2-1 149. **Seven** 150. Leeds

 Quiz 20   **The League Cup**

151. What was the final aggregate score when Charlton beat Wimbledon in the second round of the 1995-96 competition?

152. Which minnows put Manchester United out of the 1995-96 Cup?

153. Which Yorkshire side put Nottingham Forest out of the 1995-96 tournament?

154. A goal from which veteran gave Reading victory over Southampton in the fourth round in 1995-96?

155. Who was sent off in the 1995-96 quarter-final between Arsenal and Newcastle?

156. Who scored a brace in the 1995-96 quarter-final between Arsenal and Newcastle?

157. Who scored the only goal in the Midlands derby quarter-final between Villa and Wolves in 1995-96?

158. What was the aggregate score in the 1995-96 semi-final between Birmingham and Leeds?

159. Which two Africans were on the score-sheet when Leeds beat Birmingham in the 1995-96 semi-finals?

160. Who scored a brace for Arsenal in their semi-final clash with Aston Villa in 1995-96?

161. Who netted two for Aston Villa when they met Arsenal in the 1995-96 semi-finals?

162. Who played in goal for Leeds in the 1996 final when they lost 3-0 to Aston Villa?

163. Who scored Villa's opening goal in the 1996 final?

164. Who was the top scorer in the 1995-96 tournament, his side reaching the semi-finals?

165. Who scored the third and final goal in the 1996 final to top off a tremendous season?

151. 8-7 152. York City 153. **Bradford City** 154. Trevor Morley 155. **David Ginola** 156. Ian Wright 157. **Tommy Johnson** 158. 5-1 159. **Tony Yeboah and Phil Masinga** 160. Dennis Bergkamp 161. **Dwight Yorke** 162. John Lukic 163. **Savo Milosevic** 164. Ian Wright 165. **Dwight Yorke**

 **Quiz 20**   ### The League Cup

166. Which Second Division side reached the semi-finals of the 1996-97 tournament?

167. Which player, who had been at both clubs, was sent off in the 1996-97 clash between Birmingham and Coventry?

168. How many goals did Middlesbrough put past Hereford in the second round in 1996-97?

169. Which Premiership side did York City put out of the 1996-97 tournament?

170. Which side gave Chelsea a scare in 1996-97 when they won 3-1 at Stamford Bridge?

171. Who did Charlton hold to a draw at the Valley in the 1996-97 season?

172. Who put holders Villa out of the 1996-97 tournament?

173. Who did Middlesbrough beat in the quarter-finals of the 1996-97 competition?

174. Who scored Leicester's only goal when they overcame Ipswich in the 1996-97 quarter-finals?

175. Who scored the winner when Stockport beat Southampton to reach the 1996-97 semi-finals?

176. What was the aggregate score when Middlesbrough beat Stockport in the 1996-97 semi-finals?

177. Whose goal gave Leicester a win over Wimbledon in the semi-finals in 1996-97 on the away goals rule?

178. Who was the Stockport manager who led them into the Coca-Cola Cup semi-finals?

179. Who scored the opening goal of the Wimbledon v Leicester semi-final in 1997?

180. In what month was the final of the 1996-97 competition held?

 **Quiz 21**   **British Stadiums**

1. **Which club plays at the Underhill Stadium?**

2. Which club's stadium has terraces called Pontefract Road End and Spion Kop?

3. **To which club's ground is Bordesley the nearest railway station?**

4. Which club plays their home games at Dean Court?

5. **Which club plays at Twerton Park?**

6. Which club's ground has a 22, 085 capacity and has a terrace called Bee Hole Lane End?

7. **What is the name of Bury's stadium?**

8. Which team plays at Ninian Park?

9. **Which country play their international football and rugby union games at the same stadium?**

10. Who play their home games at Brunton Park?

11. **Which ground had temporary seating in the Shed End in 1995-96?**

12. Whose club's ground was the first to go all-seater in England?

13. **Who play their home games at Belle Vue?**

14. Which club's ground is the nearest to Anfield?

15. **There are two grounds in England which each share their names with two clubs. Who are the teams?**

 **Quiz 21**   **British Stadiums**

16. Which team were facing a possible ground share with Chelsea, but managed to save their ground?

17. **At which ground can you buy a fanzine called Brian Moore's Head (Looks Uncanily Like The London Planetarium)?**

18. Which team's ground is situated in Cleethorpes?

19. **Name Hartlepool United's stadium.**

20. Name Leyton Orient's ground.

21. **Which club play their home games at Sincil Bank?**

22. Which ground in 1994 had only 0.0711% of the capacity (32 seats) for the disabled?

23. **Which club plays at Glanford Park?**

24. Name Oldham Athletic's ground.

25. **Which team play their home games at London Road?**

26. Which team plays their home games at the Millmoor Ground?

27. **Which team has a stand for away fans called the Stone's Best Bitter Stand?**

28. Which team's stadium is on the banks of the river Severn?

29. **Which Premiership ground has a Clock End?**

30. Who play their home games at Plainmoor?

 **Quiz 21** British Stadiums

31. **Which club play at Prenton Park, which has a stand called the Cowshed?**

32. Which Premiership club's stadium is named the Boleyn Ground?

33. **Which ground holds the record for the highest crowd for a friendly?**

34. Which team's record attendance of 23,002 against QPR in 1949 came when they were a non-league side?

35. **Which ground has stands named after John Ireland, Jack Harris and Stan Cullis?**

36. Whose home stadium is the Racehorse Ground?

37. **What is Wycombe Wanderers's ground called?**

38. Which team play their home games at Bootham Cresent?

39. **In which year did Wembley first stage the FA Cup final?**

40. Which team's former ground were called Oozebooth, Pleasington Cricket Ground and Alexandra Meadow?

41. **At what ground were the first floodlights introduced in October 1878?**

42. At what ground was the first match to have a gate higher than 10,000 for a match outside Glasgow?

43. **Which club ground's nearest railway station is Castle station?**

44. Where was the first English FA Cup final held?

45. **Where was the only official FA Cup final during the First World War held?**

31. Tranmere 32. West Ham **33. Newcastle's St. James' Park 34.** Gillingham **35. Molineux (Wolves) 36.** Wrexham **37. Adams Park 38.** York City **39. 1923** 40. Blackburn **41. Bramall Lane, Sheffield 42.** Bramall Lane (for the first floodlights) **43. Northampton** 44. The Kennington Oval **45. Old Trafford**

 Quiz **21**   **British Stadiums**

46. Which club moved ground in 1997-98 after 102 years at Burnden Park?

47. **When did Wembley Stadium first introduce floodlights?**

48. Whose 1997-98 Premiership ground is called the Reebok Stadium?

49. **Since which year has every Scottish FA Cup final been played at Hampden?**

50. In what year did Wembley get the monopoly for all England home internationals?

51. **Which ground held the first ever home England international in 1873?**

52. Where was the first Welsh home international held, in 1877?

53. **Where were the two semi-finals played in the 1966 World Cup?**

54. What were the four quarter-final grounds in the 1966 World Cup?

55. **Where did England play their third place play-off in the 1990 World Cup?**

56. Which club played their final game at the Manor Ground in 1996-97?

57. **What was the ground, other than Wembley, that was used for Group A in Euro 96?**

58. At what ground was the second semi-final in Euro 96 played?

59. **At what ground did Denmark play all of their Euro 96 group matches?**

60. Which were the four grounds in Euro 96 that were not used for the quarter-finals?

46. Bolton Wanderers 47. 1955 48. Bolton Wanderers 49. 1925 50. 1951
51. The Kennington Oval 52. Acton Park, Wrexham 53. Wembley and
Goodison Park 54. Wembley, Goodison, Hillsborough, Roker Park 55. Bari
56. Oxford United 57. Villa Park 58. Old Trafford 59. Hillsborough 60. City
Ground, Hillsborough, Elland Road, St James' Park

 **Quiz 21**   **British Stadiums**

61. Which British club play their home games at Gayfield Park?

62. Zampa Road is the address of which English ground?

63. At what ground was the first Match of the Day televised from?

64. At which ground were Manchester United when they lost out to Blackburn on the final day of the 1994-95 season?

65. At which ground is the National Football Museum?

66. At which ground did Huddersfield gain promotion to the First Division in 1995?

67. Before Old Trafford in May 1997, where was the last ground other than Wembley, to hold an England international?

68. Which club play their home games at Dean Court?

69. Which ground holds the record for the highest crowd in a European Cup final?

70. At which Stadium was the record for the smallest League Cup attendance at a top division ground set in 1992?

71. Which ground holds the record for the highest crowd at an FA Cup game other than the final, with 64,851?

72. Which club's ground is situated in Waterloo Road?

73. Disasters at which two grounds led to the Popplewell report being published?

74. When was the Charity Shield first played at Wembley?

75. At which ground was the 1970 FA Cup final replay held?

---

73. Bradford (fire) and Birmingham (riots) 74. 1974 **75. Old Trafford**
72. Wolverhampton Wanderers **Park, with 40,149 on a big screen at Anfield** 72. Wolverhampton Wanderers
- Real Madrid vs Eintracht Frankfurt, 1960 70. Selhurst Park **71. Goodison**
66. Wembley (in play-offs) **67. Elland Road** 68. Bournemouth **69. Hampden Park**
61. Arbroath 62. Millwall 1930 **63. Anfield** 64. Upton Park **65. Deepdale**

 **Quiz 21**   **British Stadiums**

76. Where were the two semi-finals of the 1996 FA Cup played?

77. **where was the 1984 League Cup final replayed, when Liverpool beat Everton 1-0?**

78. At what ground was the 1981 League Cup replay held?

79. **At which ground did Nottingham Forest beat Liverpool in the 1978 League Cup final replay?**

80. At which two grounds did the two 1977 League Cup final replays occur?

81. **Which ground holds the record for the highest attendance in the Vauxhall conference of 9,432 in 1988?**

82. What ground was named England's national stadium in 1996?

83. **Where do Northern Ireland play their home internationals?**

84. At which ground did North Korea beat Italy in the 1966 World Cup?

85. **Which is Britain's most southwesterly League ground?**

86. Which club have moved ground 14 times since 1885?

87. **Which ground saw the first synthetic pitch in the British League?**

88. Which club started the 1997-98 season at the Britannia Stadium?

89. **Which Premiership club's stadium was used as a rifle range during World War One?**

90. Which club spent the first 23 years of their existance playing at Cassio Road?

 **Quiz 21** **British Stadiums**

91. **Which club was the first to try executive boxes in their Grant Stand in 1898?**

92. To which club's stadium is Pokesdown railway station the nearest?

93. **In which ground is there a Charlie Brown Stand?**

94. Which ground holds the record for an abandoned match?

95. **At which ground is there a Bath End?**

96. At which ground is there a Cemetry End and a Manchester Road End?

97. **Which club's stadium has a Canton Stand and a Grangetown End?**

98. Which team moved out of their Sealand Road ground to move in with Macclesfield, and then moved out again to their current Deva Stadium?

99. **Which ground has an M & B Stand?**

100. What is the name of Crewe Alexandra's stadium?

101. **Which ground has an Arthur Wait Stand?**

102. Norwood Junction is the nearest railway station to which ground?

103. **Which team's stadium has an ASDA End with a grassy knoll?**

104. Which stadium backs onto Gwladys Street and Bullens Road?

105. **Which team's ground has a Pontoon End and a Findus Stand?**

91. **Celtic Park** 92. Bournemouth 93. **Bradford City's Valley Parade**
94. Newcastle's St James' Park 95. **Bristol Rovers** 96. Gigg Lane 97. **Cardiff City's Ninian Park** 98. Chester 99. **Coventry - Highfield Road**
100. Gresty Road 101. **Selhurst Park** 102. Selhurst Park 103. **Doncaster Rovers' Belle Vue** 104. Goodison Park 105. **Grimsby Town**

Quiz 21   British Stadiums

106. Which club play their home games at Edgar Street?

107. Which team play at Boothferry Park?

108. Which club has a Churchman's Stand and a Pioneer Stand?

109. On which Premiership ground do Hunslet Rugby League Club play?

110. South Bermondsey is the closest railway station to which club's stadium?

111. Which Norwich player scored the last goal in front of the Kop at Anfield before it became an all-seater stand?

112. Which stadium stands on the banks of the river Trent?

113. Which ground has the Lookers Stand and the Rochdale Road Stand?

114. Who scored the last two goals at Middlesborough's Ayesome Park before their move to the Riverside Stadium?

115. Which stadium has a Cuckoo Lane End and a London Road End?

116. Which club's stadium has a Glebe Road Terrace and a Moys End Terrace?

117. In which ground could you buy a fanzine called more Dead Wood Than The Mary Rose?

118. Which club's ground has a British Coal Opencast Stand?

119. Which ground has a South Africa Road Stand?

120. Which club plays their home games at the Spotland Stadium?

 **Quiz 21**   **British Stadiums**

121. **Which club's home ground is called the McCain Stadium?**

122. Which ground has the Presto End?

123. **Which team play at Edgeley Park?**

124. At which stadium is there a Rous Stand and a Rookery End, which backs onto allotments?

125. **Which British club's ground became the first all-seater stadium in 1978?**

126. Which Scottish club's home ground is called Dens Park?

127. **Which British club play their home games at Tannadice Park?**

128. Which League ground hosted a semi-final in the 1997 Rugby League Silk Cut Challenge Cup?

129. **Which team play at Tynecastle Park?**

130. Who play their home games at Easter Road?

131. **Which club's home ground is called Fir Park?**

132. Which team play at Brockville Park, the smallest League pitch in Scotland?

133. **Which Scottish team play in a stadium designed for the 1970 Commonwealth Games?**

134. Wales have played every home game since 1921 in Cardiff, Wrexham and Swansea apart from one, in 1977. Where was this played?

135. **What is the most common name of a terrace/stand at British Football grounds?**

135. Spion Kop

131. Motherwell 132. Falkirk 133. Meadowbank Thistle 134. Anfield
128. The McAlpine Stadium 129. Heart of Midlothian 130. Hibernian
Road 125. Aberdeen's Pittodrie Stadium 126. Dundee 127. Dundee United
121. Scarborough 122. Hillsborough 123. Stockport 124. Watford's Vicarage

Quiz 22   Name The Team

Name........

1. The Wimbledon team that won the 1988 FA Cup Final.

2. England's side for the Euro '96 semi-final clash with Germany.

3. The Manchester United side who played Borussia Dortmund in the European Cup semi-final, first leg in 1997.

4. England's 1996 World Cup Final side.

5. The Arsenal side that clinched 'the double' when they beat Liverpool in the 1971 FA Cup Final.

6. The Everton side that beat Rapid Vienna in the 1985 European Cup-Winners' Cup Final.

7. The Arsenal team that beat Parma in the 1994 European Cup-Winners' Cup Final.

8. The Crystal Palace side that beat Liverpool in the 1990 FA Cup semi-final.

9. The Luton side that won the 1988 League Cup Final.

10. Scotland's Euro '96 side that played against England at Wembley.

1. **Beasant, Goodyear, Phelan, Jones, Young, Thorn, Gibson** (Scales), Cork (Cunningham), **Fashanu, Sanchez, Wise.** 2. Seaman, Southgate, Adams, Pearce, Ince, Anderton, Platt, Gascoigne, McManaman, Sheringham, Shearer. 3. **Van der Gouw, G.Neville, Johnsen, Pallister, Irwin, Beckham, Butt, Keane, Giggs** (Scholes), **Cantona, Solskjaer** (Cole). 4. Banks, Cohen, Wilson, Stiles, J.Charlton, Moore, Ball, Hurst, Hunt, R.Charlton, Peters. 5. **Wilson, Rice, McNab,** Storey (Kelly), **McLintock, Simpson, Armstrong, Graham, Radford,** Kennedy, George. 6. Southall, Stevens, Van den Hauwe, Ratcliffe, Mountfield, Reid, Steven, Sharp, Gray, Bracewell, Sheedy. 7. **Seaman, Dixon, Bould, Adams,** Winterburn, Davis, Morrow, Selley, Campbell, Smith, Merson (McGoldrick). 8. Martyn, Pemberton, Shaw, Gray, O'Reilly, Thorn, Barber, Thomas, Bright, Salako, Pardew. 9. **Dibble, Breacker, Johnson, Hill, Foster, Donaghy, Wilson, B.Stein, Harford** (M.Stein), **Preece** (Grimes), **Black.** 10. Goram, McKimmie, Calderwood, Hendry, Boyd, T.McKinlay (Burley), McCall, McAllister, Collins, Spencer (McCoist), Durie (Jess).

 **Quiz 22** — **Name The Team**

11. **Liverpool's side that won the 1984 European Cup Final.**

12. The Ipswich side that won 3-0 at Portman Road in the 1981 Uefa Cup Final, first leg.

13. **The Celtic side that won the European Cup in 1967.**

14. Newcastle's team that lost 4-3 to Liverpool in the 1995-96 season.

15. **The Norwich City side that beat Bayern Munich 2-1 in the Uefa Cup, first leg in 1993-94.**

16. The Republic of Ireland side that beat England in the 1988 European Championship.

17. **The Nottingham Forest side that played the re-arranged FA Cup semi-final in 1989.**

18. Blackburn's team that beat Norwich City 7-1 in the 1992-93 season.

19. **The Everton side that escaped relegation by beating Wimbledon 3-2 in 1994.**

20. The Arsenal side that beat Liverpool 2-0 at Anfield to win the 1989 League Championship.

---

11. Grobbelaar, Neal, Kennedy, Lawrenson, Whelan, Hansen, Dalglish (Robinson), Lee, Rush, Johnston (Nicol), Souness. 12. Cooper, Mills, McCall, Thijssen, Osman, Butcher, Wark, Muhren, Mariner, Brazil, Gates **13. Simpson, Craig, Gemmell, Murdoch, McNeill, Clark, Johnstone, Wallace, Chalmers, Auld, Lennox** 14. Snicek, Beresford, Howey (Peacock), Albert, Watson, Batty, Lee, Beardsley, Ginola, Asprilla, Ferdinand. **15. Gunn, Culverhouse, Butterworth, Newman, Bowen, Crook, Goss, Fox, Sutton, Robins (Sutch), Prior** 16. Bonner, Morris, Hughton, McCarthy, Moran, Whelan, McGrath, Houghton, Aldridge, Stapleton (Quinn), Galvin (Sheedy). **17. Sutton, Laws, Pearce, Walker, Wilson, Hodge, Gaynor (Starbuck), Webb, Clough, Chapman, Parker (Glover).** 18. Mimms, Brown, Wright, Sherwood, Hendry, Moran (Marker), Cowans, Ripley (Wilcox), Atkins, Shearer, Wegerle. **19. Southall, Snodin, Ablett, Unsworth, Watson, Stuart, Horne, Ebbrell, Cottee, Rideout, Limpar. 20.** Lukic, Dixon, Winterburn, Thomas, O'Leary, Adams, Rocastle, Richardson, Smith, Bould (Groves), Merson (Hayes)

Quiz 22 — Name The Team

21. **Nottingham Forest's 1979 European Cup Final team.**

22. Coventry's side that beat Tottenham in the 1987 FA Cup Final.

23. **The Republic of Ireland side that beat Italy in the 1994 World Cup.**

24. The Liverpool side that beat Crystal Palace 9-0 in the 1989-90 season.

25. **Dundee United's side that beat Rangers in the 1994 Scottish Cup Final.**

26. The England side that beat Cameroon in the 1990 World Cup.

27. **Scotland's team that beat Holland in the 1978 World Cup.**

28. The Wales team that beat West Germany in an European Championship qualifier in 1991.

29. **The Leeds side that lost to Sunderland in the 1973 FA Cup Final.**

30. Oxford United's team that won the 1986 League Cup Final.

---

21. Shilton, Anderson, Clark, McGovern, Lloyd, Burns, Francis, Bowyer, Birtles, Woodcock, Robertson. 22. Ogrizovic, Phillips, Downs, McGrath, Kilcline (Rodger), Peake, Bennett, Gynn, Regis, Houchen, Pickering. **23. Bonner, Irwin, Babb, McGrath, Phelan, Houghton (McAteer), Sheridan, Keane, Townsend, Staunton, Coyne (Aldridge) 24.** Grobbelaar, Hysen, Burrows, Nicol, Whelan, Hansen, Beardsley (Aldridge), Rush, Barnes, McMahon, Gillespie (Molby). **25. Van de Kamp, Cleland, Malpas, McInally, Petric, Welsh, Bowman, Hannah, McLaren (Nixon), Brewster, Dailly. 26.** Shilton, Parker, Walker, Wright, Butcher (Steven), Pearce, Waddle, Gascoigne, Platt, Barnes (Beardsley), Lineker. **27. Rough, Kennedy, Donachie, Rioch, Forsyth, Buchan, Dalglish, Hartford, Jordan, Gemmill, Souness. 28.** Southall, Phillips, Melville, Bodin, Aizlewood, Ratcliffe, Nicholas, Saunders (Speed), Rush, Hughes, Horne. **29. Harvey, Reaney, Cherry, Bremner, Madeley, Hunter, Lorimer, Clarke, Jones, Giles, Gray (Yorath). 30.** Judge, Langan, Trewick, Phillips, Briggs, Shotton, Houghton, Aldridge, Charles, Hebberd, Brock.

Quiz 23 British Clubs in Europe

1. **Which two British players have played in European Cup Finals for more than one club?**

2. Who were the last two men to manage English clubs to European Cup success?

3. **Who scored Manchester United's goal at Old Trafford against Rotor Volgograd in the Uefa Cup in 1995?**

4. Who is the last person to score in an European Final for a British club?

5. **Name the five clubs that have won the European Cup at Wembley?**

6. Who were Nottingham Forest's first opponents in the European Cup?

7. **Who is the only British manager to have won the European Cup-Winners Cup with different clubs?**

8. Which team did Manchester United play in their first European Cup tie?

9. **Which club did Manchester United defeat to reach the 1968 European Cup Final?**

10. Which team did Chelsea beat in the final to win the European Cup-Winners Cup in 1971?

11. **Which other English team did Chelsea beat in the semi-finals to reach the 1971 European Cup-Winners Cup Final?**

12. The 1971 European Cup-Winners Cup Final went to a replay. Who scored in both games of the Final?

13. **Which British club beat AC Milan on a toss of a coin in the Inter-Cities Fairs Cup third round in 1966?**

14. Which two present day managers played in that tie?

15. **Which English club recorded a 21-0 aggregate score over Luxembourg club Jeunesse Hautcharage in the European Cup-Winners Cup in 1971-72?**

 Quiz 23 British Clubs in Europe

16. Who were the first British club to play in a European Cup Final?

17. **Which Yugoslavian side knocked Arsenal out of the 1979 Uefa Cup?**

18. Who did Arsenal beat to reach the 1980 European Cup-Winners Cup Final?

19. **Who scored the winning goal in the second leg of that game?**

20. Arsenal were beaten in the 1980 European Cup-Winners Final on penalties. By which Spanish side?

21. **Which England international missed the decisive penalty?**

22. Which Russian club won 5-2 at Highbury to knock Arsenal out of the 1982-83 Uefa Cup?

23. **Which club knocked Arsenal out of the 1972 European Cup on their way to winning to the trophy?**

24. Which English club beat Anderlecht 4-3 on aggregate to win the 1970 Inter-Cities Fairs Cup?

25. **When they defended the Cup the following season, which German club beat them in the fourth round?**

26. In what season did Arsenal make their first appearance in European competition?

27. **Who were they beaten by in the second round?**

28. Who did Arsenal beat to win the 1994 European Cup-Winners Cup?

29. **Who scored the only goal?**

30. In defence of their title, Arsenal lost in the 1995 European Cup-Winners Cup Final. Which Spanish side beat them?

 **Quiz 23** — British Clubs in Europe

31. Where was that Final played?

32. Which former Tottenham player scored the winning goal in that Final with a 40-yard lob over David Seaman?

33. Which England international missed the 1994 European Cup-Winners Cup Final through suspension?

34. Who won the European Cup with Juventus before moving to England?

35. Who were the first English winners of the European Cup-Winners Cup?

36. Which English club reached the European Cup semi-final in their first season of the competition?

37. Liverpool collected their first European trophy when they won the 1966 European Cup-Winners Cup. Who did they beat in the Final?

38. Who scored the only goal?

39. Which German club were beaten 8-0 by Liverpool in the 1967-68 Inter-Cities Fairs Cup at Anfield?

40. Which English club beat Irish club Dundalk 14-0 on aggregate in the 1969-70 Inter-Cities Fairs Cup?

41. Which two English clubs contested one of the 1971 Inter-Cities Fairs Cup semi-finals?

42. And who won through to the Final?

43. Liverpool won the 1973 Uefa Cup by beating which German side over two legs?

44. Despite losing the second leg 2-0, Liverpool won the 1973 Uefa Cup final 3-2 on aggregate. Who scored Liverpool's goals in the first leg?

45. Who did Liverpool beat in the semi-finals of the that year?

31. **Paris** 32. Nayim 33. **Ian Wright** 34. Gianluca Vialli (Juventus) 35. **Tottenham** 36. Liverpool 37. **Borussia Dortmund** 38. Roger Hunt 39. **Munich 1860** 40. Liverpool 41. Leeds and Liverpool 42. Leeds 43. **Borussia Moenchengladbach** 44. Kevin Keegan (2), Larry Lloyd 45. **Tottenham**

Quiz 23 — British Clubs in Europe

46. In the 1974-75 European Cup-Winners Cup first round, Liverpool beat Stromsgodset 11-0 at Anfield. How many different players were on the scoresheet?

47. **Liverpool beat Belgian side FC Bruges twice in three years in European Finals. What competitions?**

48. How many years did Liverpool win consecutive European Finals in the mid-1970's?

49. **Kevin Keegan made his final appearance for Liverpool in the 1977 European Cup Final. Did he score?**

50. What were the similiarities between Liverpool's European Cup success in 1977 and 1984?

51. **Where did Liverpool win the 1978 European Cup Final?**

52. Who scored Liverpool's winning goal?

53. **Which team did Liverpool meet in successive European Cup seasons in the last-1970's?**

54. Before the ban on English clubs, how many successive seasons did Liverpool play in the European Cup?

55. **Which Scottish club were beaten 5-0 on aggregate by Liverpool in the 1980-81 European Cup?**

56. Was it Ray Kennedy or Alan Kennedy who scored the only goal in Liverpool's 1981 European Cup Final success?

57. **Who did Liverpool beat in that Final?**

58. Who knocked the reigning champions, Liverpool, out of the 1982 European Cup?

59. **Who scored Liverpool's goal in open-play in the 1984 European Cup Final?**

60. Name the four Liverpool players who scored from the spot in the 1984 European Cup Final penalty shoot-out?

 **Quiz 23** British Clubs in Europe

61. The 1985 European Cup Final between Liverpool and Juventus was marred by crowd violence at the Heysel stadium. But who scored the only goal for the Italian club?

62. Who resigned as Liverpool manager after that game?

63. How did Liverpool beat Cologne in the 1965 European Cup quarter-final?

64. Who scored West Ham's two goals in their 1965 European Cup-Winners Cup Final success?

65. Where was that Final played?

66. How many British clubs have competed in European Finals at Wembley?

67. What round did West Ham reach in the European Cup-Winners Cup in 1980-81?

68. Who were Manchester United beaten by in the group stages of the 1996-97 Champions League?

69. Who beat West Ham in the 1976 European Cup-Winners Cup Final?

70. Who did Everton beat over two legs in the semi-finals of the 1985 European Cup-Winners Cup?

71. Everton beat which Austrian club in the European Cup-Winners Cup Final of 1985?

72. Who scored Everton's goals in that Final victory?

73. Which Scottish side beat Everton in the 1962-63 Uefa Cup?

74. Which English club did Inter Milan beat on their way to winning the 1964 European Cup?

75. Who captained Everton to their European Cup-Winners Cup success in 1985?

---

61. Michel Platini 62. Joe Fagan **63. On a toss of a coin 64.** Alan Sealey **65. Wembley 66.** Three. Manchester United, Liverpool & West Ham **67. Quarter-finals 68.** Juventus (twice) and Fenerbahce **69. Anderlecht 70.** Bayern Munich **71. Rapid Vienna 72.** Andy Gray, Trevor Steven & Kevin Sheedy **73. Dunfermline 74.** Everton **75. Kevin Ratcliffe**

Quiz 23   British Clubs in Europe

76. Which England international goalkeeper had to be taken off after only eight minutes of the 1982 European Cup Final?

77. **Which youngster replaced him?**

78. Manchester United reached the semi-finals of the European Cup in 1957. Which legendary team beat them?

79. **Manchester United were beaten the following year again in the semi-finals. Who inflicted defeat this time?**

80. When Manchester United beat Benfica to win the European Cup in 1968, who scored twice for United?

81. **On defending the European Cup in 1969, Manchester United were beaten in the semi-finals. By who?**

82. Which two English teams met in the European Cup-Winners Cup second round in the 1963-64 season?

83. **Who won the tie?**

84. Which Italian club beat Manchester United in the 1984 European Cup-Winners Cup semi-final?

85. **Who scored Manchester United's other two goals in the 1968 European Cup Final?**

86. Who scored for Celtic in their memorable European Cup Final success in 1967?

87. **Who was Celtic's victorious captain on that day?**

88. Which Manchester United striker missed the 1968 European Cup Final through injury?

89. **Which former European Footballer of the Year played against Manchester United in the 1968 European Cup Final?**

90. Who were nicknamed 'The Lisbon Lions' after their European Cup success?

 **Quiz 23** British Clubs in Europe

91. **How many European Cup Finals have Celtic appeared in?**

92. Who has scored twice in European Cup Finals for Celtic?

93. **Which Dutch side beat Celtic in the European Cup Final of 1970?**

94. Which English side were beaten by Bayern Munich in an European Cup Final?

95. **Which brothers played in the Leeds side that played in the 1975 European Cup Final?**

96. Which club played in five European Cup Finals in the 1960's, winning twice?

97. **Which Dutchman won the Uefa Cup in 1981 for Ipswich and had a brother that won the European Cup in 1972?**

98. Which Spainsh club did Leeds beat to reach the 1975 European Cup Final?

99. **Which former Wales manager played for Leeds in the 1975 European Cup Final?**

100. Which English side beat Real Madrid 4-1 in the European Cup second round first leg, only to be beaten 6-5 on aggregate?

101. **Who scored a hat-trick in that first leg, and also scored in the return?**

102. Which English side won the European Cup at the first attempt?

103. **Who scored the winning away goal for Nottingham Forest against Cologne in the 1979 European Cup semi-final, second leg?**

104. Which former Nottingham Forest manager played for the club in the 1979 European Cup Final?

105. **Who scored the only goal for Nottingham Forest in the 1979 European Cup Final?**

Quiz 23 — British Clubs in Europe

106. Which Brazilian, who would later play in the Premiership, scored for Genoa against Liverpool in the 1992 Uefa Cup?

107. Who did Nottingham Forest beat in the 1980 European Cup semi-finals?

108. Who scored the winning goal for Nottingham Forest in the 1980 European Cup Final?

109. Which England captain played against Nottingham Forest in the 1980 European Cup Final?

110. Which English club did Rangers beat in the European Cup-Winners Cup semi-final in 1961?

111. Which Italian club beat Rangers in the 1961 European Cup-Winners Cup Final?

112. What round did Scottish club Dunfermline reach in the 1962 European Cup-Winners Cup?

113. Rangers lost to who in the 1963 European Cup-Winners Cup?

114. Rangers reached the 1967 European Cup-Winners Cup Final. Who did they play?

115. Which British club reached the European Cup-Winners Cup semi-final in 1968?

116. Which Scottish team reached the semi-finals in the same competition a year later?

117. Which English club won the European Cup-Winners Cup in 1970?

118. Who were their scorers in the Final?

119. Which Scottish club won the European Cup-Winners Cup in 1972?

120. Who did they beat in the Final?

106. Branco. **107. Ajax** 108. John Robertson **109. Kevin Keegan** 110. Wolves **111. Fiorentina** 112. Quarter-Finals **113. Tottenham** 114. Bayern Munich **115. Cardiff City** 116. Dunfermline **117. Manchester City** 118. Neil Young and Francis Lee (pen) **119. Rangers** 120. Dynamo Moscow

 **Quiz 23** British Clubs in Europe

121. Leeds reached the European Cup-Winners Cup Final in 1973. Who beat them in the Final?

122. Which Irish team reached the 1974 European Cup-Winners Cup quarter-finals before being beaten by Borussia Moenchengladbach?

123. Who were England's representatives in the 1973-74 European Cup-Winners Cup?

124. Which Hungarian side knocked Liverpool out of the 1975 European Cup-Winners Cup on their way to the Final?

125. Who did West Ham beat in the 1976 European Cup-Winners Cup semi-final?

126. Who scored twice for West Ham in the second leg of that semi-final?

127. Who beat West Ham in the 1976 European Cup-Winners Cup Final?

128. Which English club did Anderlecht beat in the 1977 European Cup-Winners Cup quarter-finals?

129. Which English team beat Porto 5-2 in the second leg of the 1978 European Cup-Winners Cup second round, but still lost 6-5 on aggregate?

130. Which English side lost on away goals to Barcelona in the quarter-finals of the 1979 European Cup-Winners Cup?

131. Who played in European Cup-Winners Cup Finals for Chelsea and Arsenal?

132. Which British club played in consecutive Fairs Cup Finals in the 1960's?

133. Which British club were the first to reach an European club final?

134. Which three British clubs were in the 1966 Uefa Cup quarter-finals?

135. Leeds played in consecutive Fairs Cup Finals in the 1960's. Which years?

THE ULTIMATE FACT AND QUIZ BOOK

 **Quiz 23** British Clubs in Europe

136. On reaching the two Finals, Leeds beat Scottish clubs in both semi-finals. Who were they?

137. Which European trophy did Newcastle win in 1969?

138. Which two English clubs contested the 1972 Uefa Cup Final?

139. Which Premiership manager played for Tottenham in the 1972 Uefa Cup Final?

140. Who beat Tottenham on away goals to reach the 1973 Uefa Cup Final?

141. Who beat Tottenham in the 1974 Uefa Cup Final?

142. Aston Villa were beaten by Barcelona in the Uefa Cup qaurter-finals in 1978. But who scored their consolation goal at the Nou Camp?

143. Which Midlands club reached the Uefa Cup quarter-finals in 1979?

144. Which two Ipswich players scored in both legs of the 1981 Uefa Cup Final?

145. Which English club lost in the 1959 European Cup first round?

146. Which English club did Barcelona beat 9-2 on aggregate in the 1960 European Cup?

147. What English team reached the quarter-finals of the European Cup in 1961?

148. Who was in goal for Manchester United when Barcelona beat them 4-0 in the Champions League in 1994-95?

149. Which other British club were beaten by Bayern Munich in the 1995-96 Uefa Cup?

150. Which club did Real Zaragoza beat to reach the 1995 European Cup-Winners Cup Final?

136. Kilmarnock and Dundee 137. **Fairs Cup** 138. Tottenham and Wolves
139. **Joe Kinnear** 140. Liverpool 141. **Feyenoord** 142. Brian Little 143. **W.B.A**
144. John Wark and Frans Thijssen 145. **Wolves** 146. Wolves 147. **Burnley**
148. Gary Walsh 149. **Raith Rovers** 150. Chelsea

Quiz 23 — British Clubs in Europe

151. Who did Newcastle lose to in the second round of the 1995 Uefa Cup?

152. Which club of Swedish part-timers beat Blackburn in the first round of the 1994-95 Uefa Cup?

153. To qualify for the 1992-93 Champions League, the English champions faced the Scottish champions. Who won the tie?

154. What was the aggregate score?

155. Rangers missed out on qualifying for the European Cup Final of 1993 by one point in the group stage. Who topped the group?

156. Who scored twice for Manchester United in their 1991 European Cup-Winners Cup Final victory over Barcelona?

157. English clubs were allowed back into European competitions in 1990-91. Why did they not have a representative in the European Cup?

158. Which Premiership striker played in the 1992 European Cup Final?

159. Who did Arsenal lose to in the European Cup second round in 1991-92?

160. How many group matches did Blackburn win in the 1995-96 Champions League?

161. Who scored a hat-trick for Blackburn in the 1995-96 Champions League?

162. Which German, Romanian and Italian side were in Rangers' Champions League group in 1995-96?

163. Who beat Celtic on their way to winning the 1996 European Cup-Winners Cup?

164. Nottingham Forest lost in the Uefa Cup quarter-finals in 1996 to Bayern Munich 7-2 on aggregate. What was the score after the first leg in Germany?

165. Who, in 1993-94, became the first British side to beat Bayern Munich in an European competition in Germany?

---

151. Athletico Bilbao 152. Trelleborgs 153. Rangers 154. 4-2 155. Marseille 156. Mark Hughes 157. Because Liverpool were banned for another three years 158. Gianluca Vialli (Sampdoria) 159. Benfica 160. One 161. Mike Newell 162. Borussia Dortmund, Steaua Bucharest and Juventus 163. Paris St Germain 164. 2-1 to Munich 165. Norwich City

 **Quiz 23** British Clubs in Europe

166. Who scored the two goals when Norwich beat Bayern Munich in the Uefa Cup second round, first leg in 1993-94?

167. **Who scored both Inter Milan goals in their 2-0 aggregate victory over Norwich in 1994 Uefa Cup third round?**

168. Which Italian club did Arsenal beat on their way to the 1994 European Cup-Winners Cup Final?

169. **Who did Manchester United lose to on away goals in the 1994 European Cup second round?**

170. Rangers also lost on away goals in the second round of the 1994 European Cup. Who to?

171. **When was the last European final to be played at Wembley?**

172. Manchester United's lost their first Champions League match of the 1996-97 season. Who to?

173. **Who scored the only goal?**

174. Who did Arsenal lose to in the first round of the 1996-97 Uefa Cup?

175. **Who were the only two British clubs to reach the second round of the Uefa Cup in 1996-97?**

176. Who scored Manchester United's first goal in the 1996-97 Champions League?

177. **Which former West Ham forward scored twice for Ajax in Rangers' 4-1 Champions League defeat in 1996-97?**

178. Who was sent-off for Rangers in that match?

179. **What was the score in Liverpool's second round, second leg tie against FC Sion?**

180. Who knocked Newcastle out of the 1997 Uefa Cup?

Quiz 24 — Moonlighting Footballers

1. **'Fever Pitch' is a book on one fan's obsession with his favourite football club. Which Premiership club does he support?**

2. Which famous actor narrated 'Hero', the official film of the 1986 World Cup?

3. **Which former England international appeared in the film 'When Saturday Comes'?**

4. What was the name of the award winning television drama about the Hillsborough disaster?

5. **Which club was the subject of the documentary 'Yours for a Fiver'?**

6. What was the title of the Cutting Edge television documentary that chronicled Graham Taylor as England manager?

7. **Which international manager wrote the television show 'Hazel'?**

8. Which England international had a hit record with 'Do The Right Thing'?

9. **Which footballers have appeared in adverts for Brut aftershave?**

10. Glenn Hoddle and Chris Waddle had a hit song when they were playing at Tottenham. What was the title of the song?

11. **Ruud Gullit used to be a member of a band. What music did they play?**

12. Which Premiership player appeared in the film 'Le Bonheur Est Dans Le Pre'?

13. **Name the title of the famous play and television programme An Evening with ....**

14. Which Nottingham Forest striker is a singer in a band?

15. **Who wrote the book 'Fever Pitch'?**

---

1. **Arsenal** 2. Michael Caine 3. **Tony Currie** 4. 'Hillsborough' 5. **Leyton Orient** 6. 'The Impossible Job' 7. **Terry Venables** 8. Ian Wright 9. **Kevin Keegan and Paul Gascoigne** 10. Diamond Lights 11. **Reggae** 12. Eric Cantona 13. **Gary Lineker** 14. Paul McGregor 15. **Nick Hornby**

Quiz 24 — Moonlighting Footballers

16. Which famous footballer orchestrated the football action in 'Escape to Victory'?

17. Which former England international has advertised Walkers Crisps?

18. The war film 'Escape to Victory' featured a football match between Allied prisoners and West Germany. Who was the manager of the Allies?

19. Which former England captain was in the Allies team in 'Escape to Victory'?

20. What position did Sylvester Stallone's play in 'Escape to Victory'?

21. Which England international writes a weekly article for The Times?

22. Which Croatian footballer had his own column in the Daily Telegraph during Euro '96?

23. Which former Arsenal and England striker occasionally writes for the Daily Telegraph?

24. Which two former Scotland internationals write for The Express?

25. Which England goalscorer wrote for the Observer?

26. Which former England international has a column in the football magazine 'Four-Four-Two'?

27. Which television summariser appeared on a Littlewoods Pools advert in 1997?

28. Which two Premiership players featured in a Nike advertisment in 1996?

29. Which England international has appeared in advertisments for sportswear Adidas?

30. Which Premiership footballer appeared in television adverts for Eurostar?

16. Pele 17. **Gary Lineker** 18. Michael Caine 19. **Bobby Moore** 20. Goalkeeper 21. **Steve McManaman** 22. Slaven Bilic 23. **Alan Smith** 24. Alan Hansen and Andy Gray 25. **Gary Lineker** 26. Chris Waddle 27. **Alan hansen** 28. Eric Cantona and Juninho 29. **Paul Gascoigne** 30. Eric Cantona

Quiz 24   Moonlighting Footballers

31. Which Manchester United and Manchester City players became partners in two lady boutiques?

32. Which two players from England's 1966 World Cup squad went into partnership in a football kit company?

33. Which team sung the number one hit 'Back Home' in 1970?

34. Tottenham's 1981 FA Cup Final song reached number five in the charts. Whose dream were they singing about?

35. Which nation's World Cup song was titled 'Easy, Easy'?

36. 'Blue is the Colour' was a number five hit for which club in February 1972?

37. Which England goalkeeper worked as a deck-chair assistant before turning professional?

38. Which FA Cup winning manager was a clerk in an education office before he took up football?

39. Which England 1966 World Cup star sung a version of 'You'll Never Walk Alone', but it never reached the charts?

40. Which former England captain had a number 31 hit with 'Head Over Heels in Love' in June 1979?

41. Which Spanish singer was once a Real Madrid goalkeeper?

42. Which Tottenham and Wales striker invested in two butchers shops after finishing his career?

43. Which French footballer appeared in a Renault advertisement?

44. Which television commentator supplied the voice-over for that advert?

45. Highbury was at the centre of which movie?

31. **George Best and Mike Summerbee** 32. Geoff Hurst and Jimmy Greaves
33. **England's World Cup squad** 34. Ossie's (Ardiles) 35. **Scotland in 1974**
36. Chelsea 37. **Ray Clemence** 38. Lawrie McMenemy 39. **Jack Charlton**
40. Kevin Keegan 41. **Julio Iglesias** 42. Cliff Jones 43. **David Ginola** 44. John
Motson 45. **The Arsenal Stadium Murder Mystery**

Quiz 25 — Britain's Biggest Transfers

1. In which year did Middlesbrough make Sunderland's Alf Common the first £1,000 player, 1903, 1904, 1905?

2. Who made the first five-figure move in 1928?

3. Who left Tranmere for £3,000 in 1925 and three years later set a goalscoring record which has stood for 70 years?

4. In 1996 Queens Park Rangers manager Ray Wilkins put a valuation on winger Trevor Sinclair. Was it £8million, £9.5million, £10m?

5. Which two internationals moved from Derby County to Liverpool in July 1991 for a combined total of over £5million?

6. What sum did Lazio ORIGINALLY offer Tottenham for Paul Gascoigne in 1991?

7. How much did Tottenham eventually receive for Gascoigne?

8. Who was Wimbledon's first £1million signing in 1996?

9. At the start of the 1996-7 season who was Rochdale's most expensive buy?

10. What was the name of the Norwegian agent at the centre of the "bung" transfer scandal in 1996?

11. Denis Law became Britain's first £100,000 player in 1962. From which club did Manchester United buy him?

12. In 1968 the world transfer record was shattered by a £440,000 Italian internal move. Name the player and clubs involved.

13. Who was involved in Britain's first £200,000 transfer?

14. In 1973 Johan Cruyff was involved in the first £1million transfer. Which two clubs were involved?

15. When Kevin Keegan left Liverpool in 1977 how much did Hamburg pay for his services?

---

1. 1905 2. David Jack - Bolton to Arsenal 3. Dixie Dean (Everton) 4. £10m
5. Mark Wright and Dean Saunders 6. £8.5m 7. £5.5m 8. Ben Thatcher
9. Andy Flounders 10. Rune Hauge 11. Torino 12. Pietro Anastasi from varese
to Juventus 13. Martin Peters from West Ham to Tottenham in 1970
14. Ajax and Barcelona 15. £550,000

 **Quiz 25**   **Britain's Biggest Transfers**

16. Also in 1977 the record fee for a transfer between British clubs soared to £440,000. Name the player and clubs involved.

17. **How much did Kevin Keegan spend in his first four years as Newcastle manager?**

18. In February 1996 Coventry signed a defender and a forward for a combined £3.1million. Who were they?

19. **Which two foreign players were prevented from switching Premiership clubs when the DoE initially refused new work permits in February 1996?**

20. Which clubs did the pair eventually join?

21. **In which year was Britain's first £1million transfer?**

22. Who was the player involved, the clubs and the fee?

23. **At the start of the 1996-97 season only one British player had been transferred for more than £5million on three occasions. Name him.**

24. Name the first 10 British players to cost £5million or more.

25. **Which Premiership club had three players costing £5million or more on their books at the start of the 1996-97 season?**

26. How much did Paul Gascoigne cost Rangers when he moved from Lazio in July 1995?

27. **What was the fee when striker Tony Cascarino joined Gillingham from non-League Crockenhill in 1982?**

28. How much did Cascarino cost Aston Villa when he moved from Millwall in March 1990?

29. **Why was Jimmy Greaves fee settled at £99,999 when he joined Tottenham from AC Milan in December 1961?**

30. Which Scottish club shattered the £2,000 barrier for West Ham's Syd Puddefoot in February 1922?

 **Quiz 25** Britain's Biggest Transfers

31. **Denis Law's record-breaking £100,000 move to Torino in June 1961 was followed by another 13 months later. What was the buying club and his new valuation?**

32. Who made English football's first big-money move to Italy and for how much?

33. **Which England striker moved from Chelsea to Notts County for £20,000 in November 1947?**

34. Name the player who scored in the first Wembley FA Cup Final and joined Arsenal in October 1928 for a record £10,890.

35. **The biggest immediate post-war transfer fee went North of the border. Which club collected £15,000 when Billy Steel moved to Derby in September 1947?**

36. The "clown prince" of football transferred from Newcastle to Sunderland in February 1948 for £20,500. Who was he?

37. **Name the player and the clubs involved in the first £150,000 English transfer?**

38. Which Welsh international moved from Leeds to Juventus for £65,000 in April 1957?

39. **Which club was known as the "Bank of England club" when knocked out of the FA Cup by non-League Yeovil in 1949?**

40. A member of England's world cup winning squad was involved in a big transfer within weeks of the 1966 triumph. Name the player, the clubs and the fee involved.

41. **Before Alan Shearer's £15million move from Blackburn to Newcastle, which Italian was the world's most expensive player?**

42. In which month is the annual transfer deadline?

43. **Name the subject of the world's first £1million transfer and the clubs involved .**

44. Who became the most expensive player in Britain when he moved from Middlesbrough to West Bromwich Albion in January 1979 for £516,000?

45. **In 1992 AC Milan spent £23,000 on two players within a month. Who were they?**

 **Quiz 25**   **Britain's Biggest Transfers**

46. Beazer Homes League club Rushden and Diamonds shattered the record fee for a non-League player in March 1996. Who was the player, the fee and the other club involved?

47. **Which club did Welsh international Dean Saunders join for £1.5million when he left Aston Villa in July 1995?**

48. Diego Maradona left Napoli for which club in a £4million deal in September 1992?

49. **From which club did Newcastle purchase striker Faustino Asprilla for £6.7million in February 1996?**

50. Just before the start of the 1995-96 season Wigan signed Spaniards Jesus Seba, Roberto Martinez and Isidro Diaz. By what name were they collectively known?

51. **Which club did Jurgen Klinsmann leave to join Tottenham?**

52. Who moved to Barcelona from Manchester United in May 1986 for £2.3m?

53. **Who moved from Manchester United to AC Milan for £1.5m in 1984?**

54. Who moved to Liverpool from Newcastle for £1.9m in July 1987?

55. **Which French club did Clive Allen join from Tottenham?**

56. From which club did Manchester United buy Peter Schmeichel?

57. **How did James Oakes come to play for both clubs in the same League fixture in the 1932-33 season?**

58. How much did Ruel Fox cost Tottenham when he joined from Newcastle in October 1995?

59. **Also in 1995 Andy Cole's transfer from Newcastle to Manchester United set a new British record. How much?**

60. Which player moved from Manchester United to Newcastle as part of the Andy Cole deal?

 ## Quiz 25   **Britain's Biggest Transfers**

61. Another record British transfer was set when striker Duncan Ferguson moved from Dundee United to Rangers in 1993. How much was the fee?

62. The record went a year later when Chris Sutton moved from Norwich to Blackburn for how much?

63. In 1996 Manchester United were found guilty of an illegal approach to the teenaged son of a League club manager. Who was he?

64. Striker Marco Gabbiadini has cost which two clubs over one million pounds?

65. What was the fee when Ray Wilkins left Paris St. Germain for Rangers in November 1987?

66. Which Belgian defender did Newcastle sign in August 1994?

67. How much did Phillipe Albert cost Newcastle?

68. Andy Cole's £7m signing by Manchester United in 1995 set a new British record fee. Who was the second most expensive player on the Old Trafford books at the time?

69. Name the four French clubs Eric Cantona played for before his £900,000 move to Leeds in 1992?

70. Gary Pallister became the most expensive defender in Britain when he joined Manchester United from Middlesbrough in 1989 for how much?

71. How much did Ruud Gullit cost Chelsea when he arrived as a player in August 1995?

72. Who cost Blackburn £2.7m from Sheffield Wednesday in August 1993?

73. How much did Crystal Palace collect when Ian Wright went to Arsenal in September 1991?

74. In 1979 West Bromwich Albion sold a forward to Real Madrid. Who was he and what was the fee?

75. Which player was paraded around the Baseball Ground as Derby County's latest big signing in 1972 - only to change his mind and join Manchester United instead?

 Quiz 25 Britain's Biggest Transfers

76. Which forward was sold for a Huddersfield record £2.7million to Sheffield Wednesday in 1996?

77. **Who became Britain's most expensive teenager when he moved from Charlton to Leeds in July 1996?**

78 How much did Bowyer cost?

79. **Who joined a London club in a £1million-plus deal but never played a first-team game for them?**

80. Which other London club did he join after just three weeks?

81. **Chris Armstrong left Crystal Palace for Tottenham in June 1995 for how much?**

82. Ian Rush left Liverpool in 1987 for which club and how much was the fee?

83. **How much did Rush cost Liverpool when he returned in August 1988?**

84. When Richard Gough left Tottenham for Rangers in October 1987 the £1.5million deal set three records. What were they?

85. **At which English club did Richard Gough start his playing career?**

86. Tottenham shattered the British record fee when they signed winger Cliff Jones from Swansea in February 1985. How much did he cost?

87. **Which Staffordshire-born player shattered the British transfer record twice in a year at the end of the 1960's while yet to be capped by his country?**

88. Which clubs and fees were involved in Clarke's moves?

89. **Which striker moved from Birmingham to Everton for £350,000 in February 1974?**

90. From which club did Welsh international midfielder Peter Nicholas join Chelsea in August 1988?

Quiz 25 — Britain's Biggest Transfers

91. What was the fee?

92. Brighton set a new fee record for a non-League player when they forked out £115,000 in September 1988. Who was the player and the other club involved?

93. A week later Brighton signed another Barnet player for an identical sum. Who was he?

94. Which record was set by David Leworthy when he moved from Farnborough to Dover in August 1993 for £30,000?

95. Who was the first £1million British goalkeeper?

96. Which clubs were involved in Martyn's November 1989 move?

97. Two years later five more goalkeepers had moved on in Britain for £1million or more. Who were they?

98. Back in 1964 the record fee for a British goalkeeper was collected by Crystal Palace from Coventry. Who was the goalkeeper and what was the fee involved?

99. Manchester United paid record fees for goakeepers in 1966 and 1988. Who were they?

100. Queens Park Rangers collected record fees for goalkeepers in 1979 and 1990. Who were they?

101. Which goalkeeper was transferred twice for a record £50,000 within five months of the year 1966?

102. Name the clubs involved in Stepney's moves.

103. Which two records did Alexei Mikhailichenko's transfer from Sampdoria to Rangers set in 1991?

104. How much was the fee?

105. In August 1991 three players left Liverpool for around £1million each. Who were they?

---

91. **£350,000** 92. Nicky Bissett 93. **Robert Codner** 94. The highest fee between non-league clubs 95. **Nigel Martyn** 96. Bristol Rovers and Crystal palace 97. **David Seaman, John Lukic, Tony Coton, Andy Goram and Chris Woods** 98. Bill Glazier - £35,000 99. **Iex Stepney and Jim Leighton** 100. Phil Parkes and David Seaman **101. Alex Stepney** 102. Millwall-Chelsea, Chelsea-Manchester United **103. Record fee for a Scottish club, most expensive foreign import** 104. £2m **105. Steve Staunton, Peter Beardsley, Gary Gillespie**

 **Quiz 26** Who said?

1. **Which former Manchester City manager said: "I'm not a believer in luck, although I do believe you need it"?**

2. Which manager said of his side's FA Cup chances: "I honestly believe we can go all the way to Wembley.....unless someone knocks us out"?

3. **Which former manager stated: "I promise results, not promises"?**

4. Which former Aston Villa manager said of chairman Doug Ellis: "He said he was right behind me, so I told him I'd rather have him in front of me where I could see him"?

5. **Which legendary manager once said: "Mind, I've been here during the bad times too. One year we finished second"?**

6. Which charismatic manager said: "John Bond has blackened my name with his insinuations about the private lives of football managers. Both my wives are upset."

7. **Who said of women in football: "Women should be in the kitchen, the discotheque and the boutique, but not in football"?**

8. Which former QPR and England striker once said: "If I had a choice of a night with Raquel Welch or going to a betting shop, I'd choose the betting shop"?

9. **Which former manager said: "The ideal board of directors should be made up of three men - two dead and one dying"?**

10. Which former manager said: "Football hooligans? Well, there are ninety-two club chairmen, for a start"?

 **Quiz 26**   **Who said?**

11. Which former England striker said of Kenny Dalglish: "He has about as much personality as a tennis racket"?

12. Who said: "Trevor Brooking floats like a butterfly, and stings like one too"?

13. Which commentator said: "Lukic saved with his foot which is all part of the goalkeeper's arm"?

14. Which former manager said of Ray Wilkins: "He can't run, he can't tackle and he can't head the ball. The only time he goes forward is to toss the coin"?

15. What television commentator said: "The game is balanced in Arsenal's favour"?

16. Which commentator stated: "With the very last kick of the game, Bobby McDonald scored with a header"?

17. Which international manager once said: "If history is going to repeat itself, I should think we can expect the same thing again"?

18. Which former England manager said: "The first ninety minutes are the most important"?

19. Which TV commentator said: "The European Cup is seventeen pounds of silver and it's worth it's weight in gold"?

20. Which international striker said: "Moving from Wales to Italy is like going to a different country"?

Quiz 26 — Who said?

21. **Which commentator said: "The ball has broken 50-50 for Keegan"?**

22. Which England international remarked: "I never predict anything and I never will do"?

23. **Which former Liverpool manager said: "Without picking out anyone in particular, I thought Mark Wright was tremendous"?**

24. Which former England captain once said: "If you never concede a goal, you're going to win more games than you lose"?

25. **Name the former Newcastle manager who said: "There's no job I've ever wanted. This is the only job in football I've ever wanted."**

26. Which international manager once said: "It may have just been going wide, but nevertheless it was a great shot on target"?

27. **Which radio commentator said: "Fifty-two thousand people here at Maine Road tonight, but my goodness me, it seems like fifty-thousand"?**

28. Which former Manchester United manager said: "Yes, Woodcock would have scored but his shot was too perfect"?

29. **Name the radio commentator who said: "Ian Rush. Deadly ten times out of ten. But that wasn't one of them."**

30. Who is the TV commentator who said: "Oh, he had an eternity to play that ball......but he took too long over it"?

21. **David Coleman** 22. Paul Gascoigne 23. **Graeme Souness** 24. Bobby Moore
25. **Kevin Keegan** 26. Terry Venables 27. **Bryon Butler** 28. Ron Atkinson
29. **Peter Jones** 30. Martin Tyler

THE ULTIMATE FACT AND QUIZ BOOK

 **Quiz 26** Who said?

31. **Which former Manchester City and Everton defender once said: "I can't promise anything but I can promise 100 per cent"?**

32. Name the TV commentator who said: "McCarthy shakes his head in agreement with the referee."

33. **Who said of his side's 4-3 win over Leicester: "Games like this are probably why Kevin Keegan went grey and Terry McDermott's hair is white"?**

34. Which Dutch striker said of an extra £7,000 a week offered to him as: "Good enough for the homeless but not an international striker"?

35. **Which former World Footballer of the Year said of being a substitute: "At the moment I feel like a Ferrari being driven by a traffic warden"?**

36. Which Premiership defender said of coming to England: "It won't be easy here, and any normal, intelligent person would have stayed at Inter"?

37. **Which player said after being sent-off for foul and abusive language: "Industrial language is part and parcel of the game. If I had been sent off every time I have sworn at an official I'd only have completed 100 games in my career"?**

38. Which international striker said of coming to England: "I did not come here on holiday or to enjoy myself. I came here to play and become a legend in London with Chelsea"?

39. **Which manager said of Florin Raducioiu: "He went missing on the way to the Stockport game because he thought he was going to be sub. He had every chance of playing that night, but he was shopping with his in-laws in Harvey Nichols"?**

40. Which manager of Exeter said of his side's chances of beating Aston Villa in the FA Cup: "I've seen Desert Orchid fall. I've seen Bestie refuse a drink. I've seen Emlyn Hughes buy one. So you never know"?

39. Harry Redknapp 40. Alan Ball

35. Roberto Baggio 36. Gianluca Festa **37. John Aldridge 38.** Gianluca Vialli

31. **Paul Power** 32. Martin Tyler **33. Kenny Dalglish** 34. Pierre Van Hooijdonk

 Quiz 26   Who said?

41. Which former England international said: "Playing is like a bug with me. I don't know when I'll be cured. I still get the same buzz. It's a magnificent life, being a professional footballer, and I'm frightened of going too soon"?

42. Name the former Newcastle manager who said: "Sir John Hall was a multi-millionaire when I came back to Newcastle. With all the players I've bought, I'm trying to make him just an ordinary millionaire."

43. Which former Tottenham manager once said: "I always tell young managers to pick their best team at the start of the season, write it on a piece of paper and tuck it away in a drawer. Half way through the season, if things are going wrong, look at those names again......because the first team you pick each season is always you best team"?

44. Who said after Manchester United were knocked out of the European Cup by Galatasaray: "I just sat at home watching TV - and it wasn't even switched on"?

45. Which radio commentator said: "Ray Wilkins sends an inch-perfect pass to no-one in particular"?

46. Which manager once said: "Who's want to be a football manager? People like me who are too old to be a player, too poor to be a director and too much in love with the game to be an agent"?

47. Which goalkeeper said: "One of the old trainers, John Latimer, said to me: 'Goalkeepers have got to be crackers and daft. You, son, have got the qualities of an international.' I took it as a compliment"?

48. Who said of living with a footballer: "I've been married for 17 years and been to 14 clubs, lived in six houses, five hotels and seven rented places. As for John, he is so wrapped up in his job, I've even heard him giving Gerald Sinstadt a TV interview.....in his sleep"?

49. Which manager said: "I know we are the team everyone loves to hate. They blame us for everything, from England's failure in the World Cup to the rising price in plums"?

50. Which former Premiership striker said: "A goalscorer is paid to get hurt inside the 18-yard box and to die inside the 6-yard box"?

Quiz 26 — Who said?

51. **Who said after suffering a horrific injury in a challenge with Wimbledon's John Fashanu: "John Fashanu was playing professional football without due care and attention"?**

52. Which former manager said of Kevin Keegan: "It was great for the game that Keegan came back to Newcastle. For a long period the club had been not through thick and thin, but through thin and thinner"?

53. **Who said of a Tony Yeboah goal: "It was in the net in the time it takes a snowflake to melt on a hot stove"?**

54. Who said of Eric Cantona: "He is so mild-mannered when the volcano inside him isn't erupting"?

55. **Which former Luton manager said of their 3-2 win at Wolves: "I told my players that Alex Ferguson was here, that they could do themselves a bit of good. He was actually here to watch his lad Darren playing for Wolves, but my lot wouldn't know that, would they?"?**

56. Which former World Cup winning manager said: "The art of picking a national team is not necessarily to choose the best 11 players in the country, but the 11 who fit together best"?

57. **Who said of John fashanu: "I think John Fashanu is worth £30 million really. I only said £12 million because it's nearly Christmas"?**

58. Which Premiership striker said after leaving Cambridge United: "I knew I couldn't take any more when, one day in training, a player shouted 'feet' meaning that's where he wanted the ball - and he was punished by being made to do 40 press-ups"?

59. **Who said of Paul Gascoigne leaving for Lazio: "I am pleased for him but it's like watching your mother-in-law drive off the cliff in your new car"?**

60. Which Scottish player said on the eve of their vital European Championship tie in Switzerland: "Our attitude is exactly right. Every player in the squad would give his left arm to play in this game. Well, maybe not the goalkeepers"?

.

51. **Gary Mabbutt** 52. Tommy Docherty 53. **Howard Wilkinson** 54. Alex Ferguson 55. **David Pleat** 56. Enzo Bearzot 57. **Sam Hammam** 58. Steve Claridge 59. **Terry Venables** 60. Andy Goram

 **Quiz 26**   Who said?

61. Which TV pundit said: "Trevor Steven might have scored there if he'd chanced his arm with his left foot"?

62. Who said on the eve of the 1992 European Championship: "I expect to win. Let me do the worrying - that's what I'm paid for. You get your feet up in front of the telly, get a few beers in and have a good time"?

63. Which radio commentator said of the 3,231 fans at a Wimbledon-Luton match: "The spectators showed the stewards to their seats"?

64. Which former Sheffield United manager said: "They've been loyal to me. When I came here, they said there would be no money, and they've kept their word"?

65. Which veteran striker said: "It's best being a striker. If you miss five, then score the winner, you're a hero. The goalkeeper can play a blinder, then let one in.....and he's a villain"?

66. Who replied when asked what an American was doing playing in goal for Millwall: "Trying to keep the ball out"?

67. Which former Blackburn manager said: "If we score more goals than they do, we will win"?

68. Who said on his first game as Newcastle manager: "You just sit there, pretend you know what you are doing, and hope you get it right"?

69. Which legendary England winger said: "I played in the First Division until I was 50. That was a mistake. I could have gone on for another two years"?

70. Which former Scotland manager said: "To me, pressure is being homeless or unemployed, not trying to win a football match"?

 **Quiz 26**   Who said?

71. **Name the veteran manager who said on his return to management at Bristol Rovers: "It's hard to believe that so many professional in this country haven't been taught how to kick a football correctly."**

72. Which club owner said of Vinnie Jones' video that showed violence and cheating: "He must be a mosquito brain to say what he's said"?

73. **Which former Premiership manager said in 1990: "Ten years from now, Paul Gascoigne might have proved himself the biggest name in football, or he might have blown it. Either way, I will not be surprised"?**

74. Who said of Graeme Souness' decision to leave Rangers to manager Liverpool: "I believe he is making the biggest mistake of his life. Time will tell"?

75. **Who said on being awarded the OBE in June 1990: "My wife says it stands for 'Old Big'Ead'"?**

76. "Now the players applaud the crowd at the end of a match. When I was playing, it was the other way round"?

77. **Which legendary manager said of playing youngsters: "If you don't put them in, you'll never know what you've got"?**

78. Which former Liverpool striker said: "When my playing career is over, I'll return to Liverpool and stand on the Kop just like I used to when I was a kid"?

79. **Which former QPR manager said: "I am not difficult to get on with. I am just difficult to get to know"?**

80. Which former England striker said: "There is no point in looking back in life. I had a marvelous time playing football, travelled the world, played with and against some great players. But I got old. People ask me why I gave up football. I tell them I didn't. Football gave me up"?

 **Quiz 26** Who said?

81. **Name the former Argentinean manager who said: "The player who kicks the last penalty either has the key to the hotel or the plane tickets home"?**

82. Which England veteran said in October 1989: "Every year I play now is an extra. The longer it's gone on, the more I've enjoyed it"?

83. **Which former Wolves manager remarked: "People say Steve Bull's first touch isn't good, but he usually scores with his second"?**

84. When he was in charge of Derby, who said: "A mistake is only a mistake when it is done twice"?

85. **Which legendary player said of his first experience of watching England: "My father took me, as a very young boy, to see the great England, and I went to the match expecting so much. That was the day they lost 1-0 to the U.S.A. in the World Cup"?**

86. Which international goalkeeper said: "From watching Gordon Banks, I learnt about positioning. From watching Peter Bonetti, I learnt about agility. And from watching Lev Yashin, the great Russian goalkeeper dressed in all black, I learnt about projecting an invincible image"?

87. **Who said on life in Italy: "The most incredible thing was the way the Juventus players took their minds off a match. Ninety minutes before kick-off, some smoked cigarettes or drank a glass of wine. Everyone seemed to find that normal - except me"?**

88. Who gave this advice to Kenny Dalglish when he signed for Liverpool: "Don't over-eat and don't lose your accent"?

89. **Which England midfielder said after signing a seven-year contract in November 1991: "I never seriously thought about going abroad. Knowing I can play out my career with Spurs is brilliant"?**

90. Which England international said: "I got eight O-levels at school.....zero in every subject"?

90. Paul Gascoigne

85. Pele 86. Peter Shilton **87. Ian Rush** 88. Bill Shankly 89. **Chris Waddle**

81. Carlos Bilardo 82. Peter Shilton 83. **Graham Turner** 84. Arthur Cox

 Quiz 26 Who said?

91. **Which Premiership manager told his team: "If you have the ball, you command the game. If you kick and rush, it depends on luck"?**

92. Which former England coach said: "There is nothing you can know about football that cannot be learned from watching Germany. Physically, tactically, technically, mentally, they get it right almost every time"?

93. **Which former legendary manager said once: "I'm only surprised that people are surprised by surprise results in football"?**

94. Which Premiership manager said: "You have to remember, a goalkeeper is a goalkeeper because he can't play football"?

95. **Which international manager said of allowing players' wives and girlfriends into the team camp: "I've nothing against it. Love is good for footballers, as long as it is not at half-time"?**

96. Which Premiership manager had this message on his answerphone: "I'm sorry I'm not here at the moment. If you are the president of AC Milan, Barcelona or Real Madrid, I'll get back to you"?

97. **Which former manager said: "Southampton is a very well-run outfit from Monday to Friday. It's Saturday we've got a problem with"?**

98. Who said after his side drew with Newcastle in May 1996: "Me feel sorry for Kevin Keegan? When he's got Asprilla and Barton and Clark on the bench?"?

99. **Which England captain said after England's 1-1 draw in a friendly against Portugal: "At least we got a point"?**

100. Which Premiership manager said of his trade: "Management is a seven-days-a-week job. The intensity of it takes it's toll on your health. Some people want to go on for ever, and I obviously don't. I saw Alan Hansen playing golf three times a week, and it got me thinking"?

 **Quiz 26**   Who said?

101. **Which manager left this message on his answerphone after being sacked by Birmingham: "Kristine (his wife) has gone shopping and I'm at the job centre, looking for employment. Funny old game, isn't it?"?**

102. Which radio commentator said: "Barmby stood out like a Pamela Anderson in a sea of Claire Raynors"?

103. **Which fromer England manager said: "This is a great job – until a ball is kicked"?**

104. Which legendary manager once said: "The secret of being a manager is to keep the six players who hate you away from the five who are undecided"?

105. **Which England goalscorer said in 1970: "It's easy to beat Brazil. You just stop them getting twenty yards from your goal"?**

106. Which former European Footballer of the Year said: "In my life I have had two big vices: smoking and playing football. Football has given me everything, but smoking nearly took it all away"?

107. **Which famous Brazilian said of the difference between South American and European football: "Our football comes from the heart, theirs comes from the mind"?**

108. Which former Manchester United player once said: "I could join Alcoholics Anonymous. Only problem is I can't remain anonymous"?

109. **Which Italian defender said of his treatment of Maradona during a match: "It is not dancing school"?**

110. Which famous Hungarian stated: "I am grateful to my father for all the coaching he did not give me"?

 ## Quiz 26 — Who said?

111. **Which former England manager said: "All managers are frustrated players"?**

112. Which former Newcastle and England star said of his club: "I have heard of players selling dummies. But this club keeps buying them"?

113. **Which Brazilian remarked in 1982: "Football became popular because it was an art. But now too many pitches are becoming battlefields"?**

114. Which former manager said: "I'm as bad a judge as Walter Winterbottom - he gave me only two caps"?

115. **Which Irish player remarked after he swapped shirts with Ruud Gullit in the 1988 European Championship: "When he gets mine home, he'll wonder who the bloody hell's it is"?**

116. Who said of Italian club Pisa's bid for his son: "They couldn't afford him even if they threw in the leaning tower"?

117. **Which WBA player said of seeing the Great Wall of China: "When you've seen one wall, you've seen the lot"?**

118. Which former Aberdeen manager said of signing Charlie Nicholas in 1988: "He has two arms and legs, same as the rest of our players, but once he finds his feet I'm convinced he'll do well"?

119. **Who said after scoring for Liverpool in 1988: "As the ball came over I remembered what Graham Taylor said about my having no right foot - so I headed it in"?**

120. Who once said of Paul Gascoigne: "he is accused of being arrogant, unable to cope with the press and a boozer. Sounds like he's got a chance to me"?

 **Quiz 26** Who said?

121. Which television pundit said of Italian Marco Tardelli: "He's been responsible for more scar-tissue than the surgeons of Harefield hospital"?

122. Which charismatic manager said in 1983: "It's bloody tough being a legend"?

123. Which manager said: "One of the main reasons why I never became England manager was because the Football Association thought that I would take over and run the show. They were dead right"?

124. Juventus owner, Gianni Agnelli, described which England player as being "a soldier of war with the face of a child"?

125. Which former England captain said of his drinking days: "Even after a skinful, I don't have a hangover and can still be up with the others"?

126. Which manager said in the 1990 World Cup: "We'll start worrying about the Italians when we sober up tomorrow"?

127. Which television summariser said in the 1990 World Cup: "I've just seen Gary Lineker shake hands with Jurgen Klinsmann - it's a wonder Klinsmann hasn't fallen down"?

128. About which Dutch player was it stated: "He knows the game from A to Z and if the alphabet had any more letters, he would know those as well"?

129. Who said to his team before extra-time in a World Cup Final: "You've done it once, now win it again"?

130. Which famous club chairman once said: "I know I'm difficult to deal with. It's because I'm not logical"?

THE ULTIMATE FACT AND QUIZ BOOK

 **Quiz 26**   **Who said?**

131. Which former Aston Villa manager said: "I have told my players never to believe what I say about them in the papers"?

132. Which Scottish manager once remarked: "They serve a drink in Glasgow called the Souness - one half and you're off"?

133. Which manager in 1987 described Wimbledon as "the borstal of football"?

134. Which former England manager said in 1991: "A manager can never say always and can never say never"?

135. Who said when he become the first paid football director: "Only women and horses work for nothing"?

136. Which international manager said in Euro '96: "If I walked on water, my critics would say it was because I couldn't swim"?

137. Which international defender said on life in English football: "I came to this country to play football, not to be a kick-boxer, but there seems to be one in every side we play"?

138. Which England legend said of European football: "They know on the Continent that European football without the English is like a hot dog without mustard"?

139. Which legendary European footballer said: "The failure to understand the physical and mental strains on a professional is behind the widely held belief that footballers are stupid"?

140. Which manager said of the support on the eve of his team's game with England in Euro '96: "It's 2,000 of us against 70,000 drunkards"?

131. **Graham Taylor** 132. Tommy Docherty 133. **Dave Bassett** 134. Graham Taylor 135. **Doug Ellis** 136. Berti Vogts 137. **Derby County's Igor Stimac** 138. Bobby Charlton 139. **Johan Cruyff** 140. Javier Clemente

 **Quiz 26**   Who said?

141. **Which TV summariser previewed the Portugal-Czech Republic Euro '96 game by stating: "I'm looking forward to seeing some sexy football"?**

142. Which former England goalscorer said: "Football is a simple game where 22 players play against each other and in the end Germany wins"?

143. **Which England international said in 1971: "Soccer in England is a grey game, played on grey days by grey people"?**

144. Which legendary footballer once said: "A penalty is a cowardly way to score a goal"?

145. **Which Dutch international once said: "If I'd wanted to be an individual, I'd have taken up tennis"?**

146. Which former England manager once stated: "Football is a simple game. The hard part is making it look simple"?

147. **Who told Gareth Southgate after his penalty miss in Euro '96: "Why didn't you just belt it?"?**

148. Which Scottish player said on the eve of Euro '96: "For the first match we'll be underdogs, and for the next two we'll be even bigger under-dogs - even underpups"?

149. **Which TV summariser said during the England-Spain game in Euro '96: "Three fresh men, three fresh legs"?**

150. Which international manager said in 1983: "There's no rapport with referees these days. If you say anything you get booked, and if you don't they send you off for dumb insolence"?

141. **Ruud Gullit** 142. Gary Lineker 143. **Rodney Marsh** 144. Pele 145. **Ruud Gullit** 146. Ron Greenwood 147. **Barbara Southgate** 148. Ally McCoist 149. **Jimmy Hill** 150. Jack Charlton

Quiz 27 — British Managers, Home And Abroad

1. **Which manager won three FA Cups in the 1960s with Tottenham?**

2. Which manager won two successive FA Cups in the 1980s with Tottenham?

3. **Who was Southampton's manager when they lifted the FA Cup in 1976?**

4. Who was the coach for Coventry City's victory in the 1987 FA Cup?

5. **Which manager won the FA Cup with Manchester City in 1969?**

6. What was unusual about Preston North End's manager when they won the 1938 FA Cup?

7. **Who was West Ham's manager for their 1975 FA Cup victory?**

8. Who was West Bromwich Albion's manager for their last FA Cup victory in 1968?

9. **Which manager won two FA Cups, nine years apart, and with the same club, in the 1960s and 1970s?**

10. Who managed Nottingham Forest for their FA Cup win in 1959, when they beat Luton Town 2 - 1?

11. **Which manager took over at Hereford United in August 1995?**

12. Which two managers took control at Rotherham United in September 1994?

13. **At the start of the 1996/7 season, who was the longest serving manager in the first division, having taken over his club in March 1984?**

14. How many Division One teams had player-managers at the start of the 1996-7 season?

15. **Who was appointed Swansea City player-manager in February 1996?**

---

1. **Bill Nicholson** 2. Keith Burkinshaw 3. **Lawrie McMenemy** 4. John Sillett 5. **Joe Mercer** 6. There was no manager 7. **John Lyall** 8. Alan Ashman 9. **Bill Shankly** 10. Billy Walker 11. **Graham Turner** 12. Archie Gemmill and John McGovern 13. **John Rudge (Port Vale)** 14. 9 - Barnsley, Grimsby, Oldham, Portsmouth, QPR, Reading, Southend, Swindon, Tranmere 15. **Jan Molby**

 **Quiz 27** British Managers, Home And Abroad

16. Which Premiership club has, at the start of the 1996-97 season, had the most manager changes since the Second World War?

17. **Which Nationwide side has, at the beginning of the 1996/7 season, had the most managers since World War Two?**

18. Which 1996/7 Premiership manager has on his answerphone: "I'm sorry I'm not here at the moment. If you are the president of AC Milan, Barcelona or Real Madrid, I'll get back to you"?

19. **Which Premiership manager has his birthday on New Year's Eve?**

20. Who was the 1995/6 Division One Manager of the Year?

21. **With which team did Tony Pullis receive his Division Three Manager of the Year award at the end of the 1995-96 season?**

22. Which manager led Plymouth to a promotion in 1996, making it four promotions in seven years, following two with Notts County and one with Huddersfield?

23. **Bolton Wanderers manager Charles Foweraker was the first to do what?**

24. Which manager took his team to both of the two Rumbelows Cup finals?

25. **Which manager saw his team win the 1995-96 Scottish Coca Cola Cup?**

26. Who was the losing manager in the 1995/6 Scottish FA Cup final?

27. **For which club was Paul Fairclough the Vauxall Conference Manager of the Year, in 1995/6?**

28. Which former Premiership manager was sacked after ten matches as the coach of Mexican club Guadalajara?

29. **Who became the shortest serving manager in League history, surviving only three days at Scunthorpe in 1959?**

30. Who, in 1984, was named as manager at Crystal Palace, but changed his mind four days later, without signing a contract?

16. Coventry City - 20 17. **Darlington - 25** 18. Joe Kinnear 19. **Alex Ferguson** 20. Peter Reid 21. **Gillingham** 22. Neil Warnock 23. **Win the FA Cup** 24. Alex Ferguson 25. **Roy Aitken (Aberdeen)** 26. Jim Jefferies (Hearts) 27. **Stevenage Borough** 28. Ossie Ardiles 29. **Bill Lambton** 30. Dave Bassett

Quiz 27 — British Managers, Home And Abroad

31. **Which League club has had the fewest number of managers, by the end of the 1996-97 season?**

32. Who was the first man to achieve the Championship/FA Cup double as player-manager?

33. **Who was England's longest serving manager?**

34. Which manager won the 1958 and 1959 League championships with Wolves?

35. **Who was the first manager to achieve the League and Cup double at Arsenal?**

36. How many matches was John Toshack manager of Wales?

37. **Who was the first player-manager, in the old First Division, when he played for QPR, 1968-9?**

38. Who is the only manager to win the League Championship with Ipswich Town?

39. **For how long was Brian Clough manager of Leeds United in 1974?**

40. Who was the first manager to win the FA Cup with two different sides?

41. **Name the three managers that have won League Championships with two different clubs.**

42. Who was Coventry City's player-manager in 1990-91?

43. **Who is the longest serving manager in Scottish League football, spending 17 years in charge?**

44. How many trophies did Bob Paisley win with Liverpool?

45. **Which manager coached both Watford and Sheffield United in the 1987-8 season?**

31. **West Ham** 32. Kenny Dalglish 33. **Walter Winterbottom, 1946-62** 34. Stan Cullis 35. **Bertie Mee (Arsenal, 1971)** 36. One 37. **Les Allen** 38 Alf Ramsay (1961-2) 39. **44 days** 40. Billy Walker (Sheffield Wednesday and Nottingham Forest) 41. **Herbert Chapman (Huddersfield and Arsenal), Brian Clough (Derby County and Nottingham Forest), Kenny Dalglish (Liverpool and Blackburn)** 42. Terry Butcher 43. **Jim McLean (Dundee United, 1971-88)** 44. 20 (6 Leagues, 3 European cups, 1 UEFA cup, 1 European Super cup, 6 Charity Shields) 45. **Dave Bassett**

 **Quiz 27**   British Managers, Home And Abroad

46. With what club did Aston Villa manager Brian Little spend only 49 days in charge?

47. **Which 1996/7 manager has scored the fastest ever first class goal at Wembley?**

48. Who was the last Second Division manager to win the FA Cup?

49. **Which two 1995-96 Premiership managers have been sent off for England in full internationals?**

50. Which British manager took over the Kuwait national side in 1986, and later went on to manage Vitoria Setubal in Portugal?

51. **Which British manager coached at Athletico Bilbao in 1987?**

52. Which English manager was sacked from his foreign club in September 1987?

53. **Which British manager was sacked after only 94 days at Athletico Madrid?**

54. Which British manager had spells at Celta Vigo and Athletico Madrid?

55. **Who moved from Real Madrid to manage Real Sociedad in 1989?**

56. Who moved from Tottenham to take over at Espanol for only 41 days?

57. **Which British manager has coached four different teams, in three different countries since 1992?**

58. Who went from being the Czech national manager to Aston Villa in 1990?

59. **Who left Swedish team Malmo to become coach at Southend in August 1992?**

60. Which foreign manager joined the Premiership after leaving WBA in 1992?

Quiz 27 — British Managers, Home And Abroad

61. Which ex-Chelsea manager moved to Kuwait to head Al-Arabi Sporting Club?

62. Who, in 1995, signed a contract to manage Norwegian club FC Start?

63. Which 1996-97 Premiership manager has led clubs in France and Japan?

64. Which Premiership manager has coached in Turkey?

65. Which Englishman managed a country in the 1994 World Cup and helped them qualify for Euro 96?

66. Which European manager snubbed Blackburn Rovers in 1997?

67. Who became Celtic's manager in 1993, twenty years after leaving as a player?

68. Who resigned as Coventry manager in October 1993, ten minutes after 5-1 defeat by QPR?

69. Which Brit became Zambian manager, two months after the side lost 18 players in an air crash?

70. Which St. Mirren manager resigned to persue a coaching career in Florida?

71. Which Brit became coach of Spanish club Seville in May 1986?

72. Who left Sampdoria to become player-manager at Glasgow Rangers?

73. Who has managed clubs which include Middlesborough, Millwall, Bolton and Arsenal in recent years?

74. Who made his move into management by becoming player-manager at Sheffield Wednesday?

75. Which two men became joint player-coaches at Charlton, in July 1991?

61. Bobby Campbell 62. Steve Perryman 63. Arsene Wenger (Monaco, Grampus Eight, Arsenal) 64. Graeme Souness (Galatasaray) 65. Roy Hodgson 66. Sven Goran Eriksson 67. Lou Macari 68. Bobby Gould 69. Ian Porterfield 70. David Hay 71. Jock Wallace 72. Graeme Souness 73. Bruce Rioch 74. Trevor Francis 75. Steve Gritt and Alan Curbishley

 **Quiz 27**   **British Managers, Home And Abroad**

76. Which manager was released as a player by Monaco, following an ankle injury, in April 1991?

77. **Who managed Italy to their 1982 World Cup win?**

78. Who was the Argentinian manager when they lifted the World Cup in 1986?

79. **Who are the only two men to have won the World Cup as both players and managers?**

80. In the 1994 World Cup, who was the manager of the only team to have played in all of the World Cup finals?

81. **Who were the two managers in charge for Holland's 1994 World Cup campaign?**

82. Who was the Spanish manager during the 1994 World Cup?

83. **Who went from managing Millwall to the Republic of Ireland?**

84. Who took England to four successive World Cup finals?

85. **Who was the manager of AC Milan when they lifted the World Club Championship in 1994?**

86. Who was in charge when England failed to reach the 1978 World Cup final?

87. **Who was England's manager for the 1982 World Cup?**

88. Who took England to a quarter-final and a semi-final in two successive World Cups?

89. **Who was manager when England finished third in the European Championships?**

90. How many England managers have represented their country at senior level football?

---

76. Glenn Hoddle 77. **Enzo Bearzot** 78. Carlos Bilardo 79. **Mario Zagalo (Brazil) and Franz Beckenbauer (Germany)** 80. Carlos Alberto Parreira 81. **Dick Advocaat (qualifiers) and Johan Cruyff (finals)** 82. Javier Clemente 83. **Mick McCarthy** 84. Walter Winterbottom 85. **Fabio Capello** 86. Don Revie 87. **Ron Greenwood** 88. Bobby Robson 89. **Sir Alf Ramsey (1968)** 90. 6 - Ramsey, Mercer, Revie, Robson, Venables, Hoddle

Quiz 27 — British Managers, Home And Abroad

91. Who was in charge of England when the World Cup was held in Chile?

92. Who have been the last three Scottish managers?

93. Who was Northern Ireland's manager for 13 years, from 1980-93?

94. Who took over from Roy Hodgson as manager of Switzerland for Euro 96?

95. Who was the French coach for Euro 96?

96. Which manager won Euro 96?

97. Who was the Italian manager that was sacked after Italy's poor results in Euro 96?

98. Who led Holland in Euro 96?

99. Which manager won the League Cup three years in a row in the Eighties?

100. Who was West Ham's manager when they won the 1965 Cup Winners' Cup?

101. Which two managers have led English sides to two consecutive European Cups?

102. Who was the manager of the 1995 European Cup champions?

103. Which acting manager lost out in the 1995 Cup Winners' Cup final?

104. Who was manager for Everton's 1985 Cup Winners' Cup victory?

105. Who is the last manager to have won the European Cup with a British side?

91. **Walter Winterbottom** 92. Alex Ferguson, Andy Roxburgh, Craig Brown
93. **Billy Bingham** 94. Artur Jorge 95. **Aime Jacquet** 96. Berti Vogts
97. **Arrigo Sacchi** 98. Guus Hiddink 99. **Bob Paisley** 100. Ron Greenwood
101. **Brian Clough and Bob Paisley** 102. Louis van Gaal 103. **Stewart Houston** 104. Howard Kendall 105. **Bob Paisley**

106. George Graham **107. Keith Burkinshaw** 108. **109. Dave Sexton**
110. Brian Little **111. Don Revie** 112. Glenn Hoddle **113. Terry Venables**
114. Joe Royle **115. Bruce Rioch** 116. Trevor Francis **117. Walter Smith**
118. Jimmy Nichol **119. Tommy Burns** 120. Barry Fry

Quiz 27 — British Managers, Home And Abroad

106. Who was in charge for a British club's last victory in the Cup Winners' Cup?

107. Who was the manager when a British club last lifted the UEFA Cup?

108. Who was the manager of the last Scottish team to win a European trophy?

109. Which manager led Chelsea to an FA Cup victory in 1970 and a Cup Winners Cup victory in 1971?

110. Who was the manager of the British team that beat Inter Milan in the 1994/5 UEFA Cup?

111. Who was the manager to lead his British club to win the last Fairs Cup, before it became the UEFA Cup?

112. Who was the losing FA Cup final manager in 1994?

113. Who managed the FA Cup final team that lost to Tottenham in 1982?

114. Which manager won the 1995 FA Cup?

115. Who was the losing manager in the 1995 Coca Cola Cup final?

116. Which manager lost in the final of both the FA Cup and League Cup finals in 1993?

117. Who was the manager of the Scottish league champions in the 1994/5 season?

118. Who is the only manager to have led Raith Rovers to a Scottish League Cup success, when they beat Celtic in 1995?

119. Who was the manager of Celtic when they won the Scottish FA Cup?

120. Which manager wnet from Birmingham City to own Peterborough United?

Quiz 27   British Managers, Home And Abroad

121. **Which former Everton player was managing third division Chester City at the start of the 1995/6 season?**

122. Which former England international was in charge at the beginning of the 1995/6 season?

123. **Who moved from Aston Villa to Wolves to Watford, with a pwriod as a national coach in between?**

124. Which ex-england internatioal took over at Portsmouth in February 1995?

125. **Who took Wycombe Wanderers from non-league football to the Second division for the start of the 1994/5 season?**

126. Who was manager of Oldham Athletic from July 1982 until November 1994?

127. **Who went from the Scottish Premier league to manage Brighton and Hove Albion in 1993?**

128. Who took over as player-manager at Plymouth Argile in March 1992?

129. **Which player-manager won the 1994/5 First division title?**

130. Which manager moved to Leicester and then Wolves after being player-manager at Reading?

131. **Who went from being a player-manager at Barnsley to assistant coach at Premiership Middlesborough?**

132. Which manager rejoined Norwich for his second spell, following an unsuccessful time at Everton?

133. **Who brought Nottingham Forest back into the top division, and then returned to manage Manchester City?**

134. Which former Portsmouth boss took Derby County into the Premiership?

135. **Who did Bryan Robson succeed as Middlesborough manager?**

121. **Kevin Ratcliffe** 122. Ray Clemence 123. **Graham Taylor** 124. Terry Fenwick 125. **Martin O'Neill** 126. Joe Royle 127. **Liam Brady** 128. Peter Shilton 129. **Bryan Robson** 130. Mark McGhee 131. **Viv Anderson** 132. Mike Walker 133. **Frank Clark** 134. Jim Smith 135. **Lennie Lawrence**

 **Quiz 27** British Managers, Home And Abroad

136. Which FA Cup winning manager took over at Ipswich fron Mick McGiven?

137. Which Premiership manager won the 1983 Player of the Year award?

138. Who was the last Scottish manager to beat England in an international?

139. Which former Liverpool player was Oxford manager when they were relegated in 1988?

140. Which former international manager was also in charge at Everton?

141. Which club sacked manager Don O'Riordan the day after his side were beaten 8-1 by Scunthorpe in October 1995?

142. Which former England captain managed Arsenal btween 1962 and 1966?

143. Which England legend managed Bolton Wanderers between 1968 and 1970?

144. Which European Cup winning manager was in charge at Brighton and Hove Albion from 1973 to 1974?

145. Who managed Bristol Rovers before moving to QPR?

146. Who was the manager of Fulham in 1968, before moving to coach abroad?

147. Who was the manager of Leeds United that went on to manage Scotland?

148. Who was the Leeds United manager before Howard Wilkinson?

149. What club did Jack Charlton manage before becoming the Republic of Ireland manager?

150. Who managed Sheffield Wednesday from 1983 to 1988?

Quiz 28 — Discipline

1. **What is the highest number of sendings off to occur in a season (1994-95) in all competitions from clubs in the Premier League and the Nationwide divisions?**

   A. 365, B. 376, C.367

2. Which League club had the worst record for sendings off in the 1995-96 season with 10?

   A. Hartlepool, B. Wimbledon, C. Norwich City

3. **Which three League clubs did not have a player sent off in first team football in the 1995-96 season?**

4. How many players were shown the red card on November 20 1982, to set a record for the number of sendings off in a day in League football?

   A. 10, B. 8, C. 15

5. **What is the lowest number of League dismissals in a season since the Second World War?**

   A. 3, B. 12, C. 10

6. Against which team was Alan Mullary the first ever Englishman to be sent off in a full international?

   A. Norway, B. Scotland, C. Yugoslavia

7. **Who was sent off for England in a World Cup qualifier against Poland?**

   A. Malcolm McDonald, B. Graham Roberts, C. Alan Ball

8. Who was the third player ever to be sent off in a full England international?

   A. Ray Wilkins, B. Trevor Cherry, C. Terry Butcher

9. **What was Ray Wilkins shown the red card for when he became the only Englishman to be sent off in the World Cup Finals?**

   A. Dissent, B. Throwing the ball at the referee, C. Professional foul

10. Against which team was Robbie Fowler sent off in an England Under 21 international?

    A. Wales, B. Austria, C. Germany

---

1. 376 2. Hartlepool 3. **Tottenham, Watford and Swindon** 4. 15 5. 12, in 1946-47 season 6. Yugoslavia 7. **Alan Ball** 8. Trevor Cherry vs Argentina, 1977 9. **Second yellow card when he threw the ball at the referee** 10. Austria

Quiz 28 — Discipline

11. Against which country was Kevin Keegan sent off in an England Under 23 international in 1972?

A. West Germany, B. East Germany, C. Romania

12. Who was shown the red card in an England Under 21 match against Scotland in 1982?

A. Bryan Robson, B. Peter Beardsley, C. Mark Hateley

13. Who is the only person to be sent off in an England B match, in 1990?

A. Neil Webb, B. Paul Gascoigne, C. Steve Bull

14. Who were the teams involved when five players were sent off in the 1996-97 season?

A. Chesterfield and Gillingham, B. Plymouth and Watford, C. Chesterfield and Plymouth

15. Which League team were the first to have four players sent off in one game, and still managed a 1-1 draw, in 1992?

A. Wigan, B. Hereford United, C. Scarborough

16. How many people were sent off in the 1994 Anglo-Italian Cup match between Sheffield United and Udinese?

A. 6, B. 2, C. 4

17. How many players were sent off in the 1993 South American Super Cup quater final between Gremio from Brazil and Penarol from Uruguay?

A. 9, B. 7, C. 8

18. Who was shown the red card five times in the 1987-88 season?

A. Vinnie Jones, B. Dave Caldwell, C. Terry Hurlock

19. What is the world record for the quickest sending off, held by Giuseppe Lorenzo in an Italian League match in 1990?

A. ten seconds, B. five seconds, C. eight seconds

20. Who holds the record for the fastest Premier League sending off at just 72 seconds?

A. Vinnie Jones, B. Tim Flowers, C. Roy Keane

11. East Germany 12. Mark Hateley **13. Neil Webb** 14. Chesterfield and Plymouth **15. Hereford United** 16. 5 (4 players and United manager Dave Bassett) **17. 8** 18. Dave Caldwell **19. 10 seconds** 20. Tim Flowers

 **Quiz 28**   Discipline

21. **Jose Batista holds the record for the fastest World Cup sending off at 55 seconds in the 1986 tournament. Which country was he playing for?**

    A. Spain, B. Argentina, C. Uruguay

22. Which Scotsman holds the record for the most sendings off in a career?

    A. Willie Johnston, B. Graeme Souness, C. Billy Bremner

23. **Who is the only player to have been sent off in an FA Cup final?**

    A. Andrei Kanchelskis, B. Paul Gascoigne, C. Kevin Moran

24. Who was sent off in the 1994 League Cup final?

    A. Roy Keane, B. Dalian Atkinson, C. Andrei Kanchelskis

25. **Which two players were sent off in the 1974 Charity Shield?**

    A. Tommy Smith and Norman Hunter, B. Johnny Giles and John Toshack, C. Billy Bremner and Kevin Keegan

26. Which country were the last to have somebody sent off at Wembley?

    A. Japan, B. England, C. Holland

27. **Which two players had their dismissals revoked in the 1995-6 season?**

    A. Vinnie Jones and Mick Harford, B. Henning Berg and Roy Keane, C. Vinnie Jones and Henning Berg

28. Which club holds the record for the most bookings for a single League team in one game, at 10?

    A. Wimbledon, B. Mansfield Town, C. Exeter City

29. **Team mates Mick Flanagan and Derek Hales were sent off for fighting each other at which club in 1979?**

    A.Colchester United, B. Charlton, C. Derby County

30. Who was suspended for nine matches and fined a then record #3,000 for breaking Glenn Cockerill's jaw?

    A. Paul Davis, B. Steve Davis, C. Pat Jennings.

---

21. Jose Batista for Uruguay 22. Willie Johnston with 21 23. **Kevin Moran,**
1985 24. Andre Kanchelskis 25. **Billy Bremner and Kevin Keegan** 26. Japan in
the Umbro Cup 1995 27. **Vinnie Jones and Henning Berg** 28. Mansfield Town
29. Charlton 30. Paul Davis

 Quiz 28   Discipline

31. Who was suspended for nine matches and fined £600 for a clash of heads with a referee whilst on loan with WBA in 1992?

A. Graham Roberts, B. Micky Droy, C. Frank Sinclair.

32. Who was originally banned for 12 matches in 1995 for violent conduct against Raith, and later jailed for three months for assault?

A.Duncan Ferguson, B. Mark Hateley, C. Joe Jordan.

33. Which manager was banned from the touchline for the rest of the season after striking spectators at a League Cup match in 1989?

A.Alex Ferguson, B. Brian Clough, C. Graham Souness.

34. Who was fined 8,500 following a newspaper criticism of his former club in 1989?

A.Cive Allen, B. Ian Bright, C. Paul McGrath.

35. Which two clubs were fined 50,000 pounds each and deducted points following a mass player brawl in 1990?

A.Liverpool and Manchester United, B. Leeds and Manchester United, C. Arsenal and Manchester United.

36. Which player received a three match ban for 'feigning injury' in 1992, later cancelled?

A.Paul Gascoigne, B. Gordon Durie, C. David Hopkin.

37. Who was fined 1,000 pounds for spitting at Leeds fans in 1993?

A. Roy Keane, B. Julian Dicks, C. Eric Cantona.

38. What was Tottenham's original punishment for their financial irregularities in 1994?

A. £600,000 fine and 12 Premiership points deducted, B. £150,000 fine and 12 points deducted. C. £300,000 fine and 6 points deducted.

39. Who was fined for dropping his shorts at spectators?

A. Robbie Fowler, B. Dennis Wise, C. Arthur Fowler.

40. Who was fined for swearing at Kevin Keegan after a match in 1995?

A. Alex Ferguson, B.Vinnie Jones, C. David Ginola.

 Quiz **28** Discipline

41. **Who was the first person to reach 61 disciplinary points in a season?**

    A. Trevor Brooking, B. Terry Hurlock, C. Ron Harris.

42. Who were suspended for 2 games by UEFA for brawling in a European game?

    A. Ian Wright(Arsenal) and Jari Litmanen (Ajax). B. Jari Litmanen and Vanio Shishkov (CSKA Sofia), C. David Batty and Graeme Le Saux (Blackburn).

43. **Faustino Asprilla was found guilty of an elbowing/headbutting incident with which player?**

    A. Nigel Winterburn, B. Keith Curle, C. Phil Babb.

44. Who was Sunderland's club captain that was banned for their 1985 Milk Cup final?

    A.Peter Reid, B. Shaun Elliot, C. Tony Coton.

45. **Which former West Ham player had his sending off revoked in the 1994-95 season?**

    A. Alvin Martin, B. Julian Dicks, C. Ian Dowie.

46. Who has the time of five seconds for the second fastest booking, behind Vinnie Jones's record of 3 seconds?

    A.Gary Lineker, B. Vinnie Jones, C. Tony Adams.

47. **Which two teams were involved in the 1991 Scottish Cup quarter-final when four players were shown the red card?**

    A. Raith-Rangers, B. Rangers-Celtic, C. Celtic-Hearts.

48. The sending off of how many players from one team resulted in the abandonment of a Brazilian Cup match in 1993?

    A. 3, B.2, C.5.

49. **Which team had three players sent off in a Second Division League game against Derby in April 1992?**

    A.Newcastle, B.Brentford, C.Southend.

50. Which goalkeeper holds the record for the fastest dismissal in English domestic football?

    A.Dave Beasant, B.Mark Smith, C.-Mike Walker.

Quiz 28 — Discipline

51. Sergei Dirkach holds the record for the fastest European game sending off. For which club was he dismissed, after 90 seconds, in 1991?

A.Galatasaray, B.Dynamo Moscow, C. Barcelona.

52. Which Premiership club had the most sendings off in the 1995-96 season, all in the League?

A.QPR, B. Wimbledon, C. Leeds.

53. How many sendings off were there in the Premiership in the 1995-96 season?

A. 57, B. 36, C. 82.

54. How many sendings off were there in the play-off games in the 1995-96 season?

A.9, B. 12, C.1.

55. Who was the last person to be sent off for Northern Ireland?

A. Iain Dowie, B.Norman Whiteside, C. Mick McCarthy.

56. Who was shown the red card for Scotland against Japan in 1995?

A.Craig Burley, B. Gordon Durie, C. John Spencer.

57. Who was sent off for the Republic of Ireland in their game against Mexico in 1996?

A.Paul McGrath, B. Liam Daish, C.Andy Townsend.

58. Julian Dicks and Jason Dodd were both sent off against which country in different games for the England Under 21s?

A. USA, B. Mexico, C. West Germany.

59. Who was the first player to be sent off for England at any level?

A. Dixie Dean, B.Stan Anderson, C. Samuel Weaver.

60. Who was sent off for England in an Under 21 game in May 1996?

A.Terry Cooke, B. Chris Waddle, C. Kevin Beattie.

 ## Quiz 28 — Discipline

61. Which country was Gilbert Dresch representing when he was sent off at Wembley against England in a 1977 World Cup qualifier?

A. Belgium, B. Luxembourg, C. France.

62. Four clubs saw their club captains suspended for their League Cup finals in which four consecutive years?

A. 1896-1899, B. 1982-1985, C. 1970-1973.

63. Which team had two players dismissed in a play-off final at Wembley in 1994?

A. Crystal Palace, B. Stockport, C. Carlisle.

64. Who was only the second person to be sent off in the FA Cup at Wembley?

A. Lee Dixon, B. Steve Foster, C. Frank Sinclair.

65. Which former QPR player was booked 64 times in ten seasons and answered two disrepute charges concerning newspaper articles?

A. Les Ferdinand, B. Stan Bowles, C. Mark Dennis.

66. Which team were fined in 1990 for failing play a League Cup game due to injuries?

A. Middlesbrough, B. Chesterfield, C. Torquay

67. In which year was the disciplinary points system introduced?

A. 1962-63, B. 1972-73, C. 1954-55.

68. Which player was fined in 1994 for making 'gestures' at QPR fans?

A. Ian Wright, B. Steve Bull, C. Sol Campbell.

69. Which English teams were banned from European competition for a year (suspended for five years) in 1996?

A. Millwall and Chelsea, B. Tottenham and Wimbledon, C. Coventry and Millwall.

70. Which club sacked Roger Stanislaus after he bacame the first British-based player to be found positive for taking performance enhancing drugs and banned for a year?

A. Leyton Orient, B. Doncaster Rovers, C. Barnet.

 **Quiz 28** Discipline

71. **To which club did Manchester United have to pay 20,000 pounds for illegally approaching 17 year-old David Brown?**

    A. Liverpool, B. West Brom, C. Oldham.

72. Which club were fined by UEFA for the behaviour of their 'unofficial' fans at an away leg in 1995?

    A. Arsenal, B. Chelsea, C.Juventas.

73. **Who was fined by the FA for a newspaper criticism of Eric Cantona in 1994?**

    A.Jimmy Greaves, B.John Giles, C. John Fashanu.

74. Who is the only player to have been sent off at Wembley in a major tournament?

    A.Kevin Keegan, B. Antonio Rattin, C. Christo Stoichkov.

75. **In what year was Boris Stankovic the first player to ever be sent off at Wembley?**

    A. 1904, B. 1948, C. 1954.

76. Which club was fined after arriving late for their League game at Darlington in 1994?

    A.Brighton, B.Preston, C. Mansfield.

77. **Which club were fined for fielding a Liverpool player registered on loan after the deadline, in 1995?**

    A.Sunderland, B. Watford, C.Motherwell.

78. Which Premiership club's chairman was fined for remarks to a referee at Arsenal in 1995?

    A.Manchester United, B.Chelsea, C. Blackburn Rovers.

79. **Which two clubs were fined after breaking rules when signing players from Australia, in 1993?**

    A.Arsenal and Notts Forest, B.Wrexham and Leicester, C.Aston Villa and Notts County.

80. Which team was fined by UEFA for a coin throwing incident during a european game in 1993?

    A.Panathinaikos, B.Atletico Madrid, C. Cardiff.

 **Quiz 29**   English Club History

1. **What were Arsenal first known as in 1886?**

2. When did they turn professional?

3. **What was their first ground?**

4. When did they move to Highbury?

5. **What is the club's record victory?**

6. And their record defeat?

7. **When were Aston Villa formed?**

8. Where did they first play?

9. **In their first game, against Aston Brook St Mary's, they played one half of soccer and the other rugby. True or false?**

10. When did Barnet play their first League game?

11. **What was the score?**

12. What were Barnsley first known as?

13. **Who has been their most capped international?**

14. What were Birmingham City first known as?

15. **Where did they first play?**

15. At a waste ground near Arthur Street, Birmingham
Peter's 13. Gerry Taggart (35 for Northern Ireland) 14. Small Heath Alliance
8. Aston Park 9. True 10. August 17, 1991 11. They lost 7-4 to Crewe 12. St
Loughborough Town in 1896 6. 0-8 to Loughborough Town 7. 1874
1. Dial Square 2. 1891 3. Plumstead Common 4. 1913 5. 12-0 over

Quiz 29 — English Club History

16. Birmingham City hold the record for the highest number of players used in a season. How many and which season?

17. When were Blackburn Rovers formed?

18. Where did they play their home games at first?

19. Who is their record goalscorer in League football?

20. How many did he get?

21. What were Blackpool first known as?

22. When did they move to Bloomfield Road?

23. Which player holds the record for appearances for the club?

24. What is the record transfer fee they have received - and for who?

25. What were Bolton Wanderers first called?

26. What is the club's nickname?

27. The club lost it's first League game 6-3 in 1888. To who?

28. Who holds the record for being the club's most capped player?

29. What is the record transfer fee Brentford have received - and for who?

30. What is the record transfer fee Brighton have paid out - and for who?

16. 46. - 1995-96 17. 1875 18. They didn't - all their games in 1875-76 were played away because they had nowhere to play 19. Simon Garner 20. 168 21. South Shore 22. 1899 23. Jimmy Armfield with 568 24. £750,000 from QPR for Trevor Sinclair 25. Christ Church FC 26. The Trotters 27. Derby County 28. Nat Lofthouse 29. £720,000 from Wimbledon for Dean Holdsworth 30. £500,000 to Manchester United for Andy Ritchie

 **Quiz 29**   **English Club History**

31. How many grounds have Brentford played their homes games at?

32. When did they move to Griffin Park?

33. Bristol Rovers have had four other names. 'Black Arabs' was one of them - true or false?

34. What were Cambridge United first known as?

35. When did they change it?

36. Who has been their most capped player?

37. What is Cardiff City's nickname?

38. What is the record transfer fee they have paid out - and for who?

39. What were Carlisle United first known as?

40. What has been the record transfer they have receieved for a player - and who is the player in question?

41. How many different homes have Charlton Athletic had?

42. How many times have they made the Valley their home?

43. The club was formed in 1905 - but by who?

44. Who is Chelsea's record goalscorer in one season - and how many did he get?

45. Who holds the record for appearances for Chelsea?

 Quiz 29   **English Club History**

46. Whose ground did Chester City share between 1990 and 1992?

47. **What is Chesterfield's nickname?**

48. What were Coventry first known as?

49. **Who has been their most capped player?**

50. Coventry have never won an European trophy. True or false?

51. **What is the record number of players who have scored for Crewe in one game?**

52. Who has been Crystal Palace's youngest League debutant - and at what age?

53. **When did Derby move to the Baseball Ground?**

54. How many grounds did Everton have before moving to Goodison Park?

55. **What was their previous name?**

56. Everton were the first club to win the Second Division title, First Division title and the FA Cup in successive seasons. True and false?

57. **Who is their record League goalscorer - and with how many?**

58. The same player holds the record for the number of individual goals scored in one season - how many?

59. **What is Exeter's nickname?**

60. How many homes have Fulham had?

46. Macclesfield Town's Moss Rose ground 47. **The Spireites** 48. Singers FC
49. **Peter Ndlovu (Zimbabwe)** 50. False - they won the European Fairs Cup in
1971 51. **Eight - when they beat Hartlepool 8-0 in 1995** 52. Phil Hoadley - 16
53. 1895 54. Three 55. **St Domingo FC** 56. True - between 1931 and 1933
57. Dixie Dean - with 349 58. 60 in 1927-28 59. **The Grecians** 60. 12

Quiz 29 — English Club History

61. **Huddersfield Town have never won the FA Cup. True or False?**

62. What remains the club's record defeat?

63. **Who holds the record for the most appearances for Ipswich?**

64. What remains Ipswich's record Cup victory?

65. **What were Leicester City first known as?**

66. How many different names have Leyton Orient had?

67. **Who founded Liverpool?**

68. When did they form?

69. **When Liverpool beat Stromsgodset 11-0 in the European Cup-Winners Cup in 1974, how many players found the net?**

70. Who holds the record for number of FA Cup goals scored for Liverpool?

71. **Whose record did he beat?**

72. **Who is Liverpool's record goalscorer?**

73. **What were Manchester City first known as?**

74. Where was their first home?

75. **What were Manchester United first known as?**

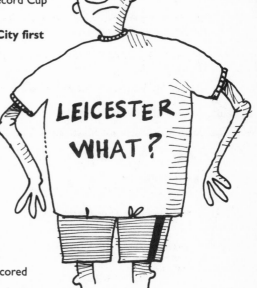

LEICESTER WHAT?

---

61. **False - they won it in 1922** 62. 10-1 to Manchester City in 1987 63. **Mick Mills - with 591** 64. 10-0 over Floriana in the European Cup in 1962 65. **Leicester Fosse FC** 66. Six 67. **The Landlord of Anfield - John Houlding** 68. 1892 69. **Nine** 70. Ian Rush 71. **Denis Law** 72. Roger Hunt 73. **Ardwick FC** 74. Clowes Street 75. **Newton Heath**

 **Quiz 29**   **English Club History**

76. Manchester United have played at Old Trafford since 1910 - apart from eight years in the 1940's. Where did they go and why?

77. **Who holds the record for the number of League goals scored in one season for Manchester United?**

78. How many League goals did Bobby Charlton score for Manchester United?

79. **What was Middlesbrough previous ground called?**

80. Who holds the record for their most capped player?

81. **Millwall used to be called Millwall Rovers and Millwall Athletic. True or False?**

82. Who is their record League goalscorer?

83. **Newcastle had two previous names. What were they?**

84. What is Northampton's present home ground called?

85. **When were Norwich City formed?**

86. Nottingham Forest used to play at the Trent Bridge cricket ground. True or false?

87. **When was the club formed?**

88. When do Notts County claimed to have been formed?

89. **What is their record Cup victory?**

90. Who holds the record for the number of appearances for the club?

90. Alf Iremonger with 564

87. 1865 88. 1862 89. 15-0 over Rotherham Town in the 1885 FA Cup

Newcastle East End 84. Sixfields Stadium 85. 1902 86. True - in 1880

Mannion - with 26 for England 81. True 82. Teddy Sheringham 83. Stanley and

77. Dennis Viollet - 32 in 1959-60 78. 199 79. Ayresome Park 80. Wilf

76. Maine Road - because of bomb damage to Old Trafford in World War Two

Quiz 29 — English Club History

91. **What competition did Notts County win in 1995?**

92. What were Oldham first known as?

93. **Who holds Portsmouth's record for the highes number of goals scored in one season?**

94. When did Port Vale move to Vale Park?

95. **Who is Preston's most capped player?**

96. How many ground changes have QPR undertaken since being formed in 1885?

97. **How many trophies did Sheffield Wednesday win in 1902-03?**

98. Who holds the record for the most number of goals scored for Southampton?

99. **When did they move to Dell?**

100. What were Stockport County first known as?

101. **What was Stoke City's first name?**

102. Swansea's record Cup win was 12-0. But in what competition?

103. **Who holds the record for the most appearances for Tottenham?**

104. What was West Ham's first name?

105. **When did Wimbledon reach Division One?**

91. **The Anglo-Italian Cup** 92. Pine Villa 93. **Guy Whittingham – with 42 in 1992-93** 94. 1950 95. **Tom Finney – with 76 for England** 96. 12 97. **Five** 98. Mick Channon 185 99. 1898 100. Heaton Norris Rovers 101. **Stoke** 102. The European Cup-Winners Cup in 1982 103. **Steve Perryman – with 655** 104. Thames Ironworks FC (1895-1900) 105. 1986

 **Quiz 30**   **British Goalscorers**

1. **Who was the first player to score 200 goals in Scotland's Premier Division in December 1992?**

2. Which player holds the individul scoring record in Scotland's Premier Division?

3. **Who are the three players to have scored a hat-trick in a major final at Wembley?**

4. Which player,in a first-class match, scored the fastest goal at Wembley?

5. **Which player scored the second fastest goal at Wembley in a first-class match?**

6. Which three players have scored a hat-trick in an FA Cup final?

7. **Who was the first player to miss a penalty in a FA Cup final?**

8. Who is the most recent player to have scored over 50 goals for a league club in one season?

9. **Who was Second Division leading scorer for 1957-58, 1958-9 and 1959-60?**

10. Which player scored five goals for England against Cyprus at Wembley on April 16 1975?

11. **Who scored 13 goals in 38 appearances for Northern Ireland?**

12. Who is the youngest player to have scored a hat-trick on his debut?

13. **Which player has scored the most League hat-tricks in his career?**

14. Which player has scored the most league hat-tricks in one season?

15. **Which two teams have had the most individual scorers in one match?**

---

1. **Ally McCoist** 2. Paul Sturrock (Dundee United) five goals against Morton. 3. **Stan Mortensen (1953 FA Cup final), Geoff Hurst (1966 World Cup final) David Speedie (1985 Full Members Cup final).** 4. Bryan Robson (England) 38 seconds v Yugoslavia in 1989. 5. **Bryan Robson (England) 44 seconds against Northern Ireland, in 1982.** 6. Billy Townley (1890), Jimmy Logan (1894) and Stan Mortensen (1953) 7. **John Aldridge (Liverpool) v Wimbledon, 1988 FA Cup final.** 8. Steve Bull 52 goals for Wolves 1987/8 season 9. **Brian Clough** 10. Malcolm Macdonald 11. **Colin Clarke. 13 goals in 38 appearances.** 12. Alan Shearer aged 17 for Southampton v Arsenal April 9 1988. 13. **37 by Dixie Dean (Everton and Tranmere)** 14. 9 by George Camsell (Middlesbrough) in Division Two 1926/7 15. Liverpool - nine against Stromsgodset in 1974, Stirling Albion - nine scorers against Selkirk in 1984

 Quiz **30**   **British Goalscorers**

16. Which goalkeeper has scored most goals in a season?

17. **Who was the last player to score five goals in a top-flight match?**

18. When Oxford United beat Shrewsbury Town 6-0 on April 23 1996 in a Division Two match, what was unusual about all six goals?

19. **Who is England's top international goalscorer?**

20. Which player has scored the most goals in one League season?

21. **Who are the two joint top international goalscorers for Scotland?**

22. Who was the first player to score more than 30 goals in three successive seasons in top division football?

23. **Who is England's second highest international goalscorer?**

24. How many goals did Kevin Keegan score in his 63 games for England?

25. **Who has scored the most goals for Southampton?**

26. Which England player, between November 1991 and June 1982, scored seven goals in six consecutive international appearances?

27. **The Republic of Ireland beat Italy 1-0 in the 1994 World Cup who scored the winning goal?**

28. Newcastle United's Player of the Year for 1996 was also the club's top goalscorer. Who was he?

29. **How many goals did Paul Gascoigne score for Rangers in the 1995/6 season?**

30. Before moving to Arsenal how many goals did Ian Wright score for Crystal Palace in his 206 full appearances?

---

16. Arthur Birch 5 (all penalties) for Chesterfield Division Three North 1923/4 17. **Andy Cole in Manchester United's 9-0 win over Ipswich, March 4 1995.** 18. They were all headers. 19. **Bobby Charlton (1958-70) 49 goals in 106 games.** 20. Dixie Dean (Everton) 60 goals 1927/8. 21. **Denis Law (1958-74) 30 goals in 55 games and Kenny Dalglish (1971-86) 30 goals in 102 games.** 22. Alan Shearer 31 goals in 1993/4, 34 in 1994/5, 31 in 1995/6. 23. **Gary Lineker (1984-92) 48 goals in 80 games.** 24. 21 (1972-82) 25. **Mike Channon with 185** 26. Paul Mariner 27. **Ray Houghton.** 28. Les Ferdinand 29. **14** 30. **90**

 **Quiz 30** — **British Goalscorers**

31. Who was Euro 96's top goalscorer?

32. In the 1992 play-offs Blackburn Rovers secured promotion to the Premiership by beating Leicester. What was the score and who scored?

33. How many goals did Jimmy Greaves score for England?

34. In the 1994 Coca-Cola Cup final Aston Villa beat Manchester United 3-1, who scored Villa's three goals?

35. Aberdeen beat Dundee 2-0 in the 1996 Scottish Coca-Cola Cup final, who scored the goals?

36. Which player scored a hat-trick for Rangers in the 1996 Scottish FA Cup final?

37. Dundee United beat Rangers in the 1994 Scottish FA Cup final. Who scored the only goal?

38. Who is Chelsea top all-time goalscorer?

39. Which player scored the extra-time winner in the 1985 FA Cup final?

40. In the 1970 FA Cup final replay between Chelsea and Leeds United who scored the winning goal?

41. In the 1973 FA Cup final Sunderland were shock 1-0 victors over Leeds United, who scored the only?

42. Who scored the 89th minute winner for Arsenal in their 3-2 win over Manchester United in the 1979 FA Cup final?

43. Who scored Arsenal's second goal at Anfield that won the 1988-89 League Championship?

44. Who scored the first goal in that match?

45. Which famous son scored twice in the 1989 League Cup final?

 **Quiz 30**   **British Goalscorers**

46. Which player has scored the most penalties for one club in a season?

47. **Which player saw his penalty saved by Nottingham Forest goalkeeper Mark Crossley in the 1991 FA Cup final?**

48. Which player scored in all four divisions of the Football League and the Premiership in his career?

49. **Which Premiership club scored four goals in four minutes against Southampton on 7 February 1993?**

50. In the 1995 Coca-Cola Cup final who scored Liverpool's two goals?

51. **In the 1995 FA Cup final who scored the only goal?**

52. Who was the leading goalscorer in Division One in 1995-6?

53. **Who was the leading goalscorer in Division Two in 1995-6?**

54. Who was the leading goalscorer in Division Three in 1995-6?

55. **Who was Chesterfield's top goalscorer in the 1995-6 season?**

56. How many goals did Neil Shipperley scored for Southampton in the 1995-6 season?

57. **Who was the leading goalscorer for Arsenal in the 1995-6 season?**

58. Which player has scored the most goals in total aggregate for one club?

59. **Which player has scored the most top-flight hat-tricks in a season since the war?**

60. Which player scored three consecutive hat-tricks in the old Division One?

46. Francis Lee (Man City) Division One 1971/2. **47. Gary Lineker** 48. Alan Cork
49. Tottenham Hotspur 50. Steve McManaman **51. Paul Rideout** 52. John
Aldridge (Tranmere) **53. Marcus Stewart (Bristol Rovers)** 54. Steve White
(Hereford) **55. Tony Lormor with 13 goals.** 56. 7 **57. Ian Wright** 58. Dixie
Dean 349 goals for Everton 1925/37. **59. Jimmy Greaves (Chelsea) 1960/1, 6.**
60. Frank Osborne (Spurs) Oct–Nov 1925

 **Quiz 30**   **British Goalscroers**

61. Which Premiership player scored five hat-tricks in the 1995-6 season?

62. For the first time in the Premiership on September 23 1995 three hat-tricks were scored on the same day, who scored them?

63. Who was Liverpool's top goalscorer in the 1995-6 season?

64. Manchester City's top goalscorer in the 1995-6 season was Uwe Rosler, how many did he score?

65. Which player has scored the most goals in an international?

66. Who is the Republic of Ireland's top international goalscorer?

67. How many goals did Geoff Hurst score for England during his international career?

68. Who was the first player in British football to settle a match with the 'golden goal' sudden death decider?

69. Who scored the winning goal for Birmingham City against Carlisle in the Auto Windscreens Shield final of 1995?

70. Which club has had the highest goal scoring aggregate in the Premiership?

71. Who was Tottenham's top goalscorer in the 1995-6 season?

72. Terry Venables made two international appearances for England as a player, how many goals did he score?

73. How many goals has Stuart Pearce scored for England?

74. Who was West Ham's top goalscorer in the 1995-6 season?

75. Who is Celtic's top all-time goalscorer?

61. Alan Shearer 62. Tony Yeboah (Leeds), Alan Shearer (Blackburn), Robbie Fowler (Liverpool). **63. Robbie Fowler with 28. 64. 9 65. Vivian Woodward with 7 for England v France in an amateur international in November 1906. Result 15-0.** 66. Frank Stapleton (1977-90) 20 goals in 71 games. **67. 24** 68. Iain Dunn (Huddersfield) on November 30 1994 in the Auto Windscreens Shield. **69. Paul Tait.** 70. Newcastle in 1993/94. **71. Teddy Sheringham with 16. 72.** None. **73. 5 74.** Tony Cottee with 10. **75. James McGrory (1922-39) with 397.**

Quiz 30 — British Goalscorers

76. Who is Rangers' top all-time goalscorer?

77. **Who was Liverpool's top goalscorer in their 1996 FA Cup run?**

78. Who is Liverpool's top all-time goalscorer?

79. **How many goals did Matthew Le Tissier score in the 1995/6 season?**

80. Who was Manchester City's top goalscorer in their 1995/6 FA Cup campaign?

81. **Who scored the goal in Nottingham Forest's 1-0 win over Malmo in the 1979 European Cup?**

82. In the 1976 UEFA Cup final 1st leg who scored Liverpool's three goals in their 3-2 win over Bruges?

83. **In the 2nd leg the score was 1-1 who scored Liverpool's goal?**

84. Which player has been Blackburn's highest scorer in a single season?

85. **Bolton Wanderers most capped player is also the club's top goalscorer, who is he?**

86. reston North End's most capped player is also the club's top goalscorer, who is he?

87. **Who has scored more goals for Portsmouth in a single season than any other player?**

88. Millwall's top all-time goalscorer scored 93 goals in total, who is he?

89. **Who is Manchester United's all-time top goalscorer?**

90. In the 1960/1 season one player scored 41 goals for Chelsea, a club record, who was he?

76. Bob McPhail (1927-39) with 236. 77. **Robbie Fowler with 6.** 78. Roger Hunt (1959-69) with 245. 79. **7** 80. Niall Quinn with 2 goals 81. **Trevor Francis** 82. Ray Kennedy, Jimmy Case, and Kevin Keegan 83. **Kevin Keegan** 84. Ted Harper 43 goals Division One 1925/6. 85. **Nat Lofthouse (1946-61) 255 goals.** 86. Tom Finney (1946-60) 187 goals. 87. **Guy Whittingham 42 goals Division One 1992/3** 88. Teddy Sheringham (1984-91) 89. **Bobby Charlton (1956-73) 199 goals.** 90. Jimmy Greaves

 **Quiz 30**   **British Goalscorers**

91. Which aromatic striker has scored more goals for Aston Villa in a single season than any other?

92. Which Championship winning Chelsea manager holds the record at Arsenal for being the top goalscorer in a single season?

93. In Blackburn Rover's European Cup campaign of 1995/6 which player scored a hat-trick against Rosenborg?

94. Everton beat Rapid Vienna 3-1 in the 1985 European Cup Winners Cup who scored Everton's goals?

95. Who scored the goal in Wimbledon's historic 1-0 win over Liverpool in the 1988 FA Cup final?

96. Who scored the winning 89th minute goal for Luton in their 3-2 Littlewoods Cup Final win over Arsenal in 1988?

97. Who was the top scorer at Crystal Palace in the 1995-6 season?

98. Which team on New Years Day 1996 scored 15 seconds from kick-off and again 15 seconds from the final whistle?

99. Grimsby knocked West Ham out of the 1995-96 FA Cup in a 4th round replay, who scored Grimsby's goals in their 3-0 win?

100. In the 1995/6 Division One Play-Off Final Leicester beat Crystal Palace 2-1, who were the goalscorers that day?

101. Who scored the winning goal for Liverpool in their 1-0 win over Real Madrid in the 1981 European Cup?

102. Geoff Hurst scored a hat-trick in the 1966 World Cup Final, who got the other one for England?

103. Who scored the only goal in Nottingham Forest's 1-0 win over SV Hamburg in the 1980 European Cup?

104. Who scored the equaliser for Leicester in the 1997 Coca-Cola Cup Final?

105. Who scored the first goal for England under Terry Venables' reign?

---

103. **John Robertson.**   104. Emilie Heskey.   105. **David Platt.**
Woods and **Jamie Forrester.**   100. Andy Roberts for Palace. Garry Parker (penalty) and Steve Claridge for Leicester.   101. **Alan Kennedy.**   102. Martin Peters.
98. Colchester United in their 3-2 win over Torquay.   99. **Gary Childs, Neil**
95. Lawrie Sanchez.   96. Mark Stein.   97. **Dougie Freedman with 20 goals.**
1934/5 **93. Mike Newell.**   94. Graeme Sharp, Trevor Steven and Kevin Sheedy.
91. **'Pongo' Waring 49 goals Division One 1930/1.**   92. Ted Drake 42 goals

 **Quiz 30**   **British Goalscorers**

106. In the 1996 Anglo-Italian Cup Final Genoa beat Port Vale 5-2, Who scored the goals for Port Vale?

107. Who scored 414 goals for Chelsea, Tottenham and West Ham in just 591 matches?

108. Who won the Golden Boot for being Europe's leading league goalscorer in 1993?

109. Who scored twice for Liverpool against Nottinghan Forest in the 1989 FA Cup semi-final?

110. Who was Sunderland's top scorer in the 1994-95 season?

111. Since signing for Sheffield Wednesday in September 1992 this player has been the clubs top goalscorer three times, who is he?

112. Which Premiership striker did Newcastle buy for 15 million in August 1996?

113. Which Premiership striker did Liverpool buy for 8.5 million June 1995?

114. Which Premiership striker did Manchester United buy for 7 million in January 1995?

115. Who was Wimbledon's top goalscorer in the 1995-96 season?

116. Who is the all-time top league goalscorer for Wolves?

117. Who scored West Ham's goal in their 1-0 win over Arsenal in the 1980 FA Cup?

118. Who won the European Golden Boot in 1984?

119. In 1978 and 1979 which English striker was voted European Player of the Year?

120. Which striker was voted by the Football Writer's Association as their Player of the Year in 1968?

106. Tony Naylor got both of them. **107. Jimmy Greaves** 108. Ally McCoist (Rangers). **109. John Aldridge.** 110. Phil Gray. **111. Mark Bright.** 112. Alan Shearer. **113. Stan Collymore.** 114. Andy Cole. **115. Robbie Earle 11 goals.** 116. Steve Bull (1986-96) 217 goals. **117. Trevor Brooking.** 118. Ian Rush. **119. Kevin Keegan.** 120. George Best.

 Quiz **31**   The Carling
Premiership 1996-97

1. **Who was Arsenal's first scorer of the 1996-97 season?**

2. Which two players scored hat-tricks on the first day of the 1996-97 season?

3. **Who scored the first goal of the 1996-97 season?**

4. Which teams played in the first Sunday game of the 1996-97 season?

5. **In which game did Alan Shearer score his first goal for Newcastle?**

6. Which teams played in the only goalless draw on the opening day of the season?

7. **Who did Sunderland beat 4-1 away from home in their second game of the season?**

8. Which clubs beat Wimbledon in their three consecutive defeats at the start of the season?

9. **Who did Middlesborough beat 4-1 on September 4?**

10. Who inflicted the firstPremiership defeat of the season on Manchester United?

11. **How many games did Manchester United go unbeaten at the start of the season?**

12. Who did Wimbledon beat to record their first win of the season?

13. **Who scored a hat-trick in Southampton's 6-3 win over Manchester United?**

14. Who were two points clear at top of the Premiership after matches on November 2?

15. **Who did Blackburn beat 3-0 to record their first win of the season in their 12th game?**

Quiz 31 — The Carling Premiership 1996-97

16. Who scored a hat-trick in Everton's 7-1 win over Southampton in November?

17. **Who were beaten 2-0 by Arsenal on the opening day of the season?**

18. Which club inflicted Newcastle's first defeat of the season?

19. **Which team did West Ham beat for their first victory of the season?**

20. Against which team did Gianfranco Zola score his first goal for Chelsea?

21. **How many goals did Robbie Fowler score against Middlesborough when they met at Anfield in December?**

22. How many games had Wimbledon gone unbeaten before they lost 5-0 to Aston Villa?

23. **Who did Chelsea beat 2-0 on Boxing Day?**

24. Who did Manchester United beat 4-0 on Boxing Day?

25. **The game between which clubs was postponed on Boxing Day?**

26. How many goals did Les Ferdinand score in Newcastle's 7-1 win over Tottenham?

27. **Who scored the first goal of the New Year?**

28. 55,133 people turned out to see Manchester United play who on New Year's Day?

29. **How many goals had the Premiership's leading marksman Ian Wright scored by January 1?**

30. Which teams played in the first Sunday game of the New Year?

16. Gary Speed 17. **West Ham** 18. Everton 19. **Southampton** 20. Everton 21. 4 22. 14 games 23. **Aston Villa** 24. Nottingham Forest 25. **Wimbledon and West Ham** 26. 2 27. **Shearer, after 4 minutes** 28. Aston Villa 29. 23 30. Tottenham and Manchester United

Quiz 31 — The Carling Premiership 1996-97

31. **Who scored an own goal for Arsenal when they lost at Sunderland in January?**

32. Who scored two goals for Sheffield Wednesday when they lost 4-2 at Middlesborough?

33. **Which team were leading the Premiership into the New Year?**

34. Which team lifted themselves from the bottom of the table with a win on New Year's Day?

35. **Manchester United went to the top of the Premiership on January 29 for the first time with a win over who?**

36. Who did Liverpool beat 4-0 at home in February?

37. **Who scored a hat-trick in Leicester's 4-2 win over Derby in February?**

38. Who scored for both teams when Derby beat Chelsea 3-2 on March 1?

39. **Which team conceded two own goals in the first five minutes at Manchester United?**

40. Who scored a hat-trick against Sunderland in a 4-0 win in March?

41. **Which team conceded six against Middlesborough, including a hat-trick from Ravanelli, in March?**

42. Sunderland players scored all three goals in the Rokerites 2-1 win over who in March?

43. **Who scored Liverpool's 90th minute winner when they beat Newcastle 4-3?**

44. Who scored two goals for West Ham in their 3-2 home victory over Chelsea in March?

45. **Who scored a hat-trick in his club's 3-1 win over Wimbledon in March?**

 **Quiz 31** The Carling Premiership 1996-97

46. How many players were on the scoresheet when Chelsea played Sunderland in March?

47. **Who scored Derby's last minute winner in their 3-2 win over Chelsea in March?**

48. Who scored the first Premiership hat-trick of the New Year?

49. **Newcastle beat which team 4-0 in March, described as the best performance under Kenny Dalglish since he took over?**

50. Dennis Bergkamp scored two goals for Arsenal against which club on March 8?

51. **Which club beat Middlesborough 3-1 on March 1?**

52. How many games did Manchester United lose between January 29 and March 29?

53. **Who was Manchester United's first scorer of the season?**

54. Who scored a first minute own goal when Tottenham lost 2-1 to Chelsea on February 1?

55. **Who were the two players sent off on New Year's Day?**

56. Who scored the last goal of the game when Tottenham lost 7-1 to Newcastle in December?

57. **Which two teams played in the last game of 1996, when they met on December 29?**

58. How many Premiership games were postponed on January 1?

59. **Blackburn lost to two goals from which player in their opening game of the season?**

60. Who was Everton's first scorer of the season?

Quiz 31 — The Carling Premiership 1996-97

61. How many goals were scored in the nine games on the first day of the season?

62. Niall Quinn scored two goals against which team in Sunderland's 4-1 victory in their second game of the season?

63. Who scored Coventry's first goal of the season?

64. Who were the four teams that Sheffield Wednesday beat in their first four games of the season?

65. Which team ended Sheffield Wednesday's unbeaten Premiership run?

66. Who scored an own goal for Leeds when they lost 4-0 to Manchester United in their fifth game of the season?

67. Which team came back from a 1-0 half time deficit to beat Sheffield Wednesday 4-1 in September?

68. Who scored the first goal when Newcastle beat Mancheter United 5-0?

69. How many points did Blackburn have after their first 11 games of the season?

70. Who scored Chelsea's only goal when they were beaten 5-1 by Liverpool in September?

71. Who scored Manchester United's goals when they lost 6-3 to Southampton?

72. What was the score of the Merseyside derby at Anfield?

73. Who scored Southampton's only goal when they lost 7-1 to Everton?

74. What was the score in the North London derby at Highbury in November?

75. Against which club did Ian Rush score his first Premiership goal for Leeds?

THE ULTIMATE FACT AND QUIZ BOOK

 **Quiz 31** The Carling
Premiership 1996-97

76. What was the score when Arsenal and Newcastle met at St James' Park on November 30?

77. **What was the score when West Ham played Manchester United at Upton Park in December?**

78. Who did Manchester United beat 5-0 on December 21?

79. **What was the score when Liverpool met Newcastle in the last Premiership game before Christmas?**

80. Against which team did Darren Huckerby score his first goal for Coventry since his move from Newcastle?

81. **Who scored the last Premiership goal of 1996?**

82. Which team did Chelsea beat 1-0 to make a winning start to 1997?

83. **Who was the first person of the season to be sent off?**

84. Which three teams won 4-0 on September 6, when they played Leeds, Coventry and Everton, respectively?

85. **Against which team did Patrick Berger score his first goal for Liverpool?**

86. Liverpool scored two goals in two minutes when they beat Newcastle 4-3. Who scored them?

87. **Who scored Newcastle's third goal in their 4-3 loss at Anfield?**

88. Who scored twice for Blackburn when they beat Liverpool 3-0 at Ewood in November?

89. **Against which team did Ruud Gullit score his only Premiership goal of the season?**

90. Middlesborough's foreigners Ravanelli, Festa, Emerson and Juninho all scored in their game against which team?

 **Quiz 32**   **Mixed Bag**

1. Who scored Marseille's winning goal in the 1993 European Cup Final?

2. Who was the World Footballer of the Year in 1994?

3. Which two 1999-97 Chelsea players played in the 1989 European Cup final?

4. Which player became the first man to win the European Cup with two different clubs?

5. Who was the first Englishman to be voted European Footballer of the Year?

6. What year was it?

7. Who is the last player to win both PFA Player of the Year and Young Player of the Year in the same season?

8. What year was it?

9. Who was the first player to twice be voted European Footballer of the Year?

10. Who is the only goalkeeper, so far, to win the European Footballer of the year award?

11. Which nationality was he?

12. Who beat Alan Shearer to the World Footballer of the Year award in 1997?

13. How many Manchester United players have been voted European Footballer of the Year?

14. Who became the first non-European to win the European Footballer of the Year?

15. Who was the last player to be the European Footballer of the Year for three consecutive years?

1. **Basile Boli** 2. Romario 3. **Ruud Gullit (AC Milan) and Dan Petrescu (Steaua Bucharest)** 4. Miodrag Belodedici 5. **Sir Stanley Matthews** 6. 1956 7. **Andy Gray** 8. 1977 9. **Alfredo Di Stefano** 10. Lev Yashin 11. **Russian** 12. Ronaldo 13. **Three** 14. George Weah 15. **Michel Platini**

 Quiz **32**   **Mixed Bag**

16. How many times has Johan Cruyff won the European Footballer of the Year title?

17. Who became the first Bulgarian to be voted European Footballer of the Year?

18. Who was the last English player to be European Footballer of the Year?

19. And what year was it?

20. Who was the last Russian player to be European Footballer of the Year?

21. What year was it?

22. Which Danish player was voted European Footballer of the Year in 1977?

23. Which European team were voted World Team of the Year in 1987?

24. Which English manager was voted World Manager of the Year in 1985?

25. Which German has conceded a penalty in both an European Cup Final and World Cup Final?

26. Which Italian club did Brazilian Zico play for?

27. Which Scottish manager was voted World Manager of the Year in 1993?

28. At which club was Kevin Keegan at when he won the European Footballer of the Year awards?

29. Which European Footballer of the Year missed a penalty in a World Cup Final penalty shoot-out?

30. Which Russian player was voted 1975 European Footballer of the Year?

FOOTBALL

Fact Book

FACTS CONTENTS

THE ULTIMATE FACT AND QUIZ BOOK

THE CARLING PREMIERSHIP

The Carling Premiership

Manchester United won four of the first five Carling Premiership titles. On the occasion that they didn't win the trophy, 1995, they finished second.

Alan Shearer was the first player to score more than 30 top-division goals in three successive seasons. He scored 31 goals in 1993-94, 34 in 1994-95 and 31 in 1995-96, all for Blackburn.

Andy Cole set a Carling Premiership record when he scored five goals for Manchester United v Ipswich Town in United's 9-0 victory in the 1994-95 season. That victory set another Carling Premiership record as the biggest win.

Up to the start of the 1997-98 season, Andy Cole (for Newcastle in 1993-94) and Alan Shearer (for Blackburn in 1994-95) share the record for the best goal tally in a Carling Premiership season with 34 goals.

Swindon Town set a new Carling Premiership record when they conceded 100 goals in the 1993-94 season.

Arsenal set a new Carling Premiership record in 1993-94, when they conceded just 28 goals in a single season.

Newcastle set a Carling Premiership record for scoring the most goals in a single season, with 82 in 1993-94.

Liverpool's Robbie Fowler produced the Carling Premiership's quickest hat-trick, when he score three times in just four-and-a-half minutes against Arsenal on August 28, 1994.

The game between Tottenham and Southampton set the record for the fastest scoring spree in the Carling Premiership. Four goals were scored in four minutes and 44 seconds.

Norwich City's Jamie Cureton holds the record for the fastest Carling Premiership goal by a substitute. He scored 13 seconds after coming on against Chelsea on December 10, 1994.

Up to the 1997-98 season, the record for fastest goal scored in the Carling Premiership is held jointly by Blackburn's Chris Sutton (v Everton, April 1, 1995) and Dwight Yorke of Aston Villa (v Coventry, September 30, 1995). Both scored after 13 seconds.

Ian Wright scored for Arsenal in seven consecutive Carling Premiership games, in 1993-94 to set a new goalscoring record.

 **Facts**   **The Carling Premiership**

Alan Shearer's five hat-tricks for Blackburn in the 1994-95 season was a Carling Premiership record.

On September 23, 1995, three players in the Carling Premiership scored hat-tricks for their respective clubs. They were, Alan Shearer (Blackburn), Tony Yeboah (Leeds) and Robbie Fowler (Liverpool).

Leeds' 28 goals in the 1996-97 season was a new Carling Premiership low.

Crystal Palace set a Carling Premiership record for the most consecutive games without a goal when they went nine matches without scoring in the 1994-95 season.

Swindon set the record for the worst start to a Carling Premiership season. They went 15 games before gaining their first victory (6 draws, 9 defeats).

In December 1994, there were no home victories in the Pemiership. Of the 11 matches played, six were away wins and five were draws.

In the weekend of December 2, 1995, seven of the ten Carling Premiership games were drawn, a record.

Leeds became the first club to fail to win a single away game in the Carling Premiership in 1992-93. In the previous season, they were League Champions.

At the end of the 1996-97 season, Alan Shearer was by far the most prolific goalscorer in the Carling Premiership. With Blackburn (1992 to 1996) and Newcastle United (1996 to present day), Shearer has scored 137 goals.

Nottingham Forest set a Carling Premiership record for the biggest away victory when they beat Sheffield Wednesday 7-1 at Hillsborough on April 1, 1995.

Manchester United set an attendance record for the Carling Premiership on January 29, 1997 when 55,314 watched the game v Wimbledon.

The oldest player to have played in the Carling Premiership was John Burridge. The veteran goalkeeper came on as a half-time substitute for Manchester City v Newcastle United on April 29, 1995 aged 43 years, 4 months and 26 days.

The Carling Premiership

Alan Shearer became the first Carling Premiership player to win the PFA Player of the Year award twice (1995, 1997).

The Carling Premiership attendances for the 1996-97 season was over 11 million, the highest figure in the Carling Premiership, and the second highest aggregate in the top-flight since 1981.

 Facts **The Carling Premiership**

The average attendance for the 1996-97 season was 28,638, the highest figure in the top division since 1978.

The goal per game ratio was at its lowest in the 1996-97 season, at 2.55. This compares to 2.57 in the previous year.

Wimbledon set the record for the lowest attendance at a Carling Premiership game on January 26, 1993 when a mere 3,039 people turned up to watch them play Everton.

The 1996-97 season saw Sunderland become the sixth club to last only one season in the Carling Premiership before being relegated to the First Division. They joined Bolton Wanderers (1995-96), Middlesbrough (1992-93), Swindon Town (1993-94), Crystal Palace (1994-95) and Leicester City (1994-95).

In 1996-97 Middlesbrough and Nottingham Forest were both relegated from the Carling Premiership in the same season for the second time. The other occasion was in 1992-93.

Crystal Palace became the first club to be relegated from the Carling Premiership twice when they were relegated in both 1992-93 and 1994-95.

Oldham Athletic suffered a nightmare run when they were relegated from the Carling Premiership in 1993-94. Three seasons later they suffered relegation from the First Division also.

Nottingham Forest set a Carling Premiership unbeaten record in the 1994-95 season when they went 25 games without defeat. They were eventually beaten 7-0 by Blackburn, after 15 wins and 10 draws.

Only three clubs that were among the original twelve that formed the Football League in 1888 were in the first Carling Premiership season in 1992-93. The trio were: Aston Villa, Blackburn Rovers and Everton.

Andy Townsend set a new discipline record in 1994, when he was suspended for 6 Carling Premiership matches. He received a three match ban for reaching 21 disciplinary points, and a further three match ban for a sending-off.

West Ham goalkeeper Neil Finn became the youngest player to have played in the Carling Premiership. He played against Manchester City on January 1, 1996 aged 17 years and 3 days.

The Carling Premiership

Facts

On September 5, 1992 Tottenham's Andy Turner became the youngest player to score a Carling Premiership goal when he scored against Everton.

The 1993-94 Carling Premiership season saw the introduction of squad numbers for players.

When the Carling Premiership was founded in 1992, it was formed of 22 clubs. This was reduced to 20 clubs for the 1995-96 season.

Newcastle United set a record in 1993-94 which Nottingham Forest equalled in 1994-95 for the highest placing in their first Carling Premiership season since winning promotion. Both finished third.

Nottingham Forest v Liverpool was the first Carling Premiership match to be shown live on TV, showon on Sky Sports. Forest won 1-0.

Bryan Robson's first Carling Premiership match for Manchester United was against Middlesbrough, the club he left United to become player-manager in May 1994.

Carling became the sponsors of the Carling Premiership when they signed the deal in February 1993.

Manchester United's Andy Cole missed the beginning of the 1996-97 season through pneumonia and then suffered two broken legs ina comeback reserve game. He still enjoyed a successful season as he collected a Carling Premiership winners medal with United.

Sheffield United's Brian Deane scored the first ever goal in the Carling Premiership. The striker scored against Manchester United on the opening day of the 1992-93 season.

The first player to reach 41 disciplinary points in the Carling Premiership was Wimbledon's Vinnie Jones.

Everton's Peter Beagrie was the first goalscorer of the 1993-94 season. His goal at Southampton came after 10 minutes.

Coventry City's Mick Quinn became the first player to score a Carling Premiership hat-trick on the opening day of a season. He scored all three goals as Coventry produced a 3-0 defeat of Arsenal at Highbury.

 Facts **The Carling Premiership**

Middlesbrough were relegated from the Carling Premiership in 1992-93, despite winning at Sheffield Wednesday 3-2 in their penultimate game of the season.

The top goalscorer in the first Carling Premiership season was Nottingham Forest's Teddy Sheringham. He scored 21 goals, one more than QPR's Les Ferdinand.

Leeds set a new record in 1992-93 by becoming the first team to go through a Carling Premiership season without an away victory. In total they collected only seven points on their travels (seven draws) as they finished two points off the relegation places.

The heaviest defeat on an opening day of the Carling Premiership was the 6-1 loss by Crystal Palace to Liverpool in 1994-95.

Kevin Campbell scored the first goal of the 1994-95 season. He scored after just two minutes in Arsenal's 3-0 home win over Manchester City.

Liverpool's Stig-Inge Bjornebye became the first player to score in the 1996-97 Carling Premiership season. The Norwegian defender netted after 4 minutes at Middlesbrough in the 3-3 draw.

Sheffield United suffered relegation in 1993-94 in the final minute of the last game. A draw against Chelsea would have been enough for them to stay above Ipswich, but Mark Stein's 90th minute goal gave Chelsea a 3-2 win, condemning United to the First Division.

After five seasons, Alan Shearer is the Carling Premiership's top goalscorer. He scored 112 goals for Blackburn and another 25 in 1996-97 for Newcastle.

Everton saved themselves from relegation with nine minutes of the 1993-94 season left. Needing a win to guarantee survival, Everton trailed 2-0 down at home to Wimbledon after only 20 minutes. But Graham Stuart's 81st minute winner gave them a 3-2 victory and another season in the top-flight.

Jurgen Klinsmann made a flying start to his Carling Premiership career. The German striker scored seven goals in his first six games for Tottenham in 1994-95.

When Wimbledon's Paul Heald was sent-off against Newcastle in October 1995, Vinnie Jones donned the goalkeeper's jersey. Unfortunately Jones failed to save the Dons, who lost 6-1.

The Carling Premiership

At the end of the 1996-97 season Arsenal's Dennis Bergkamp was the most expensive foreign signing in the Carling Premiership. The Dutch striker cost £7.5m when he arrived at Highbury from Inter Milan in June 1995.

Everton set a club record seven games without a goal during the 1994-95 Carling Premiership season.

Norwich's Efan Ekoku set a Carling Premiership record when he scored four goals against Everton in September 1993. His record was beaten by Manchester United's Andy Cole with five against Ipswich in the 1994-95 season.

 **Facts** The Carling Premiership

During the 1994-95 season, 12 Carling Premiership managers lost their jobs.

Southampton's Matthew Le Tissier scored a hat-trick on the opening day of the 1995-96 season, but still found himself on the losing side when Nottingham Forest scored four.

Manchester United wore two different kits when they played Southampton in April 1996. Playing the first half in their grey away kit, the United players complained they could not pick each other out against the crowd , so they changed to a blue strip for the second period.

The 22 clubs that played in the first Carling Premiership season were (in final order): Manchester United, Aston Villa, Norwich, Blackburn, QPR, Liverpool, Sheffield Wednesday, Tottenham, Manchester City, Arsenal, Chelsea, Wimbledon, Everton, Sheffield United, Coventry, Ipswich, Leeds, Southampton, Oldham, Crystal Palace, Middlesbrough and Nottingham Forest.

The Carling Premiership's first Manager of the Year was Alex Ferguson of Manchester United.

Three players can lay claim to scoring the first goal of the 1995-96 season. Blackburn's Alan Shearer, Danny Williamson of West Ham and Wimbledon's Efan Ekoku all scored after five minutes on the opening day.

Nottingham Forest were the first club to be relegated from the Carling Premiership, when they finished bottom in 1992-93.

The first player to score a hat-trick in the Carling Premiership was Eric Cantona. He scored three times for Leeds in a 5-0 win over Tottenham on August 25, 1992.

Ipswich have the worst losing record in a Carling Premiership season. In their 42 games in 1994-95 they lost 29 , 22 more than champions Blackburn. Unsurprisingly Ipswich finished bottom of the table.

Sponsors of the Carling Premiership, Carling, awarded their own Player of the Year. In 1994-95 the winner was Blackburn's Alan Shearer and Peter Schmeichel of Manchester United won the award in 1995-96.

The Carling Premiership

Facts

Tim Flowers holds the record for quickest dismissal in the Carling Premiership when he was sent-off for Blackburn after just 72 seconds of the match against Leeds on February 1, 1995.

Andrea Silenzi became the first Italian to play in the Carling Premiership when he joined Nottingham Forest for the 1995-96 season. Unfortunately the striker failed to register a league goal.

When Manchester United became the first Carling Premiership champions in 1992-93 they were awarded £815,210. Four years later they earned £2,114,300 for completing the same feat.

Mark Hateley made his Carling Premiership debut at the ripe old age of 34 when he turned out for QPR against Middlesbrough on December 2, 1995.

From 1994-95 season, Alan Shearer topped the goalscoring charts for three succesive seasons.

In the first five seasons of the Carling Premiership, Manchester United won 123 of their 202 matches on their way to winning four championships.

The 1996-97 season was the first Carling Premiership season that Manchester United failed to win 10 or more away fixtures. Their record is 13 in the 1993-94 season.

FA CUP

FA Cup

 Facts

Kennington Oval, Lillie Bridge in London, Fallowfield in Manchester, Goodison Park, Crystal Palace, Old Trafford, Stamford Bridge and Wembley have all hosted the FA Cup Final.

The last time the FA Cup was decided away from Wembley was in 1970 when the replay was played at Old Trafford.

Preston North End hold the record for the biggest win in the competition. They beat Hyde FC 26-0 in the first round proper in 1887.

The first winners of the FA Cup were The Wanderers, in the 1871-72 season.

David Nish became the youngest FA Cup Final captain when he skippered Leicester City in 1969. He was 21 years and seven months old.

The last team to play in an FA Cup Final while not in the top-flight were Sunderland, who lost to Liverpool in 1992.

The first all-Merseyside FA Cup Final was in 1986 when Liverpool beat Everton.

Cardiff City remain the only non-English team to win the FA Cup. They won in 1927.

Queen's Park are the only Scottish side to reach the FA Cup Final. They did so in consecutive years, 1884 and 1885, but lost both games.

 Facts   FA Cup

Manchester United have won the FA Cup more times than any other club. They have lifted the trophy nine times.

The highest score in the FA Cup Final was 6-0, when Bury beat Derby County in 1903.

Manchester United have won eight of their nine FA Cups at Wembley.

The last club outside the top flight to win the FA Cup was West Ham in 1980. They were in the Second Division when they won the trophy in 1980.

Tottenham won the FA Cup in 1901 when they were still a Southern League club.

Chesterfield became only the seventh side from the third division to reach the semi-finals of the competition in 1997.

Middlesbrough reached their first FA Cup Final in 1997. Unfortunately they were beaten by Chelsea.

Cambridge United were the last team to reach the quarter-finals from the old-Fourth Division in 1990.

Since the formation of the competition there have been four replica FA Cup trophies.

Four clubs have reached the FA Cup Final and been relegated in the same season. Manchester City in 1926, Leicester City in 1969, Brighton and Hove Albion in 1983 and Middlesbrough in 1997.

Yeovil Town are the most successful non-league club in FA Cup history. They have won recorded 17 victories over league opposition.

Tottenham Hotspur are the only club to have won the FA Cup as a non-league side, in 1901.

The first semi-final to be staged at Wembley was in 1991 when Tottenham beat Arsenal 3-1.

Up to the end of the 1996-97 season there have been five FA Cup semi-finals at Wembley.

FA Cup

Facts

When Liverpool won the FA Cup in 1986, none of their players were English. Mark Lawrenson was born in Preston but played for the Republic of Ireland.

The last club to win the FA Cup with eleven English players were West Ham, in 1975.

The last team to win the Amateur Cup and the FA Cup were Wimbledon. They won the Amateur in 1963 and the FA Cup in 1988.

On their way to winning the 1912 FA Cup Barnsley played a record 12 matches. Six of those games were replays.

Arsenal and Sheffield Wednesday took five games to decide a winner in their FA Cup third round tie. Arsenal eventually won through.

It took six games to decide the winners of the Alvechurch-Oxford City fourth qualifying round tie in the 1971-72 season. Alvechurch came out victorious.

The longest round in FA Cup history was the third round in 1962-63. The round lasted from January 5 to March 11 and included 261 postponements.

There have been only three FA Cup Final hat-tricks. Billy Townley for Blackburn Rovers in 1890, Notts County's Jimmy Logan in 1894 and Stan Mortensen of Blackpool in 1953.

The Hon. A.F Kinnaird played in nine of the first 12 FA Cup Finals. He won three with The Wanderers in 1873 (captain), 1877 and 1878 (captain) and twice as captain of Old Etonians in 1879 and 1882.

Bryan Robson captained Manchester United to three FA Cup wins in 1983. 1985 and 1990.

Ian Callaghan set a record 88 appearances in the FA Cup. He played for Liverpool, Swansea and Crewe.

Only two players have appeared in the FA Cup Final for three clubs. Harold Halse for Manchester United, Aston Villa and Chelsea and Ernie Taylor for Newcastle, Blackpool and Manchester United.

 **Facts**

FA Cup

The only player to captain both English and Scottish FA Cup winning teams is Martin Buchan – Aberdeen in 1970 and Manchester United in 1977.

Two players have appeared in FA Cup Finals before and after the war. Raich Carter (Sunderland in 1937 and Derby County in 1946) and Willie Fagan (Preston in 1937 and Liverpool in 1950).

Sunderland are the last FA Cup winners who did not include an international player in their side when they won the Cup in 1973.

There were 16 goals in the two 1990 FA Cup semi-finals. Crystal Palace 4, Liverpool 3 and Manchester United v Oldham 3-3 and 2-1 (replay). All of those 16 goals were scored by different players.

The last hat-trick in a FA Cup semi-final was scored by Alex Dawson for Manchester United in a 5-3 replay win against Fulham in 1958.

In the 1985-86 season, seven of the eight FA Cup fifth round ties went to replays – a record for that stage of the competition.

Manchester United won the FA Cup in 1990 by playing all their games away from home.

Arsenal were drawn away in every round on their way to reaching the FA Cup Finals of 1971 and 1972.

Manchester United won the FA Cup of 1948 by beating First Division sides in every round – the only team to have done so.

FA Cup

Facts

The famous FA Cup Final song "Abide With Me" was first sung at the Final in 1927 and has been sung ever since with the exception of 1959.

Blackburn Rovers hold the record unbeaten run in the Cup. They were unbeaten for 24 games.

Since the Football League was introduced in 1888, there has never been a Final that has not featured a club from the top-flight.

Tottenham Hotspur were originally banned from the 1995 competition, but were re-admitted and reached the semi-finals.

The 1991 FA Cup Final had four Guests of Honour – the Prince and Princess of Wales and the Duke and Duchess of Kent.

Norman Whiteside became the youngest player to score in an FA Cup Final when he scored for Manchester United against Brighton and Hove Albion in 1983.

Everton became the last team to lose in consecutive FA Cup Finals when they were beaten in 1985 and 1986.

Paul Bracewell ties the record for four losers medal in the FA Cup.

Brian Talbot is the last player to win successive FA Cup's with two different sides. He was a member of the 1978 Ipswich side and the 1979 Arsenal team.

Ian Wright is the last player to score for two clubs in FA Cup Finals – Crystal Palace in 1990 and Arsenal in 1993.

Les Sealey won an FA Cup winners medal while on loan to Manchester United in 1990.

Clive Allen followed his father Les by playing in an FA Cup Final for Tottenham.

Pat Van den Hauwe played in four FA Cup Finals in six years. He played for Everton in 1985,1986,1989 and Tottenham in 1991.

In 1993, Sheffield Wednesday's John Harkes became the first American to play in an FA Cup Final.

 **Facts**   **FA Cup**

George Graham was the last man to win the FA Cup, both as a player and a manager of the same club. He played in Arsenal's 1971 victory and managed them to their 1993 win.

Portsmouth's Andy Awford became the youngest player in any round of the FA Cup when he he appeared for Worcester City v Boreham Wood in the third qualifying round in 1987. He was only 15 years and 88 days old.

Paul Allen became the youngest player in a Wembley Cup Final when he played for West Ham in 1980 aged 17 years, 256 days.

The youngest player to appear in an FA Cup Final was Clapham Rovers' James Prinsep. He was 17 years, 245 days old when he played in the 1879 Final.

Peter Shilton played for Leicester City in the 1969 FA Cup Final aged 19 years, 220 days, the youngest goalkeeper to play in a Final.

The oldest player in an FA Cup match was Billy Meredith. He was 49 years, 8 months when he turned out for Manchester City in a 1924 semi-final.

The oldest scorer in a Wembley Final was Bert Turner, who scored for Charlton against Derby County in 1946. He was 36 years, 312 days old, and also scored an own goal in the same match.

Wimbledon were the 42nd team to win the FA Cup when they defeated Liverpool in the 1988 Final.

Manchester United have made more FA Cup Final appearances than any other club – 14.

Stan Cullis is the youngest man to manage an FA Cup Final wining team when Wolves won in 1949. He was 33 years, 187 days old.

Queen's Park and Cardiif City are the only two non-English clubs to have played in FA Cup Finals – both making two appearances.

Tottenham have won eight of their nine Final appearances. Their only defeat was to Coventry City in 1987.

Leicester City have played in four FA Cup Finals, and lost them all.

FA Cup

Facts

West Bromwich Albion are the only team to have won the FA Cup and promotion from the Second Division in the same season.

Pat Jennings is the only player who has won FA Cup's with both North London teams Tottenham and Arsenal.

Two players have won successive FA Cup winners medals with two different teams. Arthur Kinnaird (Wanderers and Old Etonians) and Brian Talbot (Ipswich and Arsenal).

Arthur Turner won an FA Cup winners medal with Charlton in 1946, but did not play a League match for the club. There was no League football that season and he had left the club before the start of the following campaign.

When Laurie Cunningham came on as a substitute for Wimbledon against Liverpool in the 1988 Final he completed a unique double. He had played for Real Madrid against Liverpool in the 1981 European Cup Final.

Peter Boyle and Harold Johnson both won the FA Cup with Sheffield United in 1899 and 1902. That was was followed by their sons, Thomas Boyle and Harold Johnson, who also won the Cup with United in 1925.

Manchester United were the last team to appear in three consecutive Finals. They won in 1994, lost in 1995 and won in 1996.

Old Etonians, Queen's Park, West Bromwich Albion, Derby County, Newcastle United, Manchester United and Everton have all lost in successive FA Cup Finals.

Only once has the same two teams contested successive FA Cup Finals. In 1884 and 1885 Blackburn Rovers beat Queen's Park.

The only pair of brothers to have played against each other in an FA Cup Final were Herbert and William Rawson. William was in the Oxford University team that beat Herbert's Royal Engineers in 1874.

Gary and Phil Neville were the last brothers to play in a FA Cup winning team. They both played in the 1996 Final for Manchester United.

The last cousins to play in an FA Cup Final were Clive and Paul Allen for Tottenham in 1987.

 Facts   **FA Cup**

Bobby and Jack Charlton have both played in three FA Cup Finals each, for Manchester United and Leeds respectively.

Denis and Leslie Compton both played in Arsenal's 1950 FA Cup Final win. They also played county cricket for Middlesex and Denis became one of England's finest batsmen.

Jim Standen and Geoff Hurst both played in West Ham's 1964 FA Cup winning team and played first class cricket, Standen for Worcestershire and Hurst for Essex.

Jesper Olsen, Jan Molby, John Jensen, Peter Schmeichel and Jakob Kjeldbjerg are the only Danish players to have played in an FA Cup Final. They have six winners medals between them and Kjeldbjerg is the only one never to collect a winners medal.

Brothers Edward and George Robledo are the only Chileans to have won the Cup. They both played in Newcastle's 1952 triumph, George scored the only goal of the game and played in the Final the previous year as well.

FA Cup

Jimmy Cochrane (Kilmarnock 1929 and Sunderland 1937) and Alex Ferguson (Aberdeen 1982,1983,1984,1986 and Manchester United 1990,1994,1996) are the only two managers who have led FA Cup-winning teams in both Scotland and England.

Four men have led FA Cup winning teams on three occasions – John Nicholson (Sheffield United 1902,1915,1925), Charles Foweraker (Bolton Wanderers 1923,1926,1929), Bill Nicholson (Tottenham 1961,1962,1967) and Alex Ferguson (Manchester United 1990,1994,1996).

Henry Cursham of Notts County is the highest goalscorer in the history of the FA Cup. He scored 48 goals between 1880 and 1887.

Ian Rush is the highest post-war goalscorer in the competition. He has scored 42 goals (39 for Liverpool, 3 for Chester City) from 1979 to present day.

Rush has also scored the most goals in FA Cup Finals. He scored twice in 1986 and 1989 and once in 1992 to register a record five goals.

The last man to score a hat-trick in an FA Cup Final was Stan Mortensen for Blakpool in 1953. Only two others have achieved the feat – William Townley (Blackburn Rovers 1890) and Jimmy Logan (Notts County 1894).

Only two players have scored in three different Cup Finals – Fred Priest (Sheffield United 1899,1901,1902) and Ian Rush (Liverpool 1986,1989,1992)

Jack Smith is the only player to have scored in both English and Scottish FA Cup Finals. He was on the scoresheet for Kilmarnock in 1920 and for Bolton Wanderers in 1923.

The youngest ever Cup Finalist was James Prinsep, who was 17 years, 245 days when he played for Clapham Rovers in the FA Cup Final of 1879.

David McCreery is the only man to have played in two FA Cup Finals as a teenager. He was an used substitute for Manchester United in 1976 and 1977.

Tottenham's Gary Mabbutt is the last man to score for both teams in an FA Cup Final when he scored both goals in the 1987 Final between Tottenham and Coventry.

 Facts   FA Cup

The first FA Cup Final to be televised was the 1937 Final
between Sunderland and Preston.

*The first FA Cup Final to be televised in colour was the 1968 match
between West Bromwich Albion and Everton.*

The FA Cup has been received in South Africa. Having won the
Cup the previous season, Newcastle took the trophy with them
when they went on a tour of the country in 1952.

*The official record crowd at an FA Cup Final is 126,047 for the 1923
Final between Bolton and West Ham.*

The biggest crowd for an FA Cup match other than the Final
was for a sixth round tie between Manchester City and Stoke
City in 1934. The attendance was 84,569.

*The last player to score in every round of the competition in the
same season was Chelsea's Peter Osgood in 1970. Others who
achieved the feat before him were Sandy Brown (Tottenham 1901),
Ellis Rimmer (Sheffield Wednesday 1935), Frank O'Donnell (Preston
1937), Stan Mortensen (Blackpool 1948), Jackie Milburn (Newcastle
1951), Nat Lofthouse (Bolton Wanderers 1953), Charlie Wayman
(Preston 1954) and Jeff Astle (West Bromwich Albion 1968).*

Three captains missed the FA Cup Final because of suspension
in consecutive years in the 1980's. Glenn Roeder missed QPR's
replay against Tottenham in 1982, Brighton's Steve Foster
missed the Final with Manchester United although he returned
for the replay and in 1984 Wilf Rostron was absent from
Watford's defeat to Everton.

*Manchester United were the first team to win the FA Cup "third-
place play-off" between the two losing semi-finalists. They beat
Watford in 1970.*

The "third-place play-off" was scrapped after only five seasons.
Past winners are Manchester United (1970), Stoke City (1971),
Birmingham City (1972), Wolves (1973) and Burnley (1974).

*The first FA Cup match to be decided on penalties was the 1972
"third-place play-off" between Birmingham City and Stoke City. The
Blues won the shoot-out 4-3.*

FA Cup

Southampton reached the FA Cup Final as a non-league club twice in three years. The Saints were a Southern League side when they reached the 1900 and 1902 Finals – they lost both.

The most successful non-league club in recent FA Cup history is Telford United, who reached the fifth round in 1985.

Only four non-league clubs have beaten the Cup holders – Tottenham beat Bury in 1901, Southampton beat Tottenham in 1902, Norwich City beat Sheffield Wednesday in 1908 and Crystal Palace beat Wolverhampton Wanderers in 1909.

The last non-league side to beat a Division One side were Sutton United. They beat Coventry in the third round in 1989.

Since 1948, six First Division sides have been beaten by non-league opposition.

The last amateur player to play in the Cup Final was Bill Slater of Wolves in 1951.

Blackburn Rovers have had the longest unbeaten run in the FA Cup. They went 24 matches undefeated from December 1882 to November 1886.

Six teams have won the League and FA Cup 'double' – Preston (1889), Aston Villa (1897), Tottenham (1961), Arsenal (1971), Liverpool (1986) and Manchester United (1994,1996).

Manchester United are the only club to have done the 'double' twice (1994 and 1996).

Arsenal are the only club to have won both FA and League Cups in the same season (1993).

Nottingham Forest are the only team to have played FA Cup ties in all four home countries. In 1885 they played Queen's Park in a semi-final replay in Edinburgh. They played Linfield in the first round of 1889. And in 1922 threy lost in the third round at Cardiff City.

Seven Scottish sides have appeared in the FA Cup. They were: Cowlairs, Rangers, Queen's Park, Hearts, Partick Thistle, Third Lanark and Renton.

 Facts

FA Cup

**Three Irish clubs that have appeared in the competition –
Cliftonville, Belfast Distillery and Linfield Athletic.**

*The only FA Cup match to be decided on a toss of a coin was in the
1873-74 season when Sheffield Club won through to the second
round at the expense of Shropshire Wanderers.*

**The first penalty awarded in an FA Cup Final was in the 1910
replay. Albert Shepherd scored for Newcastle against Barnsley.**

*The first penalty to be awarded in a Wembley Final was in 1938.
George Mutch scored the only goal from the spot to give Preston a 1-0
victory over Huddersfield.*

FA Cup

Facts

Only three times in the history of FA Cup Finals has a penalty been the only goal of the game – Huddersfield's win over Preston in 1922, Preston's defeat of Huddersfield in 1938 and in 1982 Tottenham's replay win over QPR in 1982.

Charlie Wallace of Aston Villa became the first man to miss a penalty in an FA Cup Final when he sent his spot-kick wide in the 1913 Final.

John Aldridge (Liverpool) and Gary Lineker (Tottenham) are the only two players to have had their penalty kicks saved at Wembley. Aldridge in 1988 and Lineker in 1991.

Manchester City's goalkeeper Bert Trautmann played the last 15 minutes of the 1956 FA Cup Final with a broken neck. City won 3-1.

Ray Wood, Manchester United's goalkeeper, suffered a fractured cheekbone in a collision with Aston Villa's Peter McParland in the 1957 Final. Jackie Blanchflower took over in goal while Wood returned to play on the wing before playing the final minutes back in goal. United lost 2-1.

Nottingham Forest's Roy Dwight scored but then broke his leg in his side's 2-1 Final win over Luton in 1959. Dwight would later become famous for being the uncle of Elton John.

In 1992 Liverpool became the first team to reach the FA Cup Final after winning a penalty shoot-out in the semi-final. They had drew 1-1 and 0-0 with Portmsouth before winning 3-1 on penalties.

The highest score in a semi-final was when Newcastle beat Fulham 6-0 in 1908.

The last non-league side to reach the semi-finals were Swindon Town in 1912.

Five men have been sent-off in semi-finals. The last man to do so was Arsenal's Lee Dixon in 1993.

Millwall, Norwich City, Stoke City and The Swifts have all reached threee FA Cup semi-finals – and lost them all.

42 different venues have been used for FA Cup semi-finals.

Everton hold the record for most appearances in the semi-finals – 23.

 Facts   **FA Cup**

The 1980 semi-final between Arsenal and Liverpool is the only to go to a third replay. Arsenal eventually won through.

At the end of the 1992 Final Sunderland were mistakenly awarded the winners medals, despite losing 2-0 to Liverpool.

In 1970 Chelsea's David Webb was refused to collect his winners medal because he was wearing a Leeds shirt he had exchanged after the game and an official believed he was a Leeds player.

The last team to reach the FA Cup Final without conceding a goal was Everton in 1966.

Only two other teams have reached the Final without conceding a goal – Preston in 1889 and Bury in 1903. Both teams went on to win the Cup.

Preston and Bury are the only teams to have won the Cup without conceding a goal in the season's competition.

In Wolves 3-1 defeat of Newcastle United in the 1908 Cup Final, the goalscorers were Kenneth Hunt, George Hedley, Billy Harrison and Jimmy Howie. Amazingly they were the only four players on the pitch with a surname that started with the letter H.

Bob Stokoe has twice beaten Don Revie in Cup Final's. In 1955 Stokoe was a member of the victorious Newcastle side that beat Manchester City, with Revie playing centre-forward. And in 1973, Sunderland, managed by Stokoe, beat Revie's Leeds side.

An hour before the 1960 FA Cup Final Blackburn Rovers' Derek Dougan asked for a transfer. Dougan then went and played for a Rovers side that lost 3-0 to Wolves.

The first FA Cup match to be played under floodlights was between Kidderminster Harriers and Brierley Hill Alliance in a preliminary round in 1955.

Barnsley played a record number of 12 matches on their way to winning the Cup in 1912.

Liverpool's 'Anfield Rap' is the most successful FA Cup Final song recorded. It reched number three in the charts in 1988.

The first FA Cup Final song to hit the top 40 was Arsenal's 'Good Old Arsenal' in 1971. It was in the charts for seven weeks.

FA Cup

Facts

The Wanderers were the first club to win the FA Cup on three occasions – 1872,1873,1876.

The first own goal in a Final was scored by Lord Kinnaird, playing for The Wanderers in 1877.

Alexander Bosnor became the first player to score in successive FA Cup Finals. He scored for Old Etonians in the 1875 and 1876 Finals.

The first player to score in successive FA Cup Finals at Wembley was Bobby Johnstone of Manchester City (1955 and 1956).

The 1967 Final between Tottenham and Chelsea was the first at which teams were allowed to name a substitue for the the Final.

The first substitute used in a Final was West Bromwich Albion's Derek Clarke. He replaced John Kaye in the 1968 Final.

Eddie Kelly became the first substitute to score in an FA Cup Final when he scored Arsenal's equaliser in the 1971 Final against Liverpool.

Everton's Stuart McCall beat Ian Rush of Liverpool by two minutes to become the first substitute to score twice in an FA Cup Final. Rush had the last laugh, helping Liverpool win 3-2.

West Bromwich Albion were the first team to win the Cup with eleven English-born players when they received the Cup in 1888.

 **Facts** FA Cup

The first player to play in winning English and Scottish FA Cup sides was Harry Campbell. He won the Scottish Cup with Renton in 1888 and played in the successful Blackburn Rovers that won the FA Cup in 1890.

The first Wembley FA Cup Final goal was scored by David Jack of Bolton in 1923.

The first man to score at Wembley and finish on the losing side was Alex Jackson of Huddersfield in 1928.

The first club to score first and lose at Wembley in a Final was Arsenal in 1932. They lost 2-1 to Newcastle.

David O'Leary ended his 20-year association with Arsenal by winning an FA Cup winners medal in 1993.

The first man to play for and then manage the same club in the FA Cup Final was Stan Seymour. He played for Newcastle in 1924 and managed them in their 1951 and 1952 victories.

King George V was the first reigning monarch to attend an FA Cup Final – in 1914.

The first Wembley FA Cup Final to go to a replay was in 1970 when Chelsea drew 2-2 with Leeds. The replay was played at Old Trafford.

The first FA Cup Final to be replayed at Wembley was the 1981 match between Tottenham and Manchester City.

Manchester United's Kevin Moran became the first player to be sent-off in an FA Cup Final. He was ordered off by referee Peter Willis in the 1985 Final against Everton.

In February 1969, all eight fifth round ties were postponed because of the weather.

The first FA Cup tie to be played on a Sunday was between Cambridge United and Oldham in a third round match in 1974.

The first FA Cup Final to produce gate receipts of £1million was the 1985 match between Everton and Manchester United.

When Wimbledon won the FA Cup in 1988, Dave Beasant became the first goalkeeper to captain a winning side.

FA Cup

Facts

Beasant also became the first goalkeeper to save a penalty in a Wembley FA Cup Final in the 1988 victory.

The only other goalkeeper to save a penalty in a Wembley FA Cup Final was Nottingham Forest's Mark Crossley, who saved from Tottenham's Gary Lineker in 1991.

The first FA Cup tie to be decided by a penalty shoot-out was the first round match between Rotherham United and Scunthorpe United in 1991. Rotherham won 7-6 in the shoot-out.

The first FA Cup Final where both sets of players wore their names on the back of their shirts was in 1993 between Arsenal and Sheffield Wednesday.

Oldham and Manchester United met twice in four years in FA Cup semi-finals – 1990 and 1994.

Also in the 1993 Final, squad numbers were used rather than the traditional 1-11.

The first black player to captain an FA Cup Final side was Sheffield Wednesday's Viv Anderson in 1993.

Sheffield Wednesday also claimed the second black player to captain a FA Cup Final side when Carlton Palmer led them in the 1993 replay due to Anderson's injury.

The 1993 FA Cup Final was the first occasion where the two team managers collected medals with their sides.

Arsenal became the first Carling Premiership club to win the FA Cup – in 1993.

The last All-London FA Cup Final was in 1982 when Tottenham beat QPR.

The lowest attendance for a semi-final was in 1995 for the replay between Manchester United and Crystal Palace – 17,987. A large number of Palace fans boycotted the match after a fan died before the first game.

Aston Villa's Villa Park has staged the most FA Cup semi-finals – 45.

Sunderland became the first team to win the FA Cup without any international players.

 **Facts** FA Cup

Ian Rush has played in three FA Cup Finals for Liverpool, and scored in all of them.

H. Lyons was carried off on a stretcher against Doncaster Rovers in a first round replay in 1965, but returned later to score a hat-trick.

In 1987 (Coventry City) and 1988 (Wimbledon), both clubs won the FA Cup in their first Final.

The first winners of the Littlewoods-sponsored FA Cup were Everton in 1995.

The 1923 Final was named the White Horse Final after Billy the horse helped to contain the crowd when they overspilled onto the pitch.

Burnley's Jimmy Robson scored the 100th Cup Final goal in 1962.

Burnley and Tottenham played in three successive FA Cup ties from 1961 to 1963.

Allan Clarke played for Leicester City (1969) and Leeds (1970) in successive FA Cup Finals – and lost them both.

Arsenal and Leeds played in the Centenary Cup Final in 1972.

Mike Trebilcock scored twice for Everton in the 1966 FA Cup Final despite not having his name printed in the official match programme.

Arsenal were the first holders of the FA Cup to lose in the final when they were beaten by Leeds in 1972.

Leicester City were the first club to have their names on the back of their tracksuits before the 1961 FA Cup Final.

Tommy Docherty had lost three FA Cup Finals, once as a player, before managing manchester United to glory in 1977.

Arthur Kinnaird appeared in six FA Cup Finals for Old Etonians, as well as three for The Wanderers.

Bryan Robson captained Manchester United to three FA Cup wins in seven years.

FA Cup

Arsenal played in five FA Cup Finals in nine years from 1971.

Jimmy Case scored for Liverpool in the 1977 FA Cup Final and in 1983 grabbed the winning goal for Brighton against Liverpool in the fifth round.

At the ripe old age of 20, Manchester United's Norman Whiteside had already scored in two FA Cup Finals (1983 and 1985).

The 100th FA Cup Final was played in 1981 between Tottenham and Manchester City.

Dave Bennett has twice been an FA Cup Finalist. He was a member of the Manchester City team that lost in 1981, and played for Coventry City in 1987. Both games were played against Tottenham.

The last man to play for and then manage the same team in an FA Cup Final was Joe Royle. He played for Everton in the 1968 Final and managed the club to victory in the 1995 Final.

Steve Coppell won the FA Cup in 1977 as a player with Manchester United. As a manger he led Crystal Palace to the 1990 Final but they lost in a replay – to Manchester United.

The last player to score an own goal in an FA Cup Final was Nottingham Forest's Des Walker (1991).

Tottenham's Danny Blanchflower was the first man to captain a team to successive FA Cup Final wins, in 1961 and 1962.

Eric Cantona of Manchester United became the first foreign player to captain an FA Cup Final side when he led out United in the 1996 Final.

Arnold Muhren became the first Dutchman to play in the FA Cup Final when he played, and scored, for Manchester United in 1983.

Chelsea's Ruud Gullit became the first foreign manager to lead a FA Cup Final side when Chelsea reached the 1997 Final.

Glenn Hoddle became the last player-manager to play in an FA Cup Final when he came on as a substitute in Chelsea's 4-0 defeat to Manchester United in 1994.

Facts

FA Cup

The last two FA Cup Finals in which a player has scored for both teams have both involved Tottenham. Manchester City's Tommy Hutchinson done it in 1981 and Tottenham's Gary Mabbutt scored for his team as well as Coventry in 1987.

Joe Royle and Howard Kendall both played for Everton in the 1968 FA Cup Final, and later managed the club to Cup success.

There has only been one instance where two pairs of brothers have played in the same Final. In 1876, Hubert and Frederick Heron played for The Wanderers against an Old Etonians team that boasted the Hon. Alfred and The Hon.and Rev. Edward Lyttleton.

FA Cup

Walton and Hersham's 4-0 win over Brighton in 1973 is the biggest away victory for a non-league side in the competition.

Albert Taylor of Luton scored after just 45 seconds of his senior debut in an FA Cup tie in January 1953.

The 1986 FA Cup Final between Liverpool and Everton was dubbed 'The Friendly Final' because of the atmosphere between both sets of supporters.

Charles Alcock, secretary of the FA, invented the FA Cup in 1871.

Because of an injury crisis at the club Watford had to play Gary Plumley, a wine-bar owner who played part-time football, in goal in their 1987 semi-final against Tottenham. They lost 4-1.

The last FA Cup Final that featured the two clubs that finished first and second in the top division was in 1986 when Liverpool beat Everton to both League and FA Cup.

Ten Mansfield Town players were booked in their third round tie against Crystal Palace in 1963.

Leeds United went 16 matches without a win in the competition between February 1952 and March 1963.

Stoke City are the only founder members of the Football League not to have won the FA Cup.

Cardiff City had to apply for re-election to the Football League in 1934 – just seven years after winning the FA Cup.

In 1933, Everton and Manchester City became the first teams to wear number on the back of their shirts in an FA Cup Final.

Preston North End became the first Football League club to win the FA Cup, in 1889.

Portsmouth won the FA Cup in 1939, but kept the trophy for seven years because of the Second World War.

Nobby Stiles, George Cohen and Martin Peters are the only three memebers of the 1966 World Cup winning team that have not played in an FA Cup Final.

 **Facts**

FA Cup

Paul Gascoigne's final game for Tottenham ended with him being carried off on a stretcher after suffering a knee injury after only 16 minutes of the 1991 FA Cup Final.

Non-league side Sutton United beat First Division Coventry City in the third round in 1989, but were beaten by Norwich City 8-0 in the following round.

The last player to be sent-off in an FA Cup semi-final was Middlesbrough's Vladimir Kinder in 1997.

The last player to be named Footballer of the Year and captain his side to FA Cup glory in the same season was Manchester United's Eric Cantona.

Keith Houchen was an FA Cup goalscoring hero for two clubs in the space of two years and both times against North London clubs. He scored the only goal as York City beat Arsenal in 1985, and then scored for Coventry in the 1987 Final against Tottenham.

Up to 1998 there has not been a goalless draw in a Wembley FA Cup Final.

Paul Bracewell is the only player this century to play in three FA Cup Finals against the same club. He played for Everton (1986,1989) and Sunderland in 1992, losing to Liverpool on all three occasions.

Bryan Robson is the last man to captain a winning side and then lead a club to the FA Cup Final. He captained Manchester United to victory in 1983,1985 and 1990 and managed Middlesbrough to the 1997 Final.

Leyton Orient, now in the Third Division, last reached the semi-finals in 1978, but were beaten by Arsenal.

The first man to play in and then manage an FA Cup winning team was Peter McWilliam. He played in Newcastle's 1910 victory and then managed Tottenham to victory in 1921.

Arsenal's Steve Morrow collected a Cup winners medal before the 1993 FA Cup Final. Morrow was injured in the celebrations after the League Cup Final and could not receive his medal.

FA Cup

The 1993 FA Cup Final was also the first where the two sides, Arsenal and Sheffield Wednesday, had contested the League Cup in the same season.

Clive Allen played for QPR in the 1982 FA Cup Final but was beaten by Tottenham, then played for Tottenham in the 1987 Final, who were beaten by Coventry City.

Liverpool's Kenny Dalglish was the first man to win an FA Cup as player-manager, in 1986. Chelsea's Ruud Gullit followed that feat in 1997, but did not play in the Final.

Chelsea have appeared in two FA Cup Finals in the 1990's, led by two different player-managers – Glenn Hoddle in 1994 and Ruud Gullit in 1997.

The 1997 FA Cup Final was the first time that both clubs were led by player-managers – Ruud Gullit (Chelsea) and Bryan Robson (Middlesbrough).

West Ham's four FA Cup Finals have all featured a club from the Second Division. In 1923 and 1980 they were in Division Two and in 1964 and 1975 they beat Preston North End and Fulham respectively, who were both in the Second Division.

Mark Hughes became the first player this century to win four FA Cup winners medals. He won the trophy with Manchester United in 1985, 1990 and 1994 and with Chelsea in 1997.

FA CUP FINALS

FA Cup Finals

Facts

FA CUP WINNERS

9 - Manchester United	2 - Preston North End
8 - Tottenham	2 - Sunderland
7 - Aston Villa	1 - Barnsley
6 - Arsenal	1 - Blackburn Olympic
6 - Blackburn Rovers	1 - Blackpool
6 - Newcastle United	1 - Bradford City
5 - Everton	1 - Burnley
5 - Liverpool	1 - Cardiff City
5 - The Wanderers	1 - Charlton Athletic
5 - West Bromwich Albion	1 - Clapham Rovers
4 - Bolton Wanderers	1 - Coventry City
4 - Manchester City	1 - Derby County
4 - Sheffield United	1 - Huddersfield Town
4 - Wolves	1 - Ipswich Town
3 - Sheffield Wednesday	1 - Leeds United
3 - West Ham United	1 - Notts County
2 - Bury	1 - Old Carthusians
2 - Chelsea	1 - Oxford University
2 - Nottingham Forest	1 - Portsmouth
2 - Old Etonians	1- Royal Engineers
	1 - Southampton
	1 - Wimbledon

AT KENNINGTON OVAL

1872 The Wanderers 1, Royal Engineers 0

AT LILLIE BRIDGE, LONDON

1873 The Wanderers 2, Oxford University 1

AT KENNINGTON OVAL

1874 Oxford University 2, Royal Engineers 0
1875 Royal Engineers 1, Old Etonians 1 (Replay: 2-0)
1876 The Wanderers 0, Old Etonians 0 (Replay: 3-0)
1877 The Wanderers 2, Oxford University 1 (aet)
1878 The Wanderers 3, Royal Engineers 1
1879 Old Etonians 1, Clapham Rovers 0
1880 Clapham Rovers 1, Oxford University 0
1881 Old Carthusians 3, Old Etonians 0
1882 Old Etonians 1, Blackburn Rovers 0
1883 Blackburn Olympic 2, Old Etonians 1 (aet)
1884 Blackburn Rovers 2, Queen's Park (Glasgow) 1
1885 Blackburn Rovers 2, Queen's Park (Glasgow) 0
1886 Blackburn Rovers 0, West Bromwich Albion 0
　　　　(Replay at Derby's Baseball Ground: 2-0)

THE ULTIMATE FACT AND QUIZ BOOK

 **Facts**   **FA Cup Finals**

1887 Aston Villa 2, West Bromwich Albion 0
1888 West Bromwich Albion 2, Preston North End 1
1889 Preston North End 3, Wolverhampton Wanderers 0
1890 Blackburn Rovers 6, Sheffield Wednesday 1
1891 Blackburn Rovers 3, Notts County 1
1892 West Bromwich Albion 3, Aston Villa 0

AT FALLOWFIELD, MANCHESTER

1893 Wolverhampton Wanderers 1, Everton 0

AT GOODISON PARK

1894 Notts County 4, Bolton Wanderers 1

AT CRYSTAL PALACE

1895 Aston Villa 1, West Bromwich Albion 0
1896 Sheffield Wednesday 2, Wolverhampton Wanderers 1
1897 Aston Villa 3, Everton 2
1898 Nottingham Forest 3, Derby County 1
1899 Sheffield United 4, Derby County 1
1900 Bury 4, Southampton 0
1901 Tottenham Hotspur 2, Sheffield United 2
*   (Replay at Bolton Wanderers' Burnden Park: 3-1)*
1902 Sheffield United 1, Southampton 1 (Replay: 2-1)
1903 Bury 6, Derby County 0
1904 Manchester City 1, Bolton Wanderers 0
1905 Aston Villa 2, Newcastle United 0
1906 Everton 1, Newcastle United 0
1907 Sheffield Wednesday 2, Everton 1
1908 Wolverhampton Wanderers 3, Newcastle United 1
1909 Manchester United 1, Bristol City 0
1910 Newcastle United 1, Barnsley 1
*   (Replay at Everton's Goodison Park: 2-0)*
1911 Bradford City 0, Newcastle United 0
*   (Replay at Manchester United's Old Trafford: 1-0)*
1912 Barnsley 0, West Bromwich Albion 0
*   (Replay at Sheffield United's Bramall Lane: 1-0)*
1913 Aston Villa 1, Sunderland 0
1914 Burnely 1, Liverpool 0

AT OLD TRAFFORD

1915 Sheffield United 3, Chelsea 0

FA Cup Finals

AT STAMFORD BRIDGE

1920 Aston Villa 1, Huddersfield Town 0 (aet)
1921 Tottenham Hotspur 1, Wolverhampton Wanderers 0
1922 Huddersfield Town 1, Preston North End 0

AT WEMBLEY

1923 Bolton Wanderers 2, West Ham United 0
1924 Newcastle United 2, Aston Villa 0
1925 Sheffield United 1, Cardiff City 0
1926 Bolton Wanderers 1, Manchester City 0
1927 Cardiff City 1, Arsenal 0
1928 Blackburn Rovers 3, Huddersfield Town 1
1929 Bolton Wanderers 2, Portsmouth 0
1930 Arsenal 2, Huddersfield Town 0
1931 West Bromwich Albion 2, Birmingham City 1
1932 Newcastle United 2, Arsenal 1
1933 Everton 3, Manchester City 0
1934 Manchester City 2, Portsmouth 1
1935 Sheffield Wednesday 4, West Bromwich Albion 2
1936 Arsenal 1, Sheffield United 0
1937 Sunderland 3, Preston North End 1
1938 Preston North End 1, Huddersfield Town 0 (aet)
1939 Portsmouth 4, Wolverhampton Wanderers 1
1946 Derby County 4, Charlton Athletic 1 (aet)
1947 Charlton Athletic 1, Burnley 0 (aet)
1948 Manchester United 4, Blackpool 2
1949 Wolverhampton Wanderers 3, Leicester City 1
1950 Arsenal 2, Liverpool 0
1951 Newcastle United 2, Blackpool 0
1952 Newcastle United 1, Arsenal 0
1953 Blackpool 4, Bolton Wanderers 3
1954 West Bromwich Albion 3, Preston North End 2
1955 Newcastle United 3, Manchester City 1
1956 Manchester City 3, Birmingham City 1
1957 Aston Villa 2, Manchester United 1
1958 Bolton Wanderers 2, Manchester United 0
1959 Nottingham Forest 2, Luton Town 1
1960 Wolverhampton Wanderers 3, Blackburn Rovers 0
1961 Tottenham Hotspur 2, Leicester City 0
1962 Tottenham Hostspur 3, Burnley 1
1963 Manchester United 3, Leicester City 1
1964 West Ham United 3, Preston North End 2
1965 Liverpool 2, Leeds United 1 (aet)
1966 Everton 3, Sheffield Wednesday 2

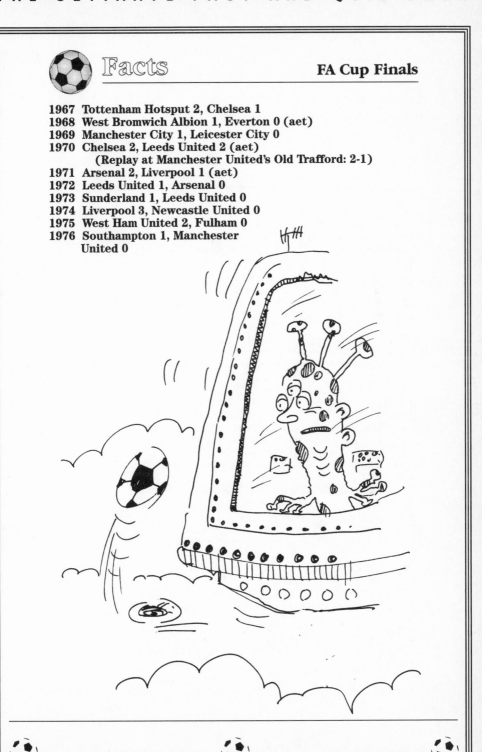

Facts   **FA Cup Finals**

1967 Tottenham Hotsput 2, Chelsea 1
1968 West Bromwich Albion 1, Everton 0 (aet)
1969 Manchester City 1, Leicester City 0
1970 Chelsea 2, Leeds United 2 (aet)
     (Replay at Manchester United's Old Trafford: 2-1)
1971 Arsenal 2, Liverpool 1 (aet)
1972 Leeds United 1, Arsenal 0
1973 Sunderland 1, Leeds United 0
1974 Liverpool 3, Newcastle United 0
1975 West Ham United 2, Fulham 0
1976 Southampton 1, Manchester
     United 0

FA Cup Finals

1977 Manchester United 2, Liverpool 1
1978 Ipswich Town 1, Arsenal 0
1979 Arsenal 3, Manchester United 2
1980 West Ham United 1, Arsenal 0
1981 Tottenham Hotspur 1, Manchester City 1 (Replay: 3-2)
1982 Tottenham Hotspur 1, Queens Park Rangers 1 (Replay; 1-0)
1983 Manchester United 2, Brighton and Hove Albion 2
     (Replay: 4-0)
1984 Everton 2, Watford 0
1985 Manchester United 1, Everton 0 (aet)
1986 Liverpool 3, Everton 1
1987 Coventry City 3, Tottenham Hotspur 2 (aet)
1988 Wimbledon 1, Liverpool 0
1989 Liverpool 3, Everton 2 (aet)
1990 Manchester United 3, Crystal Palace 3 (aet) (Replay: 1-0)
1991 Tottenham Hotspur 2, Nottingham Forest 1
1992 Liverpool 2, Sunderland 0
1993 Arsenal 1, Sheffield Wednesday 1 (aet) (Replay: 2-1aet)
1994 Manchester United 4, Chelsea 0
1995 Everton 1, Manchester United 0
1996 Manchester United 1, Liverpool 0
1997 Chelsea 2, Middlesbrough 0

APPERANCES IN FA CUP FINALS

The Wanderers, Bury, Blackburn Olympic, Bradford City,
Coventry City, Ipswich Town, Old Carthusians and Wimbledon
are all undefeated in FA Cup Finals. The Wanderers are the top
club, winning all of their five appearances.

THE SUMARY OF APPEARANCES - CLUB BY CLUB:

14 - Manchester United
12 - Arsenal
12 - Everton
11 - Liverpool
11 - Newcastle United
10 - West Bromwich Albion
 9 - Aston Villa
 9 - Tottenham
 8 - Blackburn Rovers
 8 - Manchester City
 8 - Wolves
 7 - Bolton Wanderers
 7 - Preston North End
 6 - Old Etonians

Facts

FA Cup Finals

6 - Sheffield United
6 - Sheffield Wednesday
5 - Chelsea
5 - Huddersfield Town
5 - The Wanderers
4 - Derby County
4 - Leeds United
4 - Leicester City
4 - Oxford University
4 - Royal Engineers
4 - Sunderland
4 - West Ham United
3 - Blackpool
3 - Burnley
3 - Nottingham Forest
3 - Portsmouth
3 - Southampton
2 - Barnsley
2 - Birmingham City
2 - Bury
2 - Cardiff City
2 - Charlton Athletic
2 - Clapham Rovers
2 - Notts County
2 - Queen's Park
1 - Blackburn Olympic
1 - Bradford City
1 - Brighton and Hove Albion
1 - Bristol City
1 - Coventry City
1 - Crystal Palace
1 - Fulham
1 - Ipswich Town
1 - Luton Town
1 - Middlesbrough
1 - Old Carthusians
1 - QPR
1 - Watford
1 - Wimbledon

APPEARANCES IN SEMI-FINALS

23 - Everton
21 - Manchester United
20 - Liverpool
19 - West Bromwich Albion
18 - Arsenal
18 - Aston Villa
16 - Blackburn Rovers
16 - Sheffield Wednesday
15 - Tottenham
13 - Chelsea
13 - Derby County
13 - Newcastle United
13 - Wolves
12 - Bolton Wanderers
12 - Nottingham Forest
11 - Sheffield United
11 - Sunderland
10 - Manchester City
10 - Preston North End
10 - Southampton
9 - Birmingham City
8 - Burnley
8 - Leeds United
7 - Huddersfield Town
7 - Leicester City
6 - Old Etonians
6 - Oxford University
6 - West Ham United
5 - Fulham
5 - Notts County
5 - Portsmouth
5 - The Wanderers
4 - Luton Town
4 - Queen's Park
4 - Royal Engineers
3 - Blackpool
3 - Cardiff City
3 - Clapham Rovers
3 - Crystal Palace
3 - Ipswich Town
3 - Millwall
3 - Norwich City
3 - Old Carthusians

FA Cup Finals

3 - Oldham Athletic
3 - Stoke City
3 - The Swifts
3 - Watford
2 - Barnsley
2 - Blackburn Olympic
2 - Bristol City
2 - Bury
2 - Charlton Athletic
2 - Grimsby Town
2 - Swansea City
2 - Swindon Town
2 - Wimbledon
1 - Bradford City
1 - Brighton and Hove Albion
1 - Cambridge University
1 - Chesterfield

1 - Coventry City
1 - Crewe Alexandra
1 - Darwen
1 - Derby Junction
1 - Hull City
1 - Marlow
1 - Middlesbrough
1 - Old Harrovians
1 - Orient
1 - Plymouth Argyle
1 - Port Vale
1 - QPR
1 - Rangers
1 - Reading
1 - Shropshire Wanderers
1 - York City

DISCIPLINE

Discipline

Only three teams in the Carling Premiership and three Nationwide League went through the 1995-96 season without a player being sent-off – Tottenham (Carling Premiership), Watford (Division One) and Swindon (Division Two).

November 20, 1982 became the worst day for dismissals in football history with 15 players sent-off. Twelve of those came in the third round of the FA Cup.

The most players ordered off on a League day was 13. That record number has been reached three times – December 14, 1985, August 19, 1995 and September 9, 1995.

The 376 sending-offs in the Carling Premiership and Nationwide League's in the 1994-95 season set a new record for England.

Alan Mullery became the first player to be sent-off for England when he was dismissed against Yugoslavia in an European Championship match in Florence, Italy on June 5, 1968.

Up to July 1997, only four players have been sent-off for England. Those players were: Alan Mullery v Yugoslavia (European Championship, June 5, 1968), Alan Ball v Poland (World Cup qualifyer, June 6, 1973), Trevor Cherry v Argentina (friendly, June 15, 1977) and Ray Wilkins v Morocco (World Cup finals, June 6, 1986).

 **Facts**   **Discipline**

Stranraer set a Scottish record when four of their players were sent-off against Airdrie in a Scottish Division One match on December 3, 1994.

Five players from Brazilian club America Tres Rios were sent-off in the first ten minutes of a Brazilian Cup match after a disputed goal awarded by opponents Itaperuna. As a result the game was abandoned and Itaperuna were awarded the match.

When Gremio of Brazil met Uruguay's Penarol in the South American Super Cup quarter-final in October 1993, eight players were sent-off, four from either clubs.

Up to July 1997, England have not had a player sent-off at Wembley.

Bologna's Giuseppe Lorenzo set a new world record when he was sent-off for striking an opponent after only 10 seconds of a League match against Parma on December 9, 1990.

Jose Batista of Uruguay set a World Cup finals record when he was sent-off after only 55 seconds against Scotland in 1986.

Willie Johnston has the most sending-offs in a career. The breakdown of his 21 dismissals are: Rangers 7, West Bromwich Albion 6, Vancouver Whitecaps 4, Hearts 3 and Scotland 1.

Yugoslavia's Boris Stankovic became the first player to be sent-off at Wembley when he was dismissed in an Olympic Games match against Sweden in August 1948.

Manchester United's Kevin Moran is the only player to be sent-off in a FA Cup Final. He got his marching orders in the 1985 final against Everton in 1985.

Leeds' Billy Bremner and Kevin Keegan of Liverpool became the first player to be sent-off in the same match at Wembley. The two were dismissed for fighting in the 1974 Charity Shield.

Stockport had two players sent-off in the 1994 Second Division Play-Off final against Burnley at Wembley. Mike Wallace and Chris Beaumont the culprits.

Vinnie Jones has collected two of the fastest bookings in English football. He was shown the yellow card after three seconds for Chelsea against Sheffield United on February 15, 1992 and after five seconds for Sheffield United at Manchester City on January 19,

Discipline

1991.
**Charlton's Derek Hales and Mike Flanagan were sent-off for
fighting with each other against Southern League side
Maidstone in an FA Cup third round tie on January 9, 1979.**

*Another warring pair were Hearts' Graeme Hogg and Craig Levein.
The Scottish FA banned the two for ten matches in September 1994
when they fought in a pre-season friendly against Raith Rovers.*

**Eric Cantona of Manchester United suffered the longest
suspension in modern times after his attack on a spectator
during a Premiership match at Crystal Palace on January 25,
1995. He was banned from football by the FA for eight months.**

*Newcastle United's Faustino Asprilla was fined £10,000 and banned
for the first match of the 1996-97 season by the FA after being found
guilty of elbowing/head-butting Keith Curle of Manchester City in
February 1996.*

**David Batty and Graeme Le Saux were both suspended for two
European games by Uefa after the two Blackburn players
started brawling with each other in a European Champions
League match against Spartak Moscow in November 1995.**

FOOTBALL LEAGUE

Football League

Before the introduction of three points for a win, Lincoln City set the record for most points in a season. They won 74 points in 46 games in Division Four in 1975-76.

The introduction of three points for a win was established in the 1981-82 season.

Doncaster Rovers won 18 of their 21 Division Three (North) away games in the 1946-47 season. They finished as champions.

Tottenham set the record of eight successive away wins in their 'double' season of 1960-61. They ended the previous season with two away victories and then won the first six.

Norwich City drew 23 of their 42 Division One matches in 1978-79, a record. Exeter City also drew 23 matches in the 1986-87 season (Division Four), but they played four games more.

The highest score-draw in Football League history is 6-6. Leicester City and Arsenal shared the score in a Division One match on April 21, 1930, and then Charlton Athletic and Middlesbrough also shared 12 goals on October 22, 1960 in a Second Division game.

On September 18, 1948 nine of the 11 First Division matches were drawn.

Preston North End set a new record when they remained unbeaten in the League's first season, 1888-89. Liverpool repeated that feat in the Second Division in 1893-94.

Up to the start of the 1997-98 season, only two clubs have won all their home games in a season. Liverpool set the record when they won their 14 home games (Division Two) in 1893-94, and Brentford won all 21 matches at Griffin Park in the 1929-30 Third Division (South).

Rotherham nearly equalled that record but drew their final home game of the season in the 1946-47 Third Dision (North).

The longest League run without a win was set by Cambridge United in 1983-84. They went 31 matches without a victory between October 8 and April 23, losing 21. They finished the season bottom of the Second Division.

United followed that the following season when they set an uneviable record of 18 home defeats in Division Three.

Facts

Football League

The most consecutive League defeats in a season is 18, set by First Division Darwen in the 1898-99. Since the last War Walsall have suffered the worst sequence when they went 15 Division Two games without a point in 1988-89.

Newport County hold the record of the longest non-winning start to a season. They went 25 matches without a victory in Division Four in 1970-71. The run came between August 15, 1970 and January 9, 1971 and consisted of four draws and 21 losses.

Manchester United suffered 12 consecutive defeats at the start of the 1930-31 Division One season – still a record.

Phil Neal and Alan Hansen share the playing record of eight League Championship medals. Neal won with Liverpool in 1976, 77, 79, 80, 82, 83, 84, 86, with Hansen collecting League medals in 1979, 80, 82, 83, 84, 86, 88 and 1990.

Kenny Dalglish also won eight medals with Liverpool, five as player in 1979, 80, 82, 83, 84 and three as player-manager in 1986, 88 and 1990. He also won four Scottish League championship medals with Celtic in 1972, 73, 74, 77 and a Carling Premiership medal as manager of Blackburn in 1995.

Macclesfield were the first club in four seasons to be promoted to the Third Division from the GM Vauxhall Conference when they replaced Hereford United in 1997-98. The last club to go up from non-league to the Football League were Wycombe Wanderers.

Macclesfield became the 30th club to be promoted to the Football League since 1923. The most successful of those clubs so far are Wimbledon, who entered the league in 1977 and were promoted to the First Division nine years later and have stayed there ever since. They also won the FA Cup in 1988.

Up to the start of the 1997-98 season, only nine men have won the League Championship both as player and then as manager. They are:

Ted Drake	*Arsenal (player) 1934,35,38,*
	Chelsea (manager) 1955
Bill Nicholson	*Tottenham (player) 1951,*
	Tottenham (manager) 1961.
Sir Alf Ramsey	*Tottenham (player) 1951,*
	Ipswich Town (manager) 1962.
Joe Mercer	*Everton (player) 1939, Arsenal 1948,53,*
	Manchester City (manager) 1968.

Football League

Facts

Dave Mackay	*Tottenham (player) 1961,*
	Derby County (manager) 1975.
Bob Paisley	*Liverpool (player) 1947,*
	Liverpool (manager) 1976,77,79,80,82,83.
Howard Kendall	*Everton (player) 1970,*
	Everton (manager) 1985,87.
Kenny Dalglish	*Liverpool (player) 1979,80,82,83,84,*
	Liverpool (player-manager) 1986,88,90.
George Graham	*Arsenal (player) 1971,*
	Arsenal (manager) 1989,91.

Nottingham Forest set the unbeaten League sequence – 42 games. The run consisted of the last 26 matches of the 1977-78 season and the first 16 of 1978-79. The run of 21 wins and 21 draws was started in November 1977 and ended in December 1978.

Ipswich Town won the First Division in 1961-62, their first season in the division.

Three clubs tie the record of winning sequences in the League. Manchester United (1904-05), Bristol City (1905-06) and Preston North End (1950-51) all had 14 consecutive League victories, and all were in the Second Division at the time.

There have been 12 extensions to the number of clubs in the Football League, before the introduction of the Carling Premiership in 1992-93.

Peterborough United won the Fourth Division in 1960-61, their first season in the Football League. They also set a scoring record with 134 goals.

Since the introduction of the Carling Premiership the record number of points per division are:
Carling Premiership – Manchester United (1993-94) 92.
First Division – Bolton (1996-97) 98.
Second Division – Stoke City (1992-93) 93.
Third Division – Carlisle United (1994-95) 91.

Tottenham (1960-61) set the record of best starts in the old First Division with 11 wins. Manchester United came closest to equalling that feat, when they won their first 10 matches of the 1985-86 season.

Newcastle did win their first eleven games of the 1992-93 season, but it was in the new First Division.

 **Facts** **Football League**

The longest unbeaten start to a League season is 29 matches, both achieved in the First Division, the record is shared by Leeds (1973-74, 19 wins, 10 draws) and Liverpool (1987-88, 22 wins, 7 draws). Stoke City were the first to beat Leeds in 1973-74 and Liverpool finally lost Everton, whose winning goal came from Wayne Clarke, whose older brother, Allan, played in the 1973-74 Leeds side.

Wolves and Burnley are the only clubs to have won the old Divisions One, Two, Three and Four. Wolves have also won the Third Divison (North).

Manchester City were relegated from the First Division in 1937-38 a season after winning the title. They also scored 80 goals in their relegation season, three more than champions Arsenal.

Stockport's Steve Milton had a disastrous League debut. He conceded 13 goals against Halifax Town in a Third Division (North) match on January 6, 1934.

The most League goals scored in a season by a relegated side is 89. That record was set by Manchester City (Division One) in 1925-26.

Bristol City (1980,81,82) and Wolves (1984,85,86) are the only clubs to have suffered relegation from the First Division to the Fourth in three successive seasons.

The oldest Football League club is Notts County, who were formed in 1862.

The North and South sections were abandoned by the Football League and the Fourth Division was introduced for the start of the 1958-59 season.

Tranmere Rovers' Harold Bell was ever-present for 401 consecutive League matches over nine seasons (1946-55). He also played 58 FA Cup ties which takes the record to 459.

Dave Beasant has, so far, come the closest to beating Bell's League record. He played for Wimbledon, Newcastle and Chelsea in a nine-year run which saw him make 394 consecutive League appearances.

Football League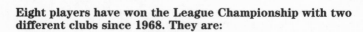

**Eight players have won the League Championship with two
different clubs since 1968. They are:**

Francis Lee	Manchester City 1968, Derby County 1975
Ray Kennedy	Arsenal 1971, Liverpool 1979,80,82
Archie Gemmill	Derby County 1972,75, Nottingham Forest 1978
John McGovern	Derby County 1972, Nottingham Forest 1978
Larry Lloyd	Liverpool 1973, Nottingham Forest 1978
Peter Withe	Nottingham Forest 1978, Aston Villa 1981
Kevin Richardson	Everton 1985, Arsenal 1989
John Lukic	Arsenal 1989, Leeds 1992

 **Facts**   **Football League**

*Players who have won League Championship and Carling Premiership
medals with different clubs are:*

Eric Cantona	*Leeds 1992,*
	Manchester United 1993, 1994, 1996, 1997
David Batty	*Leeds 1992,*
	Blackburn 1995
Bobby Mimms	*Everton 1987,*
	Blackburn 1995

**The first substitute to be used in a Football League match was
Charlton's Keith Peacock in a Division Two match at Bolton on
August 21, 1965.**

*Eric Nixon set a new record by becoming the first, and so far only,
player to play in all four divisions in one season. He played for
Manchester City and Southampton in the First Division, Bradford
in Division Two, Carlisle in Division Three and Wolves in Division
Four.*

**There have been only two instances of father and son playing in
the same League side. Alec and David Herd played for
Stockport County at Hartlepool in a Division Three (North)
match on May 5, 1951. Ian and Gary Bowyer matched that
record by playing for Hereford United against Scunthorpe in a
Division Four match on April 21, 1990.**

*Huddersfield's same goalkeeper and five defenders played in all their
42 Division Two matches in the 1952-53 season. They were: Bill
Wheeler, Ron Staniforth, Laurie Kelly, Bill McGarry, Don McEvoy
and Len Quested. Also an ever-present was outside-left Vic Metcalfe.*

**Eric Cantona has won three different League Championship in
successive seasons. He won the French First Division with
Marseille in 1990-91, English First Division with Leeds in 1991-
92 and the Carling Premiership with Manchester United in
1992-93. He also won the 1993-94, 1995-96 and 1996-97 Carling
Premiership titles.**

*Only three of the original twelve Football League clubs were founder
members of the Carling Premiership: Aston Villa, Blackburn and
Everton.*

Football League

Facts

The most penalties to be awarded in any Football League match came in March 1989, when Crystal Palace were given four spot-kicks to Brighton's one. Palace missed three of their four but still managed to win 2-1.

THE FOOTBALL LEAGUE PLAYOFFS

The Football League introduced the play-off system at the end of the 1987-88 season.

The original system meant the club that finished one place above the relegation places played off with the club that finished one place off the promotion places in the division below. The games were played on a home and away basis.

THE PLAY-OFF FINALS 1987 & 1988

**1987
Division One/Two: Charlton 1, Leeds 1 (1-0h,0-1a) (Replay at St. Andrews: 2-1). Charlton stay in Division One. Losing semi-finalists: Ipswich Town, Oldham Athletic.**

Division Two/Three: Swindon 2, Gillingham 2 (0-1a,2-1h) (Replay at Selhurst Park: 2-0). Swindon promoted to Division Two. Losing semi-finalists: Sunderland, Wigan Athletic. Sunderland relegated to Division Three.

Division Three/Four: Aldershot 3, Wolverhampton Wanderers 0 (2-0h,1-0a). Aldershot promoted to Division Three. Losing semi-finalists: Bolton Wanderers, Colchester United. Bolton relegated to Division Four.

*1988
Division One/Two: Middlesbrough 2, Chelsea 1 (2-0h,0-1a). Middlesbrough promoted to Division One. Chelsea relegated to Division Two. Losing semi-finalists: Blackburn Rovers, Bradford City.*

Division Two/Three: Walsall 3, Bristol City 3 (3-1a,0-2h) (Replay at Walsall: 4-0). Walsall promoted to Division Two. Losing semi-finalists: Sheffield United, Notts County. Sheffield United relegated to Division Three.

Division Three/Four: Swansea City 5, Torquay United 4 (2-1h,3-3a). Swansea promoted to Division Three. Losing semi-finalists:

 **Facts**   **Football League**

Rotherham United, Scunthorpe United. Rotherham United relegated to Division Four.

The format was changed for the end of the 1989 season. There was no play-off place in the First Division, which meant that four clubs from the 2nd, 3rd and 4th divisions play-off for the last promotion spot.

1989
Division Two: Crystal Palace 4, Blackburn Rovers 3 (1-3a,3-0h).
Losing semi-finalists: Watford, Swindon Town.

Division Three: Port Vale 2, Bristol Rovers 1 (1-1a,1-0h). Losing semi-finalists: Fulham, Preston North End.

Division Four: Leyton Orient 2, Wrexham 1 (0-0a,2-1h). Losing semi-finalists: Scarborough, Scunthorpe United.

The format changed again after 1989. All three Finals were played at Wembley over the Spring bank-holiday weekend. The lowest division would play on the Saturday, the middle one on the Sunday and the play-off to the First Division (Carling Premiership from 1993) on Monday.

PLAY-OFF FINALS AT WEMBLEY

1990
Division Two: Swindon 1, Sunderland 0. Swindon were denied promotion because of financial irregularities. Sunderland promoted. Losing semi-finalists: Blackburn, Newcastle.

Division Three: Notts County 2, Tranmere Rovers 0. Losing semi-finalists: Bolton, Bury.

Division Four: Cambridge United 1, Chesterfield 0. Losing semi-finalists: Maidstone United, Stockport County.

1991
Division Two: Notts County 3, Brighton and Hove Albion 1. Losing semi-finalists: Middlesbrough, Millwall.

Division Three: Tranmere Rovers 1, Bolton Wanderers 0. Losing semi-finalists: Brentford, Bury.

Division Four: Torquay 2, Blackpool 2; Torquay won 5-4 on penalties. Losing semi-finalists: Burnley, Scunthorpe.

Football League

1992
Division Two: Blackburn 1, Leicester City 0. Losing semi-finalists:
Derby County, Cambridge United.

Division Three: Peterborough 2, Stockport 1. Losing semi-finalists: Huddersfield Town, Stoke City.

Division Four: Blackpool 1, Scunthorpe 1; Blackpool won 4-3 on penalties. Losing semi-finalists: Barnet, Crewe Alexandra.

1993
Division One: Swindon 4, Leicester City 3. Losing semi-finalists: Portsmouth, Tranmere Rovers.

Division Two: West Bromwich Albion 3, Port Vale 0. Losing semi-finalists: Stockport County, Swansea City.

Division Three: York City 1, Crewe Alexandra 1; York won 5-3 on penalties. Losing semi-finalists: Bury, Walsall.

1994
Division One: Leicester City 2, Derby County 1. Losing semi-finalists: Millwall, Tranmere Rovers.

Division Two: Burnley 2, Stockport County 1. Losing semi-finalists: Plymouth Argyle, York City.

Division Three: Wycombe Wanderers 4, Preston North End 2. Losing semi-finalists: Carlisle United, Torquay United.

1995
Division One: Bolton Wanderers 4, Reading 3. Losing semi-finalists: Tranmere Rovers, Wolverhampton Wanderers.

Division Two: Huddersfield Town 2, Bristol Rovers 1. Losing semi-finalists: Brentford, Crewe Alexandra.

Division Three: Chesterfield 2, Bury 0. Losing semi-finalists: mansfield Town, Preston North End.

1996
Division One: Leicester City 2, Crystal Palace 1. Losing semi-finalists: Charlton Athletic, Stoke City.

Division Two: Bradford City 2, Notts County 0. Losing semi-finalists: Blackpool, Crewe Alexandra.

 **Facts**   **Football League**

Division Three: Plymouth Argyle 1, Darlington 0. Losing semi-finalists: Colchester United, Hereford United.

1997
Division One: Crystal Palace 1, Sheffield United 0. Losing semi-finalists: Wolverhampton Wanderers, Ipswich Town.

Division Two: Crewe Alexandra 1, Brentford 0. Losing semi-finalists: Luton Town, Bristol City.

Division Three: Northampton Town 1, Swansea City 0. Losing semi-finalists: Chester City, Cardiff City.

PLAY-OFF APPEARANCES - CLUB BY CLUB

W - Winners of their divisional play-off

Aldershot - 1987 (W)

Barnet - 1992
Blackburn Rovers - 1988, 1989, 1990, 1992 (W)
Blackpool - 1991, 1992 (W), 1996
Bolton Wanderers - 1987, 1990, 1991, 1995 (W)
Bradford City - 1988, 1996 (W)
Brentford - 1991, 1996, 1997
Brighton and Hove Albion - 1991
Bristol City - 1988, 1997
Bristol Rovers - 1989, 1995
Burnley - 1991, 1994 (W)
Bury - 1990, 1991, 1993, 1995

Cambridge United - 1990 (W), 1992
Cardiff City - 1997
Carlisle United - 1994
Charlton Athletic - 1987 (W), 1996
Chelsea - 1988
Chesterfield - 1990, 1995 (W)
Chester City - 1997
Colchester - 1987, 1996
Crewe Alexandra - 1992, 1993, 1995, 1996, 1997 (W)
Crystal Palace - 1989 (W), 1996, 1997 (W)

Darlington - 1996
Derby County - 1992, 1994

Football League

Fulham - 1989

Gillingham - 1987

Hereford United - 1996
Huddersfield Town - 1992, 1995 (W)

Ipswich Town - 1987, 1997

Leeds United - 1987
Leicester City - 1992, 1993, 1994 (W), 1996 (W)
Leyton Orient - 1989 (W)
Luton Town - 1997

Maidstone United - 1990
Mansfield Town - 1995
Middlesbrough - 1988 (W), 1991
Millwall - 1991, 1994
Newcastle United - 1990
Northampton Town - 1997 (W)
Notts County - 1988, 1990 (W), 1991 (W), 1996

Oldham Athletic - 1987

Peterborough United - 1992 (W)
Plymouth Argyle - 1994, 1996 (W)
Portsmouth - 1993
Port Vale - 1989 (W), 1993
Preston North End - 1989, 1994, 1995

Reading - 1995
Rotherham United - 1988

Scarborough - 1989
Scunthorpe United - 1988, 1989, 1991, 1992
Sheffield United - 1988, 1997
Stockport County - 1990, 1992, 1993, 1994
Stoke City - 1992, 1996
Sunderland - 1987, 1990
Swansea City - 1988, 1993, 1997
Swindon Town - 1987, 1989, 1990 (W), 1993 (W)

Torquay United - 1988, 1991 (W), 1994
Tranmere Rovers - 1990, 1991 (W), 1993, 1994, 1995

Facts   **Football League**

Walsall - 1988 (W), 1993
Watford - 1989
West Bromwich Albion - 1993
  (W)
Wigan Athletic - 1987
Wolves - 1987, 1995, 1997
Wrexham - 1989
Wycombe Wanderers 1994 (W)

York City - 1993 (W), 1994

**LEAGUE CHAMPIONSHIP
WINNERS SINCE
RE-STRUCTURE**

PREMIERSHIP

4 - Manchester United
1 - Blackburn Rovers

DIVISION ONE (NEW)

1 - Bolton Wanderers
1 - Crystal Palace
1 - Middlesbrough
1 - Newcastle United
1 - Sunderland

DIVISION TWO (NEW)

1 - Birmingham City
1 - Bury
1 - Reading
1 - Stoke City
1 - Swindon Town

DIVISION THREE (NEW)

1 - Cardiff City
1 - Carlisle United
1 - Preston North End
1 - Shrewsbury Town
1 - Wigan Athletic

**FOOTBALL LEAGUE
WINNERS**

Football League
1888-89   Preston North End
1889-90   Preston North End
1890-91   Everton
1891-92   Sunderland

FIRST DIVISION

1892-93	**Sunderland**
1893-94	**Aston Villa**
1894-95	**Sunderland**
1895-96	**Aston Villa**
1896-97	**Aston Villa**
1897-98	**Sheffield United**
1898-99	**Aston Villa**
1899-1900	**Aston Villa**
1900-01	**Liverpool**
1901-02	**Sunderland**
1902-03	**The Wednesday**
1903-04	**The Wednesday**
1904-05	**Newcastle United**
1905-06	**Liverpool**
1906-07	**Newcastle United**
1907-08	**Manchester United**
1908-09	**Newcastle United**
1909-10	**Aston Villa**
1910-11	**Manchester United**
1911-12	**Blackburn Rovers**

FIRST DIVISION WINNERS
1912-13 AND 1975-76

1912-13	Sunderland
1913-14	Blackburn Rovers
1914-15	Everton
1919-20	West Bromwich Albion
1920-21	Burnley
1921-22	Liverpool
1922-23	Liverpool
1923-24	Huddersfield Town

(won on goal average from Wolves)

Football League

Facts

1924-25	Huddersfield Town	1972-73	Liverpool
1925-26	Huddersfield Town	1973-74	Leeds United
1926-27	Newcastle United	1974-75	Derby County
1927-28	Everton	1975-76	Liverpool
1928-29	Sheffield Wednesday	1976-77	Liverpool
1929-30	Sheffield Wednesday	1977-78	Nottingham Forest
1930-31	Arsenal	1978-79	Liverpool
1931-32	Everton	1979-80	Liverpool
1932-33	Arsenal	1980-81	Aston Villa
1933-34	Arsenal	1981-82	Liverpoool
1934-35	Arsenal	1982-83	Liverpool
1935-36	Sunderland	1983-84	Liverpool
1936-37	Manchester City	1984-85	Everton
1937-38	Arsenal	1985-86	Liverpool
1938-39	Everton	1986-87	Everton
1946-47	Liverpool	1987-88	Liverpool
1947-48	Arsenal	1988-89	Arsenal (won on goal difference from Liverpool)
1948-49	Portsmouth		
1949-50	Portsmouth (won on goal average from Wolves)	1989-90	Liverpool
		1990-91	Arsenal
1950-51	Tottenham	1991-92	Leeds United
1951-52	Manchester United		
1952-53	Arsenal (won on goal average from Preston North End)		

THE PREMIERSHIP

1953-54	Wolves
1954-55	Chelsea
1955-56	Manchester United
1956-57	Manchester United
1957-58	Wolves
1958-59	Wolves
1959-60	Burnley
1960-61	Tottenham
1961-62	Ipswich Town
1962-63	Everton
1963-64	Liverpool
1964-65	Manchester United (won on goal average from Leeds)
1965-66	Liverpool
1966-67	Manchester United
1967-68	Manchester City
1968-69	Leeds United
1969-70	Everton
1970-71	Arsenal
1971-72	Derby County

1992-93	**Manchester United**
1993-94	**Manchester United**
1994-95	**Blackburn Rovers**
1995-96	**Manchester United**
1996-97	**Manchester United**

SECOND DIVISION

1892-93	Small Heath
1893-94	Liverpool
1894-95	Bury
1895-96	Liverpool (won on goal average from Manchester City)
1896-97	Notts County
1897-98	Burnley
1898-99	Manchester City
1899-1900	The Wednesday
1900-01	Grimsby Town
1901-02	West Bromwich Albion
1902-03	Manchester City
1903-04	Preston North End

Facts

Football League

1904-05	Liverpool
1905-06	Bristol City
1906-07	Nottingham Forest
1907-08	Bradford City
1908-09	Bolton Wanderers
1909-10	Manchester City
1910-11	West Bromwich Albion
1911-12	Derby County (won on goal average from Chelsea)
1912-13	Preston North End
1913-14	Notts County
1914-15	Derby County
1919-20	Tottenham
1920-21	Birmingham City (won on goal average from Cardiff City)
1921-22	Nottingham Forest
1922-23	Notts County
1923-24	Leeds United
1924-25	Leicester City
1925-26	Sheffield Wednesday
1926-27	Middlesbrough
1927-28	Manchester City
1928-29	Middlesbrough
1929-30	Blackpool
1930-31	Everton
1931-32	Wolves
1932-33	Stoke City
1933-34	Grimsby Town
1934-35	Brentford
1935-36	Manchester United
1936-37	Leicester City
1937-38	Aston Villa
1938-39	Blackburn Rovers
1946-47	Manchester City
1947-48	Birmingham City
1948-49	Fulham
1949-50	Tottenham
1950-51	Preston North End
1951-52	Sheffield Wednesday
1952-53	Sheffield United
1953-54	Leicester City (won on goal average from Everton)
1954-55	Birmingham City (won on goal average from Luton Town)
1955-56	Sheffield Wednesday
1956-57	Leicester City
1957-58	West Ham United
1958-59	Sheffield Wednesday
1959-60	Aston Villa
1960-61	Ipswich Town
1961-62	Liverpool
1962-63	Stoke City
1963-64	Leeds United
1964-65	Newcastle United
1965-66	Manchester City
1966-67	Coventry City
1967-68	Ipswich Town
1968-69	Derby County
1969-70	Huddersfield Town
1970-71	Leicester City
1971-72	Norwich City
1972-73	Burnley
1973-74	Middlesbrough
1974-75	Manchester United
1975-76	Sunderland
1976-77	Wolves
1977-78	Bolton Wanderers
1978-79	Crystal Palace
1979-80	Leicester City
1980-81	West Ham United
1981-82	Luton Town
1982-83	QPR
1983-84	Chelsea (won on goal difference from Sheffield Wednesday)
1984-85	Oxford United
1985-86	Norwich City
1986-87	Derby County
1987-88	Millwall
1988-89	Chelsea
1989-90	Leeds (won on goal difference from Sheffield United)
1990-91	Oldham Athletic
1991-92	Ipswich Town

Football League

NEW FIRST DIVISION

1992-93	**Newcastle United**
1993-94	**Crystal Palace**
1994-95	**Middlesbrough**
1995-96	**Sunderland**
1996-97	**Bolton Wanderers**

THIRD DIVISION

1958-59	*Plymouth Argyle*
1959-60	*Southampton*
1960-61	*Bury*
1961-62	*Portsmouth*
1962-63	*Northampton Town*
1963-64	*Coventry City (won on goal average from Crystal Palace)*
1964-65	*Carlisle United*
1965-66	*Hull City*
1966-67	*QPR*
1967-68	*Oxford United*
1968-69	*Watford (won on goal average from Swindon Town)*
1969-70	*Orient*
1970-71	*Preston North End*
1971-72	*Aston Villa*
1972-73	*Bolton Wanderers*
1973-74	*Oldham Athletic*
1974-75	*Blackburn Rovers*
1975-76	*Hereford United*
1976-77	*Mansfield Town*
1977-78	*Wrexham*
1978-79	*Shrewsbury Town*
1979-80	*Grimsby Town*
1980-81	*Rotherham United*
1981-82	*Burnley (won on goal average from Carlisle United)*
1982-83	*Portsmouth*
1983-84	*Oxford United*
1984-85	*Bradford City*
1985-86	*Reading*
1986-87	*Bournemouth*
1987-88	*Sunderland*
1988-89	*Wolves*
1989-90	*Bristol Rovers*

1990-91	*Cambridge United*
1991-92	*Brentford*

NEW SECOND DIVISION

1992-93	**Stoke City**
1993-94	**Reading**
1994-95	**Birmingham City**
1995-96	**Swindon Town**
1996-97	**Bury**

FOURTH DIVISION

1958-59	*Port Vale*
1959-60	*Walsall*
1960-61	*Peterborough United*
1961-62	*Millwall*
1962-63	*Brentford*
1963-64	*Gillingham (won on goal average from Carlisle United)*
1964-65	*Brighton and Hove Albion*
1965-66	*Doncaster Rovers (won on goal average from Darlington)*
1966-67	*Stockport County*
1967-68	*Luton Town*
1968-69	*Doncaster Rovers*
1969-70	*Chesterfield*
1970-71	*Notts County*
1971-72	*Grimsby Town*
1972-73	*Southport*
1973-74	*Peterborough United*
1974-75	*Mansfield Town*
1975-76	*Lincoln City*
1976-77	*Cambridge United*
1977-78	*Watford*
1978-79	*Reading*
1979-80	*Huddersfield Town*
1980-81	*Southend United*
1981-82	*Sheffield United*
1982-83	*Wimbledon*
1983-84	*York City*
1984-85	*Chesterfield*
1985-86	*Swindon Town*
1986-87	*Northampton Town*

Facts   **Football League**

1987-88	*Wolves*
1988-89	*Rotherham United*
1989-90	*Exeter City*
1990-91	*Darlington*
1991-92	*Burnley*

NEW THIRD DIVISION

1992-93	**Cardiff City**
1993-94	**Shrewsbury Town**
1994-95	**Carlisle United**
1995-96	**Preston North End**
1996-97	**Wigan Athletic**

THIRD DIVISION (SOUTH)
(1920-58)

1920-21	*Crystal Palace*
1921-22	*Southampton*
	(won on goal average from Plymouth Argyle)
1922-23	*Bristol City*
1923-24	*Portsmouth*
1924-25	*Swansea City*
1925-26	*Reading*
1926-27	*Bristol City*
1927-28	*Millwall*
1928-29	*Charlton Athletic*
	(won on goal average from Crystal Palace)
1929-30	*Plymouth Argyle*
1930-31	*Notts County*
1931-32	*Fulham*
1932-33	*Brentford*
1933-34	*Norwich City*
1934-35	*Charlton Athletic*
1935-36	*Coventry City*
1936-37	*Luton Town*
1937-38	*Millwall*
1938-39	*Newport County*
1946-47	*Cardiff City*
1947-48	*QPR*
1948-49	*Swansea City*
1949-50	*Notts County*
1950-51	*Nottingham Forest*
1951-52	*Plymouth Argyle*

1952-53	*Bristol Rovers*
1953-54	*Ipswich Town*
1954-55	*Bristol City*
1955-56	*Leyton Orient*
1956-57	*Ipswich Town*
	(won on goal average from Torquay United)
1957-58	*Brighton and Hove Albion*

THIRD DIVISION (NORTH)
(1921-58)

1921-22	**Stockport County**
1922-23	**Nelson**
1923-24	**Wolves**
1924-25	**Darlington**
1925-26	**Grimsby Town**
1926-27	**Stoke City**
1927-28	**Bradford Park Avenue**
1928-29	**Bradford City**
1929-30	**Port Vale**
1930-31	**Chesterfield**
1931-32	**Lincoln**
	(won on goal average from Gateshead)
1932-33	**Hull City**
1933-34	**Barnsley**
1934-35	**Doncaster Rovers**
1935-36	**Chesterfield**
1936-37	**Stockport County**
1937-38	**Tranmere Rovers**
1938-39	**Barnsley**
1946-47	**Doncaster Rovers**
1947-48	**Lincoln City**
1948-49	**Hull City**
1949-50	**Doncaster Rovers**
1950-51	**Rotherham United**
1951-52	**Lincoln City**
1952-53	**Oldham Athletic**
1953-54	**Port Vale**
1954-55	**Barnsley**
1955-56	**Grimsby Town**
1956-57	**Derby County**
1957-58	**Scunthorpe United**

Football League

OTHER COMPETITIONS

ANGLO-ITALIAN CUP FINALS

1970	*Napoli 0, Swindon Town 3*
1971	*Bologna 1, Blackpool 2 (aet)*
1972	*Roma 3, Blackpool 1*
1973	*Fiorentina 1, Newcastle United 2*
1993	*Derby County 1, Cremonese 3 (at Wembley)*
1994	*Notts County 0, Brescia 1 (at Wembley)*
1995	*Notts County 2, Ascoli 1 (at Wembley)*
1996	*Port Vale 2, Genoa 5 (at Wembley)*

ASSOCIATED MEMBER'S CUP

1984	**Bournemouth 2, Hull City 1 (at Hull)** **Freight Rover Trophy**
1985	**Wigan Athletic 3, Brentford 1 (at Wembley)**
1986	**Bristol City 3, Bolton Wanderers 0 (at Wembley)**
1987	**Mansfield Town 1, Bristol City 1 (aet; Mansfield won** **5-4 on penalties) (at Wembley)** **Sherpa van Trophy**
1988	**Wolves 2, Burnley 0 (at Wembley)**
1989	**Bolton Wanderers 4, Torquay United 1 (at Wembley)** **Leyland Daf Cup**
1990	**Tranmere Rovers 2, Bristol Rovers 1 (at Wembley)**
1991	**Birmingham City 3, Tranmere Rovers 2 (at Wembley)** **Autoglass Trophy**
1992	**Stoke City 1, Stockport County 0 (at Wembley)**
1993	**Port Vale 2, Stockport County 1 (at Wembley)**
1994	**Huddersfield Town 1, Swansea City 1 (aet; Swansea** **won 3-1 on penalties) (at Wembley)** **Auto Windscreens Shield**
1995	**Birmingham City 1, Carlisle United 0 (Birmingham** **won in sudden death overtime) (at Wembley)**
1996	**Rotherham United 2, Shrewsbury Town 1** **(at Wembley)**
1997	**Carlisle 0, Colchester United 0 (aet; Carlisle won 4-3** **on penalties) (at Wembley)**

ATTENDANCES

Attendances

The biggest World Cup attendance came in the final match of the 1950 tournament in Brazil. 199,850 saw Uruguay defeat Brazil to win the trophy.

The total attendance for the three World Club Cup matches between Santos and AC Milan in 1963 exceeded 375,000.

The first all-ticket match in Scotland was the 1937 international between Scotland and England at Hampden Park. 149,547 watched the game on April 17.

The biggest attendance for a British club match, apart from a Cup Final, was 143,470 for the Rangers v Hibernian at Hampden Park on March 27, 1948.

The FA Cup Final's highest attendance came in 1923 for the Bolton Wanderers-West Ham game. 126,047 were at Wembley although 150,000 were estimated to be in the ground.

120,000 watched Cameroon v Morocco in a World Cup qualifying tie in Yaounde in November 1981 – a record for a qualifying match.

The biggest British attendance for a World Cup qualifying match was 107,580 watching the Scotland and Poland at Hampden Park on October 13, 1965.

A record 127,621 saw the 1960 European Cup Final between Real Madrid and Eintracht Frankfurt at Hampden Park.

The highest attendance at an European Cup match is the 135,826 that watched the Celtic v Leeds semi-final at Hampden Park on April 15, 1970.

West Ham's victory over TSV Munich at Wembley in the 1965 European Cup-Winners' Cup Final produced a record crowd for the competition – 100,000.

Rangers and Celtic's match on January 2, 1939 provided a record attendance for a Scottish League match of 118,567.

The Scottish League Cup Final between Celtic and Rangers at Hampden Park on October 23, 1965 drew a record crowd of 107,609.

The English First Division's record attendance was set at the Manchester United v Arsenal match on January 17, 1948. 83,260 watched the match that was played at Maine Road.

 Facts   **Attendances**

The Second Division record crowd was at Villa Park on October 30, 1937 when 68,029 watched Aston Villa v Coventry City.

A record 49,309 for the Third Division watched the Sheffield Wednesday-Sheffield United match on Boxing Day in 1979.

The record attendance for a Football League season is 41,271,414 between the 88 clubs in the 1948-49 season.

The record single day attendance for Football League matches was the 1,269,934 on December 27, 1949.

Manchester United averaged a record 57,758 for matches in the 1967-68 season.

100,000 watched the 1953 FA Amateur Cup Final between Pegasus and Harwich & Parkeston at Wembley – a record for the competition.

The record British Cup tie aggregate is 265,199 for the two matches between Rangers and Morton in the Scottish Cup Final of 1948.

Attendances

Facts

Colchester United's record crowd of 19,072 turned up to watch the FA Cup first round tie against Reading on November 27, 1948 only for the game was abandoned after 35 minutes because of fog.

The lowest post-war League attendance was 450 for the Division Three game between Rochdale and Cambridge United on February 2, 1974.

The lowest First Division attendance since the war is the 3,121 that turned up to watch Wimbledon v Sheffield Wednesday on October 2, 1991.

The lowest Carling Premiership crowd is 3,039 at Selhurst Park on Boxing Day, 1993 for Wimbledon v Everton.

The smallest Wembley crowd for an England match is 15,628 for the match against Chile on May 23, 1989. The gate was affected by a tube strike.

Chile also featured in Northern Ireland's smallest gate when only 2,500 saw the match at Belfast on May 26, 1989.

The record FA Cup final attendance before Wembley was the 120,028 that saw the 1913 final between Aston Villa and Sunderland at Crystal Palace.

APPEARANCES

Appearances

Peter Shilton played his 1000th League game for Leyton Orient in December 1996, playing against Brighton and keeping a clean sheet. He became the first man to reach the thousand-mark in English football.

Tranmere Rovers' centre-half Harold Bell holds the record for consecutive appearances, playing in 459 games between 1946 and 1955 when he was ever-present for the first nine post-war seasons.

A broken finger prevented Dave Beasant extending his run of consecutive League games past 394, his nine-year run beginning in August 1981 and ending with his accident in October 1990.

Phil Neal made 366 consecutive First Division appearances for Liverpool between December 1974 and September 1983, a record for an outfield player in the top flight.

In 1952-53 the entire Huddersfield Town defence played in all 42 Second Division matches – the goalkeeper, two full-backs and three half-backs being ever-present for the whole season.

Eric Cantona played in Championship-winning teams for four consecutive seasons, first for Marseille (1990-91) and then in England for first Leeds then Manchester United.

The first substitute to be used in a League game was Keith Peacock, who came on for Charlton in a game at Bolton on August 21, 1965.

In 1992-93 Leeds United became the first club to fail to win a League match away from home in the season after claiming the Championship.

In 1986-87 goalkeeper Eric Nixon became the first player to play in all four divisions of the Football League in one season when he played for Manchester City, Southampton, Bradford City, Carlisle and Wolves.

When Preston played Bury in January 1990 the opposing keepers were brothers with Alan Kelly (Preston) lining up against Gary Kelly (Bury). Their father was a Republic of Ireland international goalkeeper.

In April 1915 a game between Middlesbrough and Oldham was abandoned after 55 minutes when Oldham defender Billy Cook refused to leave the field after his dismissal.

 **Facts**   **Appearances**

A game between Sheffield Wednesday and Aston Villa was abandoned through bad light after 79 and a half minutes in November 1898. The two teams reconvened four months later to play the last ten and a half minutes, Wednesday adding a fourth goal to make the final score 4-1.

Sweden's Tomas Ravelli overtook Peter Shilton's international goalkeeping record when he won his 126th cap for his country on June 8, 1995 in the Umbro Cup against, ironically, England.

After Peter Shilton, here are the players with most English League appearances:

Terry Paine - 824 (713 Southampton, 111 Hereford United)

Tommy Hutchinson - 797 (165 Blackpool, 314 Coventry City, 46 Manchester City, 92 Burnley, 180 Swansea City)

Robbie James - 782 (484 Swansea City, 48 Stoke City, 87 QPR, 23 Leicester City, 89 Bradford City, 51 Cardiff City)

Alan Oakes - 777 (565 Manchester City, 211 Chester City, 1 Port Vale)

Appearances

John Trollope - 770 (all for Swindon Town - a record total for one club)

Jimmy Dickinson - 764 (all for Portsmouth)

Roy Sproson - 762 (all for Port Vale)

Billy Bonds - 758 (95 Charlton, 663 West Ham United)

Ray Clemence - 758 (48 Scunthorpe United, 470 Liverpool, 240 Tottenham)

Pat Jennings - 757 (48 Watford, 472 Tottenham, 237 Arsenal)

Frank Worthington - 757 (171 Huddersfield Town, 210 Leicester City, 84 Bolton Wanderers, 75 Birmingham City, 32 Leeds United, 19 Sunderland, 34 Southampton, 31 Brighton and Hove Albion, 59 Tranmere Rovers, 23 Preston North End, 19 Stockport County)

Trevor Steven has appeared in Championship-winning teams from three different countries. Steven played for Everton in England (1985, 1987), Scotland's Rangers (1990, 1991, 1993, 1994, 1995) and Marseille in France (1992).

ENGLISH CLUB FEATS

English Club Feats

Facts

Liverpool went 85 competitive matches unbeaten from January 21, 1978 to January 31, 1981. That run covered 63 League games, nine League Cup, seven in Europe and six in the FA Cup.

Millwall were unbeaten at home in the League for 59 consecutive matches from 1964-67.

The first club to rise from the Fourth Division to the First were Northampton Town when they won promotion to Division One in 1965.

Wimbledon went from non-league football (Southern League) to Division One in just nine seasons. They reached the top-flight in 1986.

Manchester United completed the League and Cup 'double' twice in three seasons. They won both competitions in 1993-94 and 1995-96. They became the first club to win the 'double' twice.

Arsenal were the first club to win both FA and League Cup's in the same season – 1992-93.

Four clubs this century have won the League and Cup 'double'. They are Tottenham (1960-61), Arsenal (1970-71), Liverpool (1985-86) and Manchester United (1993-94 and 1995-96).

On their way to completing the first League and Cup 'double' in 1888-89, Preston North End did not lose a League match and didn't concede a goal in the FA Cup.

Liverpool's most successful League run was between 1976 and 1983 when they won the Championship six times in eight seasons.

Up to the start of the 1997-98 season, Liverpool are the only team to have won three major competitions in one season. They won the League Championship, League Cup and European Cup in the 1983-84 season.

Arsenal had seven players in the England side against Italy on November 14, 1935 – still a record.

Coventry City are the only club to have played in the Premier League, all four previous divisions of the Football League and both sections of the old Third Division (North and South).

 **Facts**   **English Club Feats**

Wolves, one of the founder members of the Football League, went from First Division to Fourth in successive seasons – 1984-5-6.

Lincoln City became the first club to be demoted from the Football League when they finished bottom of the Fourth Division in 1986-87. Scarborough, champions of the GM Vauxhall Conference, replaced them.

Aston Villa had seven ever-present players when they won the League Championship in 1980-81.

Birmingham City set a new record in the 1995-96 season by using 46 players during the League season.

Arsenal were defeated only once when they won the League Championship in 1990-91 – a record this century.

Up to the start of the 1997-98 season, only three teams have won the League Championship three times in succession. Huddersfield Town in 1923-24, 1924-25, 1925-26, Arsenal in 1932-33, 1933-34, 1934-35 and Liverpool in 1981-82, 1982-83, 1983-84.

Oxford United became the first club to win Division Three and Division Two titles in successive seasons – 1983-84, 1984-85.

The last team to win Second Division and First Division titles in successive years were Ipswich Town in 1960-61 and 1961-62.

The original 12 members of the Football League were Accrington, Aston Villa, Blackburn Rovers, Bolton Wanderers, Burnley, Derby County, Everton, Notts County, Preston North End, Stoke, West Bromwich Albion and Wolverhampton Wanderers.

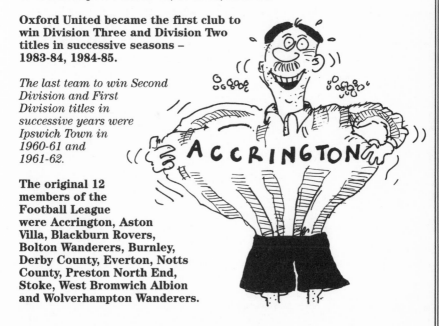

English Club Feats

Facts

Up to the start of the 1997-98 season, Liverpool is the only city to have staged top-flight football in every season since the Football League began in 1888.

League Champions in successive seasons

Preston North End (1888-89, 1889-90)
Sunderland (1891-92, 1892-93)
Aston Villa (1895-96, 1896-97, 1898-99, 1899-1900)
Sheffield Wednesday (1902-03, 1903-04, 1928-29, 1929-30)
Liverpool (1921-22, 1922-23, 1975-76, 1976-77, 1978-79, 1979-80, 1981-82, 1982-83, 1983-84)
Portsmouth (1948-49, 1949-50)
Manchester United (1955-56, 1956-57)
Wolves (1957-58, 1958-59)

The highest goal-scoring team in the Premiership have been Newcastle United. They scored 82 goals in 42 games in the 1993-94 season.

Swindon Town hold the record for most goals conceded in a Premiership season when they let in 100 goals, also in the 1993-94 season.

MANAGERS

Managers

Facts

Fred Everiss holds the record as the longest-serving manager of one club – holding the reins at West Bromwich Albion for 46 years between 1902 and 1948.

Bill Lambton became the shortest-serving manager in British history when he served only three days at Scunthorpe United in April 1959.

Herbert Chapman became the first manager to win the League Championship with two different clubs when he led Arsenal to the title in 1930-31 after two earlier triumphs with Huddersfield Town.

The only manager to win the FA Cup with two different clubs is Billy Walker, who led Sheffield Wednesday to victory in 1935 and Nottingham Forest in 1959.

Les Allen was the first man to become player/manager of a top-flight team when he was appointed to the post at QPR in 1968.

Bob Paisley is the most successful manager in English club history, leading Liverpool to 20 trophies, including six League Championships, between 1974 and 1983.

Glenn Hoddle became the ninth England manager when he took over from Terry Venables in June 1996. Joe Mercer was caretaker-manager in 1974 before Don Revie took over.

Billy Bingham has managed Northern Ireland on two occasions. First from 1967 to 1971 and then from 1980 to 1993. He also coached Greece for two years from 1971.

Dave Bassett looked to have become manager of Crystal Palace in May 1984. But four days later he changed his mind, without signing the contract, and stayed at Wimbledon.

Up to the end of the 1996-97 season, West Ham have only had eight managers in their history. The list is: Syd King, Charlie Paynter, Ted Fenton, Ron Greenwood, John Lyall, Lou Macari, Billy Bonds and Harry Redknapp.

Tom Whittaker got a dream start with his new team at Arsenal in 1947-48. They were unbeaten for the first 17 League matches on their way to winning the First Division.

 Facts **Managers**

Only two managers have won the League Championship with different clubs – Herbert Chapman, Huddersfield Town (1923-24, 1924-25) and Arsenal (1930-31, 1932-33); Brian Clough, Derby County (1971-72) and Nottingham Forest (1977-78);

Kenny Dalglish became the first manager to win the League and Carling Premiership trophy. He led Liverpool to three League Championship titles in 1985-86, 1987-88, 1989-90 and then Blackburn to the Carling Premiership trophy in 1994-95.

Dalglish also became the first manager to win the 'double' as player-manager, when he led Liverpool in 1985-86.

The last man to win the First Division title as a player and as a manager with the same club was George Graham. He won the League with Arsenal as a player in 1970-71, and as a manager in 1988-89 and 1989-90.

Ruud Gullit became the first foreign manager to win the FA Cup when he led Chelsea to victory in 1997.

Managers

Billy McNeill and Dave Bassett both managed two clubs that were relegated in the same season. McNeill was in charge of Manchester City and Aston Villa who were relegated to Division Two in 1986-87. Bassett managed Watford (relegated to Division Two) and Sheffield United (down to the Third Division) in 1987-88.

Bob Paisley remains the most successful manager in English club football. Paisley won six League Championships, three European Cups, three League Cups, one Uefa Cup, one European Super Cup and six Charity Shields (one shared) as Liverpool manager between 1974 and 1983.

Up to the start of the 1997-98 season, Kenny Dalglish is the only man to have won the League Championship as player-manager. He led Liverpool to the title in 1985-86 and 1987-88 in dual roles.

The first winner of the Manager of the Year award was Celtic's Jock Stein.

By 1997, ten of the last 12 Manager of the Year were Scottish. Howard Kendall (Everton 1987) and Howard Wilkinson (Leeds (1992) are the only two English winners. The Scottish contingent are: Kenny Dalglish (Liverpool 1986, 1988, 1990 and Blackburn 1995), George Graham (Arsenal 1989, 1991) and Alex Ferguson (Manchester United 1993, 1994, 1996, 1997) are the other winners.

Jack Charlton was named Manager of the Year in 1974 when he was manager of Middlesbrough.

The League Managers' Association created their own Manager of the Year award in 1993. Given to "the manager who has made best use of the resources available to him", the winners have been: 1993 – Dave Bassett (Sheffield United), 1994 – Joe Kinnear (Wimbledon), 1995 – Frank Clark (Nottingham Forest), 1996 – Peter Reid (Sunderland), 1997 – Danny Wilson (Barnsley).

 **Facts**

Managers

MANAGER OF THE YEAR AWARDS

1966 Jock Stein (Celtic)
1967 Jock Stein (Celtic)
1968 Matt Busby (Manchester United)
1969 Don Revie (Leeds United)
1970 Don Revie (Leeds United)
1971 Bertie Mee (Arsenal)
1972 Don Revie (Leeds United)
1973 Bill Shankly (Liverpool)
1974 Jack Charlton (Middlesbrough)
1975 Ron Saunders (Aston Villa)
1976 Bob Paisley (Liverpool)
1977 Bob Paisley (Liverpool)
1978 Brian Clough (Nottingham Forest)
1979 Bob Paisley (Liverpool)

WHY CATS DON'T PLAY FOOTBALL!

Managers

Facts

1980 Bob Paisley (Liverpool)
1981 Ron Saunders (Aston Villa)
1982 Bob Paisley (Liverpool)
1983 Bob Paisley (Liverpool)
1984 Joe Fagan (Liverpool)
1985 Howard Kendall (Everton)
1986 Kenny Dalglish (Liverpool)
1987 Howard Kendall (Everton)
1988 Kenny Dalglish (Liverpool)
1989 George Graham (Arsenal)
1990 Kenny Dalglish (Liverpool)
1991 George Graham (Arsenal)
1992 Howard Wilkinson (Leeds United)
1993 Alex Ferguson (Manchester United)
1994 Alex Ferguson (Manchester United)
1995 Kenny Dalglish (Blackburn Rovers)
1996 Alex Ferguson (Manchester United)
1997 Alex Ferguson (Manchester United)

WORLD CUP

World Cup

The top scorers for a single match in a World Cup finals are Hungary. They scored 10 goals against El Salvador in 1982. The final score was 10-1.

The record scoreline in any World Cup match was a qualifying tie in May 1997. Iran beat The Maldives 17-0.

West Germany's Gerd Muller is the highest goalscorer in World Cup finals history. He registered 14 goals – 10 in 1970 and four in 1974.

The next two top scorers are Just Fontaine (France) with 13 goals, and Pele (Brazil) with 12.

Fontaine is the highest goalscorer for a single World Cup finals. He scored 13 goals in six matches of the 1958 tournament.

The first goal scored in the World Cup Finals is credited to France's Louis Laurent against Mexico on July 30, 1930. France went on to win 4-1.

The highest attendance for a World Cup match was 205,000 in Rio de Janeiro in 1950 for Brazil v Uruguay.

Manchester United's Norman Whiteside became the youngest player to appear in the World Cup Finals when he played for Northern Ireland against Yugoslavia on June 17, 1982. he was 17 years 42 days old.

Whiteside beat the previous record, set by Pele in the 1958 tournament, by 195 days.

Brazil's Vava is the only player to have scored in successive World Cup Final's. He scored in 1958 (twice) and in 1962.

The only players, aside from Vava, to have scored in two World Finals are Pele (Brazil, 1958 and 1970) and Paul Breitner of West Germany (1974 and 1982).

Only one player has scored in every match of the Finals. Jairzinho of Brazil scored seven goals in six games in 1970.

Italy's Dino Zoff broke two records when Italy won the World Cup in 1982. He became the oldest player to win a World Cup winners medal and the oldest to captain a winning side at the age of 40.

 **Facts** World Cup

*Two goalkeepers have captained their country to World Cup victory –
and both are Italian. Giampiero Combi in 1934 and Dino Zoff in
1982.*

**Geoff Hurst is the only player to score a hat-trick in a World
Cup Final. He scored three of England's four goals in their 1966
triumph against West Germany.**

*The longest unbeaten run in World Cup Finals is 13 games by
Brazil. Between 1958 and 1962 they won 11 and drew two before
being beaten by Hungary in the 1966 tournament.*

**Holland Rob Rensenbrink scored the 1000th goal in World Cup
Finals against Scotland in 1978.**

*The first substitute used in a World Cup Finals match was Anatoly
Puzach of USSR against Mexico in 1970.*

**Brazil used only 12 players when they won the 1962 World Cup,
the lowest number used in the tournament's history.**

*Uruguay's Jose Batista became the quickest dismissal in World Cup
history when he was sent-off after only 55 seconds of the match
against Scotland in 1986.*

**Russia's Oleg Salenko is the only man to score five goals in a
single World Cup Finals match. His goals helped Russia to a 6-1
victory over Cameroon in 1994.**

*The highest aggregate match in the World Cup Finals is Austria 7
Switzerland 5 in 1954.*

**The fastest goal, officially recorded by FIFA, in the Finals is
Bryan Robson's 27-second strike for England against France in
1982.**

*When West Germany won the World Cup in 1954 they produced two
goalscoring records for a winning side. Their 25 goals in six
matches for an average of 4.16 was a record, as was the 14 goals
they conceded.*

World Cup

Facts

Before Oleg Salenko's record five goals in a match nine players had scored four goals in a World Cup game. They were Gustav Wetterson (Sweden v Cuba, 1938), Leonidas da Silva (Brazil v Poland, 1938), Ernest Willimowski (Poland v Brazil, 1938), Ademir (Brazil v Sweden, 1950), Juan Schiaffino (Uruguay v Bolivia, 1950), Sandor Kocsis (Hungary v West Germany, 1954), Just Fontaine (France v West Germany, 1958), Eusebio (Portugal v North Korea, 1966) and Emilio Butragueno (Spain v Denmark, 1986).

Pele is the only player to have won the World Cup three times as a player. He won with Brazil in 1958, 1962 and 1970.

The only player to have appeared in five World Cup Finals is Mexico's goalkeeper Antonio Carbajal. He played in 1950, 1954, 1958, 1962 and 1966.

Mario Zagalo has won three World Cups and became the first to win it as both player and manager. He played in the 1958 and 1962 tournaments for Brazil and was manager when they won in 1970.

The only other man to win the World Cup as both player and manager was West Germany's Franz Beckenbauer. He won it in 1974 and was the German manager when they won in 1990. Beckenbauer is the only man to have captained and managed a World Cup winning side.

Beckenbauer has appeared in four World Cup Finals. He played in 1966 and 1974 and managed West Germany in 1986 and 1990. He aslo played in the 1970 tournament.

Bora Milutinovic is the only man to manage three different nations in successive World Cup Finals. He led host nation Mexico in 1986, was in charge of Costa Rica in 1990 and managed USA in 1994.

Two other men have led different countries in successive World Cup Finals. Rudolf Vytlacil was in charge of Czechoslovakia in 1962 and Bulgaria in 1966, while Blagoje Vidinic was manager of Morocco in 1970 and Zaire four years later.

Five countries have won the World Cup in their own country – Uruguay (1930), Italy (1934), England (1966), West Germany (1974) and Argentina (1978).

 Facts   **World Cup**

Up to the 1998 finals, Brazil are the only country to win the World Cup outside their continent. They won in Sweden in 1958

Only two countries have hosted the World Cup twice – Italy (1934 and 1990) and Mexico (1970 and 1986).

In the 1930 World Cup Final, Argentina and Uruguay could not decide on which ball to use. So the first half was played with Argentina's ball and the Uruguayan ball was used in the second. Argentina led at half-time but Uruguay eventually won 4-2.

The 1974 World Cup Final was delayed because there were no corner-flags on the pitch.

The 1966 tournament had a special World Cup stamp published for the occasion. The original stamp was to feature the flags of the 16 competing teams but the British government refused to recognise North Korea so instead the official stamp showed various footballers.

World Cup

Facts

One of the most bizarre incidents in World Cup history occurred in 1930. The United States trainer ran onto to treat a player, but he tripped and broke a bottle of chloroform. The trainer was carried off unconscious while the player was forced to continue playing without treatment.

Two contrasting fortunes on a special day for famous players in the World Cup Finals. Kazimierz Deyna played his 100th game for Poland in the 1978 Finals but missed a penalty against Argentina in a 2-0 defeat. Italy's Dino Zoff had a better experience. He celebrated his 100th cap with a clean sheet against Poland in the 1982 tournament.

Brazil are the only country to appear in all of the World Cup Finals.

There have been 15 World Cup tournaments and six different winners.

Brazil have won the World Cup more times than any other country. Their win in 1994 was their fourth.

The other countries to win the World Cup are:

Uruguay (1930, 1950),
Italy (1934,1938,1982),
West Germany (1954, 1974,1990),
England (1966) and
Argentina (1978, 1986).

Scotland's manager Andy Beattie resigned after Scotland's opening defeat by Austria in the 1954 Finals. They lost their next game 7-0 to Uruguay.

Scotland's Mo Johnston set a Home Countries record when he scored in five qualifying matches during the 1990 qualifying campaign.

Northern Ireland were ordered not to play two of their three group matches in the 1958 Finals because the games were being played on the Sunday. They refused.

The first black African country to reach the Finals was Zaire in 1974.

Haiti's Ernest Jean-Joseph became the first player to be banned by FIFA for drug-taking during the Finals when he was sent home in the middle of the 1974 tournament.

 Facts   **World Cup**

In 1990 Walter Zenga set the record for remaining unbeaten in World Cup Finals matches. He had not been beaten for 517 minutes. After five games, he was beaten in the 67th minute by Argentinean Claudio Caniggia in the semi-final.

There has been only one goalless draw in a World Cup Final. The 1994 Final was decided on penalties with Brazil beating Italy.

Ferenc Puskas played for different countries in World Cup Finals. He played for Hungary in 1954 and Spain in 1962.

The original Jules Rimet was stolen in 1966 while on display before the tournament in England and found by a dog called Pickles. Brazil kept the trophy when they won it for the third time in 1970, but it was stolen from a display in Rio and has never been recovered.

Four players share the record for most appearances in Finals matches. Uwe Seeler (West Germany 1958, 1962, 1966, 1970), Wladyslaw Zmuda (Poland 1974, 1978, 1982, 1986), Diego Maradona (Argentina 1982, 1986, 1990, 1994) and Lothar Matthaus (Germany 1982, 1986, 1990, 1994).

The 1994 Finals in the United States were the first to be played outside Europe and South America.

The record average attendance at the Finals was set in 1994 – 68,604.

The record number of yellow cards showed in a single tournament was 227 in 1994. The previous high was 164 in 1990.

The highest number of red cards shown in the Finals was 16 in 1990.

There has been only one missed penalty in a World Cup Final. Antonio Cabrini of Italy missed in the 1982 Final against West Germany, but still collected a winners medal.

The first penalty scored in a Final was by Johan Neeskens in the 1974 defeat by West Germany.

Three goals were scored in the first 12 minutes of the 1954 World Cup Final. Despite taking an early 2-0 lead Hungary were beaten 3-2 by West Germany.

World Cup

Facts

Karl-Heinz Rummenigge has captained West Germany to two World Cup Finals – and lost them both.

The United States best World Cup tournament was in 1930, where they finished third.

Two past winners failed to qualify for the 1994 World Cup – England and Uruguay.

Republic of Ireland manager Jack Charlton received a one-match touchline ban and a £10,000 fine in the 1994 Finals after arguing with an official against Mexico.

Roger Milla became the oldest goalscorer in the Finals when he scored for Cameroon against Russia in 1994 at the age of 42. He had also scored four goals in the previous tournament in Italy.

The first player to be sent-off in a World Cup Final was Argentina's Pedro Monzon in 1986 after 65 minutes. He was succeeded by team-mate Gustavo Dezotti 21 minutes later.

Scotland have qualified for the World Cup Finals on seven occasions but have yet to get past the first round.

Paulo Rossi was top-scorer in the 1982 World Cup after returning from a two-year ban for bribery.

Mexico hosted the 1986 World Cup only eight months after 9,500 people died in two earthquakes in the space of 24 hours.

 **Facts**   **World Cup**

West Germany, Brazil and Italy have all appeared in five World Cup Finals.

Two players have scored World Cup Finals hat-tricks and still been on the losing side. Ernest Willimowski scored four in Poland's 6-5 defeat by Brazil in 1938 and Igor Belanov of the USSR scored three in the 4-3 loss to Belgium in 1986.

Alex Ferguson was caretaker-manager for Scotland in 1986 after the shock death of Jock Stein in Scotland's last qualifying match against Wales.

Mexico were banned from the 1990 Finals by FIFA after using over-age players in the World Under-20 tournament.

Cameroon became the first black African country to reach the quarter-finals in 1990.

All 15 penalties awarded in normal time in 1994 were scored.

Both semi-finals in the 1990 Finals were settled by penalty shoot-outs. Argentina beat Italy and West Germany defeated England both by the same score, 4-3.

The first players to be sent-off in a World Cup opening match were Cameroon's Andre Kana-Biyik and Benjamin Massing in 1990. Cameroon still went on to beat holders Argentina 1-0.

The only other player to be sent-off in the opening match was Bolivia's Marco Etcheverry against Germany in 1994.

28 of the 52 matches in Italy 1990 failed to produce a goal.

Johan Neeskens scored the fastest goal in a World Cup Final when he score a penalty for Holland after only two minutes. The first West German player to touch the ball was Sepp Maier when he picked the ball out of the net.

Egypt have withdrawn from the World Cup in 1938, 1958, 1962 and 1966.

The last British player to be sent-off in a World Cup Finals match was England Ray Wilkins in 1986 against Morocco.

World Cup Facts

The last time all four Home Countries were in the World Cup Finals was 1958.

West Germany were the first country to be both World Champions and European Champions in the same year. They won the European Championship in 1972 and the World Cup in 1974.

Mexico were the first team to qualify for the 1994 World Cup Final. USA (hosts) and Germany (holders) were exempt from qualification.

Costa Rica made their World Cup debut in Italia '90 and beat Scotland in their first match. They went on to beat Sweden and lose narrowly to Brazil before being beaten by Czechoslovakia in the second round.

Morocco have played in two World Cup Finals – both in Mexico, 1970 and 1986.

Spain withdrew from the 1938 World Cup because of the breakout of civil war in the country.

Scotland were eliminated from the 1974 World Cup despite not losing a game. They won once and drew the other two.

Sir Alf Ramsey was manager of the England side that won the World Cup in 1966, but he has also played in the tournament – for England in 1950.

The World Cup Finals in 2002 will be the first to be hosted by two countries – Japan and South Korea.

Bulgaria had appeared in five World Cup Finals (1962, 1966, 1970, 1974, 1986) and not won a single match.

Bulgaria won their first World Cup Finals match when they beat Greece 4-0 in the 1994 tournament. They went on to reach the semi-finals that year, beating Germany in the quarter-finals.

Famous Italian dictator Benito Mussolini presented the World Cup to Italian captain Giampiero Combi after the 1934 Final.

Czechoslovakia and Hungary have both been beaten in two World Cup Finals. Czechoslovakia in 1934 and 1962, Hungary in 1938 and 1954.

 **Facts**   **World Cup**

Two countries have lost successive World Cup Finals – Holland in 1974 and 1978 and West Germany in 1982 and 1986.

Bobby Robson has appeared in three World Cup Finals for England. He played in 1958 and was manager in 1986 and 1990.

Poland have finished third in two World Cup's – 1974 and 1982.

Despite qualifying in second place, Scotland refused to go to the 1950 World Cup Finals because they did not win the qualifying group.

India withdrew from the 1950 World Cup Finals because FIFA had refused to allow them to play barefoot.

In the 1978 World Cup Final both goalkeepers wore perculiar shirt numbers. Argentina's Ubalodo Fillol wore number seven and Jan Jongbloed of Holland wore number eight.

Uruguay were threatened with expulsion from the 1986 Finals because of persistent foul play.

The first World Cup Final was staged in Montevideo, Uruguay.

Billy Wright was England captain in three World Cup Finals – 1950, 1954, 1958.

Scotland were confident of first round progress when they were drawn against Peru, Iran and Holland in the 1978 Finals. However, they lost to Peru, drew with Iran and beat Holland but not by enough goals to go through to the second stage.

Uruguay were chosen as the host country for the first World Cup Finals because they were Olympic champions and that they also promised to underwrite the costs of the competing nations.

In a play-off match to decide who went through to the Finals of 1974, the Soviet Union refused to play their second leg in Chile because the National Stadium had been used as a prison during Chile's civil war.

Haiti made their only appearance in the Finals when they beat Mexico in qualifying for the 1974 World Cup.

The Republic of Ireland have played nine games in the Finals and won only once. The single victory was against Italy in 1994 which they won 1-0.

World Cup

Facts

Three European teams made up the 1994 semi-finals. Italy beat Bulgaria and Sweden lost to Brazil.

England were the first Home Countries to play in the World Cup, in 1950.

Despite losing twice to Mexico, 6-0 and 6-2, USA still qualified for the 1950 Finals, and beat England 1-0 in one of the biggest shocks in World Cup history.

Gary Lineker is England's top goalscorer in World Cup Finals history. He has scored 10 goals in just 11 games.

Lineker finished the 1986 World Cup as top goalscorer, the first British player to have done so.

Chilean goalkeeper Roberto Rojas was banned from international football for life when he claimed he was hit by a firecracker during Chile's important 1990 World Cup qualifying match against Brazil which they had to win. The game was abandoned with Brazil winning 1-0, but it was later discovered that Rojas had faked the injury and Brazil were awarded a 2-0 victory.

Seven of the eight quarter-finalists in the 1994 World Cup were European.

The last time two British countries reached the quarter-finals was in 1958. Northern Ireland and Wales both lost.

After being eliminated in 1938, Norway had to wait for 56 years before reaching the Finals again, losing in the first round in 1994.

Two-time winners Argentina had to beat Australia in a play-off to qualify for the 1994 Finals.

Joe Jordan is the only Scotsman to have scored in three successive World Cup Finals – 1974, 1978, 1982.

Against El Salvador in 1970, Mexico's Juan Basaguren became the first substitute to score in a World Cup Finals match.

Holland, Hungary, Sweden, Spain and Italy all boycotted the first World Cup in 1930 because they were not installed as hosts.

 **Facts**   **World Cup**

Colombia were originally named as host nation for the 1986 Finals, but they had to withdraw because of financial difficulties. Mexico took their place.

Mexico became the first country to host the Finals twice. The 1970 and 1986 tournaments were played there.

Peru beat Bulgaria in the 1970 Finals just two days after 66,794 people had died in a Peruvian earthquake.

World Cup

Facts

The first goalless draw in the World Cup Finals was between England and Brazil in 1958.

The first extra-time goal in a Final was in 1934 when Italy beat Czechoslovakia. The scorer was Italy's Angelo Schiavio.

Berne, in Switzerland, is the smallest city to have hosted a World Cup Final (1954).

Two sets of brothers have won the World Cup. Fritz and Ottmar Walter for West Germany in 1954 and England's Bobby and Jack Charlton in 1966.

Luis Monti is the only player to play in two World Cup Final's for different nations. He played for Argentina in 1930 and for Italy in 1934.

Italian Vittorio Pozzo is the only man to win two World Cup's as manager.

Vicente Feola, the 1966 Brazilian manager, stayed in Europe for a month after his country's elimination in England for safety reasons.

Poland's Laszlo Kiss was the first substitute to score three times in a World Cup Finals match against El Salvador in 1982.

All games in the first World Cup Finals in 1930 were played in Montevideo.

Argentina have reached four World Cup semi-finals – and won all of them.

Portugal players had been on strike at the start of the 1986 World Cup Finals because of a dispute over bonuses. They settled their differences and beat England in their first match.

Hungary hold an incredible international record. Between 1950 and 1956 they lost only once in 48 internationals. Their only defeat was in the 1954 World Cup Final to West Germany.

The Dutch East Indies (now Indonesia) were the first Asian country to play in the Finals. They qualified for the 1938 tournament.

 # Facts   **World Cup**

Pedro Cea of Uruguay was the first player to score in both Olympic and World Cup Final's.

Argentina have won the World Cup twice, but have also lost both opening games when they were holders. They were beaten by Belgium in 1982 and Cameroon in 1990.

Tunisia have played in just one World Cup, and despite being eliminated in the first round they boast a win against Mexico and a draw with West Germany.

The Dutch East Indies (now Indonesia) have played only one game in the Finals – a 6-0 defeat by Hungary in 1938.

Jan Tomaszewski, Poland's goalkeeper in the 1974 Finals, became the first man to save two penalties in the same tournament.

England were eliminated from the 1982 Finals without losing a game. They beat France, Czechoslovakia and Kuwait in the group stages but lost out on goal difference after goalless draws against West Germany and Spain.

Only six of the 15 tournaments have seen the host nation not reach the semi-finals. They are France (1938), Switzerland (1954), Mexico (1970), Spain (1982), Mexico (1986) and USA (1994).

Of the 16 competing teams in the 1934 Finals 12 were from Europe. The others were Argentina, USA, Brazil and Egypt.

Cuba's last appearance in the World Cup Finals was in 1938. They lost to Sweden 8-0 in the quarter-finals.

Hungary scored 27 goals in just five matches in the 1954 Finals, but still lost in the Final to West Germany.

West Germany's defeat of Hungary in the 1954 Final was a repeat of an earlier group match. On that occasion Hungary won 8-3.

WORLD CUP FINALS

1930 Uruguay 4, Argentina 2 (Montevideo, Uruguay)
1934 Italy 2, Czechoslovakia 1 (aet) (Rome, Italy)
1938 Italy 4, Hungary 2 (Paris, France)
1950 (Finals on pool basis) Winners - Uruguay, Runners-up -
    Brazil (Rio de Janeiro, Brazil)
1954 West Germany 3, Hungary 2 (Berne, Switzerland)

World Cup

1958 Brazil 5, Sweden 2 (Stockholm, Sweden)
1962 Brazil 3, Czechoslovakia 1 (Santiago, Chile)
1966 England 4, West Germany 2 (aet) (London, England)
1970 Brazil 4, Italy 1 (Mexico City, Mexico)
1974 West Germany 2, Holland 1 (Munich, West Germany)
1978 Argentina 3, Holland 1 (aet) (Buenos Aires, Argentina)
1982 Italy 3, West Germany 1 (Madrid, Spain)
1986 Argentina 3, West Germany 2 (Mexico City, Mexico)
1990 West Germany 1, Argentina 0 (Rome, Italy)
1994 Brazil 0, Italy 0 (aet; Brazil won 3-2 on penalties)
     (Los Angeles, America)

WORLD CUP-WINNING MANAGERS

1930 Alberto Supicci (Uruguay)
1934 Vittorio Pozzo (Italy)
1938 Vittorio Pozzo (Italy)
1950 Juan Lopez (Uruguay)
1954 Sepp Herberger (West Germany)
1958 Vicente Feola (Brazil)
1962 Aimore Moreira (Brazil)
1966 Alf Ramsey (England)
1970 Mario Zagalo (Brazil)
1974 Helmut Schoen (West Germany)
1978 Cesar Luis Menotti (Argentina)
1982 Enzo Bearzot (Italy)
1986 Carlos Bilardo (Argentina)
1990 Franz Beckenbauer (West Germany)
1994 Carlos Alberto Parreira (Brazil)

BRITISH TRANSFERS

British Transfers

The first £1m British player was Trevor Francis. He moved from Birmingham to Nottingham Forest for £1.18m in February 1979.

Alan Shearer became the most expensive player in the world when he moved from Blackburn to Newcastle for £15m in July 1996.

Duncan Ferguson cost £8m in two transfers in the space of 17 months. He moved from Dundee United to Rangers for £4m in July 1993, and then joined Everton for the same price in December 1994. The Dundee United-Rangers deal set a record transfer involving two Scottish clubs.

Alf Common became the first £1,000 player when he moved from Sunderland to Middlesbrough in February 1905.

Rushden & Diamonds set a new non-league transfer record when they bought Carl Alford from GM Vauxhall Conference side Kettering for £85,000 in March 1996.

The first £100,000 British player was Denis Law, when he moved to Italian club Torino from Manchester City in June 1961. Law became the most expensive British player for the second time when he returned to Manchester, but this time to United, for £115,000 in July 1962.

The first £200,000 British player was Tottenham's Martin Peters. The World Cup winning forward moved from London rivals West Ham in March 1970.

Kevin Keegan became the first £500,000 British player when he left Liverpool to join German club Hamburg in June 1977.

Paul Ince became the most expensive British player to sign for a foreign club when he moved from Manchester United to Italian club Inter Milan for £6m in June 1995.

Lee Bowyer became the most expensive teenager in British football when he left Charlton in July 1996 to join Leeds for £2.6m.

Bruce Dyer became the first £1m teenager when he joined Crystal Palace from Watford in March 1994 for £1.1m.

Alan Shearer has cost £18.3m in just two transfer deals. He moved to Blackburn from Southampton for £3.3m in July 1992 and then to Newcastle in July 1996 for £15m. Both transfer deals set British records.

 **Facts**   **British Transfers**

**Stan Collymore cost £17.7m in just three transfer deals in four
years. He moved to Nottingham Forest for £2.2m from
Southend in June 1993, then went to Liverpool in June 1995 for
£8.5m and then arrived at Aston Villa for £7m in May 1997.**

*David Platt became Britian's most expensive player in history when
Arsenal signed him from Sampdoria in July 1995. Platt cost just
under £22m in total transfer deals in just four years. He moved
from Aston Villa to Italian club Bari for £5.5m in July 1991, Bari to
Juventus for £6.5m a year later, Juventus to Sampdoria for £5.2m
in July 1993 and then to Arsenal for £4.75m in July 1995.*

British Transfers

Facts

Dutch striker Dennis Bergkamp became the most expensive foreign import when he joined Arsenal in June 1995 for £7.5m.

Stan Collymore set three British records when he signed for Liverpool for £8.5m in June 1995. He became the record English club signing, the most expensive British striker and set a record all-British deal.

The record fee paid to a Scottish club was the £5m paid to Rangers from French club Marseille for Trevor Steven in August 1991.

Croatian Slaven Bilic became the most expensive footballer in Britain when he joined Everton from West Ham in May 1997 for £4.5m.

GOALSCORING

Goalscoring

Facts

The highest number of goals scored by a British club is 36, scored by Arbroath against Bon Accord in the Scottish Cup of 1885.

On the same day as Arbroath's record-breaking haul Dundee Harp beat Aberdeen Rovers 35-0.

The highest score recorded by a club in the Carling Premiership is nine, scored by Manchester United against Ipswich in March 1995.

Dixie Dean holds the record for English League goals in a season, scoring 60 in 1927-28 for Everton.

Luton's Joe Payne holds the record for goals in a League game, netting ten against Bristol Rovers in 1936 on his debut as a centre-forward.

The British record for League goalscoring in one season is held by Jimmy Smith of Ayr, who scored 66 goals in 38 appearances in the 1927-28 season.

Arthur Rowley has scored the greatest number of goals in League history with 434 strikes for WBA, Fulham, Leicester and Shrewsbury.

The record for League goals in the top flight is held by Jimmy Greaves, who scored 357 times for Chelsea, Tottenham and West Ham before becoming a television commentator.

Dixie Dean scored 349 goals for Everton between 1925 and 1937, a British goalscoring record for a player at one club.

Pele is reputedly the world's all-time biggest scorer with 1,282 goals from 1,365 matches, although some were in friendlies for his club, Santos.

Pele's 1000th goal was scored against Vasco de Gama in the Maracana Stadium in November 1969.

The first player to score more than 30 top-flight goals in three successive seasons was Alan Shearer between 1993 and 1996.

Iain Dunn was the first player in British football to settle a match with a golden goal when he scored in the 107th minute to seal Huddersfield's win over Lincoln in an Auto Windscreens Shield tie.

 **Facts**   **Goalscoring**

The first Wembley match to be decided by a golden goal was the Auto Windscreens final of 1995, Paul Tait giving Birmingham the win over Carlisle 13 minutes into overtime.

The first penalty to be scored in a first-class match was converted by John Heath for Wolves against Accrington Stanley in September 1891.

The first major international tournament to be decided by a golden goal was the 1996 European Championships – Oliver Bierhoff scoring the winner for Germany in the 95th minute.

Paul Mariner scored in six consecutive England appearances between November 1991 and June 1992.

Swindon conceded 100 goals in the 1993-94 season, a Carling Premiership record.

In 1993-94 Arsenal conceded only 28 goals in 42 Carling Premiership games, but in 1978-79 Liverpool claimed the post-war record with only 16 goals in 42 games.

In Tottenham's Championship year of 1960-61 they scored 115 goals. Two years later they scored 111 goals but finished the season as runners-up to Everton.

In 1930-31 the top three in the championship all scored a century of goals (Arsenal – 127, Aston Villa – 128, Sheffield Wednesday – 102)

The most goals to be scored in the Football League on one day was 209 in the 44 matches on February 1, 1936.

When Oxford United beat Shrewsbury 6-0 in April 1996 all six of the goals came from headers.

Alan Cork scored in all four divisions of the Football League and the FA Carling Premiership in an 18-year career with Wimbledon, Sheffield United and Fulham.

Billy Foulkes scored his first international goal for Wales against England in 1951, scoring with his first kick in his first game for his country.

Preston scored six goals in seven minutes in their 26-0 victory over Hyde in the FA Cup of 1887.

Goalscoring

The fastest Carling Premiership hat-trick was scored in August 1994 by Robbie Fowler. He netted three goals in 4 and a half minutes against Arsenal.

The fastest recorded hat-trick in history was scored by Maglioni for Independiente against Gimnasia de la Plata in March 1973. He completed his three goals in one minute 50 seconds.

In 1923-24 Chesterfield's goalkeeper, Arthur Birch, scored five goals in their Third Division campaign. All came from the penalty spot.

In August 1962 Reading's goalkeeper Arthur Wilkie injured a hand during the match against Halifax. He came out of goal to play as a striker and scored twice in a 4-2 win.

 **Facts**   **Goalscoring**

When Liverpool beat Crystal Palace 9-0 in December 1992 there were eight of their players on the scoresheet, with defender Steve Nicol the only man to score twice.

The English record for consecutive goalscoring is held by Bill Prendergast, who scored in 13 successive games for Chester in 1938.

Steve Bull was England's highest scorer for two consecutive seasons in 1987-88 (52) and 1988-89 (50).

Jimmy Greaves was First Division top scorer six times in 11 seasons between 1968 and 1969.

When West Ham beat Newcastle 8-1 in April 1986 Alvin Martin scored a hat-trick against three different keepers – goalkeeper Martin Thomas being replaced first by Chris Hedworth and then Peter Beardsley.

Manchester City are the only club to concede and score 100 goals in one season, scoring 104 and letting in 100 when they finished fifth in 1957-58.

Jim Dyet of Scottish club King's Park enjoyed a dream debut when he played against Forfar Athletic in 1930. He scored eight goals and surprisingly kept his place for their next fixture.

Alan Shearer scored a hat-trick on his full First Division debut at the age of 17. He scored his three goals for Southampton in their 4-2 win over Arsenal.

Jim Stannard of Gillingham set a new goalkeeper's record in 1995-96 when he kept 29 clean sheets in 46 matches, beating Ray Clemence's Liverpool record of 1978-79.

Chris Woods holds the British record for the longest shut-out by a goalkeeper. He did not concede a goal for 1,196 minutes when playing for Rangers in 1986-87, until he was finally beaten by a goal from Hamilton's Adrian Sprott.

Nottingham Forest hold the record for the longest unbeaten run in the Football League, playing 42 matches in 1977-78 and 1978-79 without being beaten. Defeat finally came at Liverpool with a 2-0 defeat.

Goalscoring

Facts

In 1960 Peterborough joined the Football league and won the Fourth Division at their first attempt, setting a scoring record of 134 goals in the process.

The Leeds side of 1973-74 were unbeaten in their first 29 League matches of the season. Their record was equalled by Liverpool in 1987-88.

In 1983-84 Cambridge United set a new Football League record when they played 31 consecutive matches without winning a game. They were later relegated from the Second Division.

The worst start to a Premier League season came at Swindon in 1993-94, the County Ground side waiting 15 matches before recording a win.

Only two clubs have completed a Football League season without being beaten – Preston North End in the League's inaugural season in 1888-89 and Liverpool in 1893-94.

On Boxing Day, 1994 the Carling Premiership was an away-day celebration as none of the 11 matches ended in a home win.

In 1957-58 QPR played out six consecutive 1-1 draws to set a record for the longest sequence of draws by the same score.

In 1993-94 there were 1195 goals scored in the Carling Premiership. The following year exactly the same number were scored once again.

In the nine seasons between 1961 and 1969 Northampton travelled from the Fourth Division to the First, and all the way back down from the top flight to the bottom again.

Halifax goalkeeper Steve Milton had a nightmare League debut when his side met Stockport in January 1934. They lost 13-0.

Manchester City were the highest-scoring team in the First Division in 1937-38 with 80 goals. But they ended the season in 21st and were relegated, despite scoring three more goals than champions Arsenal.

Robert Bell scored nine goals for Tranmere against Oldham in a Division Three (North) match on Boxing Day in 1935.

Preston North End's James Ross set a League record in it's first season when he scored seven goals against Stoke City on October 6, 1888.

 **Facts** Goalscoring

Three other players have scored seven League goals in one match. They are: Ted Drake for Arsenal v Aston Villa, Division One, December 14, 1935. Tommy Briggs for Blackburn v Bristol Rovers, Division Two, February 5, 1955. Neville ('Tim') Coleman for Stoke City v Lincoln, Division Two, February 23, 1957.

On September 12, 1885, John Petrie set the all-time British individual record when he scored 13 goals in Arbroath's 36-0 win over Bon Accord in the Scottish Cup first round.

Denis Law scored seven goals in an FA Cup tie against Luton, but still finished a loser. Playing for Manchester City in 1961, Law scored all six goals in the fourth round tie but the game was abandoned with City leading 6-2. The re-arranged match was won by Luton 3-1, with Law scoring the consolation.

Vivian Woodward set a British record when he scored seven goals for England against France in an Amateur International in Paris on November 1, 1906. England won the game 15-0.

Woodward also scored six goals for England against Holland at Chelsea on December 11, 1909.

Ireland's Joe Bambrick set the British professional record when he scored six goals against Wales in Belfast on February 1, 1930.

Willie Hall set the record for fastest international hat-trick when he scored three goals in three minutes for England against Ireland at Old Trafford on November 16, 1938. Hall went on to score another two goals as England ran out 7-0 winners.

Up to the end of the 1996-97 season the top British international goalscorers are: England – Bobby Charlton (49 in 106 games), Scotland – Denis Law (30 in 55) and Kenny Dalglish (30 in 102), Northern Ireland – Colin Clarke (13 in 38), Wales – Ian Rush (28 in 73) and Republic of Ireland – Frank Stapleton (20 in 71).

Tinsley Lindley scored in nine consecutive games for England spanning three seasons. He scored in three games against each of Scotland, Wales and Ireland.

Paul Mariner has come the closest to beating Lindley's record. The England striker scored in six consecutive matches between November 1981 and June 1982.

Goalscoring

Facts

Peterborough United's Terry Bly set a new League record when he scored 52 Division Four goals in the 1960-61 season.

Albert Mundy set the quickest goal record by scoring after just six seconds for Aldershot against Hartlepool on October 25, 1958.

Two men have repeated Mundy's feat. Barrie Jones of Newport County v Torquay United, March 31, 1962; and Crystal Palace's Keith Smith v Derby County, December 12, 1964.

Huddersfield's Phil Starbuck scored after only three seconds of coming on as a substitute against Wigan in a Division Two match on April 12, 1993.

Malcolm Macdonald was officially timed with scoring a goal after just five seconds of Newcastle's 7-3 friendly win at St Johnstone on July 29, 1972.

Jimmy Scarth scored three goals in two minutes for Gillingham against Leyton Orient in a Division Three (South) match on November 1, 1952.

Arsenal scored six goals in 18 minutes in a 7-1 win over Sheffield Wednesday on February 15, 1992. The goals came between the 71st and 89th minute.

Notts County scored six goals in twelve second-half minutes when they beat Exeter 9-0 in Division Three (South) onOctober 16, 1948. Tommy Lawton and Jackie Sewell both scored hat-tricks.

The fastest international goal was set by San Marino's Davide Gualtieri against England in a World Cup qualifier on November 17, 1993. The official timing of the goal was 8.3 seconds.

The fastest First Division hat-trick since the war was set by Fulham's Graham Leggat. He scored three goals in three minutes when Fulham beat Ipswich 10-1 on Boxing Day, 1963.

Robbie Fowler set the fastest Carling Premiership hat-trick when he scored three goals in four-and-a-half minutes in Liverpool's 3-0 victory over Arsenal on August 28, 1994.

Blackburn's Chris Sutton and Dwight Yorke of Aston Villa share the record of fastest goal in the Carling Premiership. Both scored after 13 seconds, Sutton against Everton on April 1, 1995 and Yorke against Coventry on September 30, 1995.

 **Facts** Goalscoring

Jamie Cureton scored the fastest Carling Premiership goal from a substitute when he netted after only 13 seconds of coming on for Norwich against Chelsea on December 10, 1994.

The fastest Scottish hat-trick was timed at two-and-a-half minutes by Motherwell's Ian St. John. He managed the feat away at Hibernian in the Scottish League Cup on August 15, 1959.

The fastest all-time hat-trick was reported at one minute 50 seconds by Independiente's Maglioni against Gimnasia de la Plata in Argentina on March 18, 1973.

The fastest First Division own-goal was set by Arsenal's Steve Bould. He 'scored' after just 16 seconds at Sheffield Wednesday on February 17, 1990.

The fastest goal in World Cup finals history was scored by Vaclav Masek of Czechoslovakia against Mexico in 1962. The goal was timed at 15 seconds.

Up to the start of the 1997-98 season, no Carling Premiership goals have been scored by a goalkeeper.

Peter Schmeichel scored for Manchester United against Rotor Volgograd in the Uefa Cup first round, second leg on September 26, 1995.

Jan Molby's first hat-trick in English football all came from the penalty spot in Liverpool's 3-1 win over Coventry in November 1986.

Arthur Birch scored five goals for Chesterfield in the 1923-24 season – as a goalkeeper. All came from the penalty spot.

Goalscoring

Facts

Maik Taylor was beaten by his opposite goalkeeper – on his League debut. Barnet's Taylor was beaten by Chris Mackenzie of Hereford in a Division Three match on August 12, 1995.

Liverpool set a Football League record when eight players scored in the same match. Steve Nicol (twice), Steve McMahon, ian Rush, Gary Gillespie, Peter Beardsley, John Aldridge, John Barnes and Glenn Hysen all scored in the 9-0 win over Crystal Palace on September 12, 1989.

Nine different players scored for Striling Albion in their 20-0 win against Selkirk in the Scottish Cup first round on December 8, 1984.

Liverpool also hold the record for different scorers in a European match. Nine players scored in their 11-0 record home win over Stromsgodset of Norway in the European Cup-Winners' Cup first round, first leg on September 17, 1974.

Nearly matching Liverpool were Swansea City. They had eight different goalscorers when they beat Sliema of Malta 12-0 in the Cup-Winners' Cup first round, first leg on September 15, 1982.

Bill Prendergast set an English record when he scored in 13 consecutive matches for Chester City between September and December 1938.

Prendergast feat eclipsed the previous record set by Everton's Dixie Dean. Dean had scored on 12 consecutive appearances.

The Carling Premiership record for goals scored in consecutive games was set by Mark Stein. The Chelsea striker scored in seven consecutive matches between December 28, 1993 and February 5, 1994.

Brian Clough was the Second Division top goalscorer for three successive seasons while at Middlesbrough. He scored 40 goals in 1957-58, 42 in 1958-59 and 39 in 1959-60.

Middlesbrough's George Camsell scored a record nine hat-tricks in the 1926-27 season.

Dixie Dean holds the record for most League hat-tricks in a career. He scored 37 for Tranmere and Everton between 1924 and 1938.

The most Carling Premiership hat-tricks in a season was set by Alan Shearer. He scored five for Blackburn in the 1995-96 season.

 **Goalscoring**

Three players have scored three consecutive First Division hat-tricks: Frank Osborne (Tottenham) scored against Liverpool, Leicester and West Ham in 1925; Tom Jennings (Leeds), against Arsenal, Liverpool (four) and Blackburn (four) in 1926 and Jack Balmer (Liverpool) against Portsmouth, Derby County (four) and Arsenal in 1946.

Gilbert Alsop also scored three consecutive League hat-tricks for Walsall in Division Three (South). He scored against Swindon, Bristol City and Swindon (four) in 1939.

Up to the start of the 1997-98 season, there have been three hat-tricks scored from players on the same team in a League match: Nottingham Forest (Enoch West, Billy Hooper and Arthur Spouncer) against Leicester Fosse on April 21, 1909 in Division One; Wrexham (Ron Barnes, Wyn Davies and Roy Ambler) against Hartlepool on March 3, 1962 in Division Four; Manchester City (Tony Adcock, Paul Stewart and David White) against Huddersfield on November 7, 1987 in Division Two.

The record for most Football League goals scored on one day was set on February 1, 1936. In the 44 games played 209 goals were scored.

A Carling Premiership record was set on September 23, 1995 when three players scored hat-tricks on the same day. Robbie Fowler (Liverpool) scored four goals against Bolton, Tony Yeboah (Leeds) scored a hat-trick at Wimbledon and Alan Shearer (Blackburn) netted three against Coventry.

Hereford's Chris Pike scored a hat-trick against different goalkeepers on October 16, 1993. Hereford's opponents, Colchester, had two goalkeepers sent-off. The result of the game was 5-0.

Jim Dyet scored eight goals on his debut for King's Park against Forfar Athletic on January 2, 1930.

Len Shackleton holds the English record for scoring six goals on his debut for Newcastle in a 13-0 Division Two win against Newport County on October 5, 1946.

Alan Shearer became the youngest player to score a Division One hat-trick on his full debut when he scored for Southampton against Arsenal on April 9, 1988 at the age of 17.

Goalscoring

Stoke City equalled a Football League record in the 1984-85 season by scoring the fewest goals in a season. Both Stoke and Watford (1971-72) scored 24 goals.

Leeds set a new Carling Premiership record by scoring the fewest goals in 1996-97. They managed only 28 goals but still finished in 11th place.

The fewest goals scored by a relegated Carling Premiership side was Manchester City's 33 in 1995-96.

Crystal Palace set a Carling Premiership record when they went nine consecutive matches without scoring in the 1994-95 season.

The longest Football League sequence of a club not scoring a goal was 11 matches. Coventry (Division Two 1919-20) and

 **Facts**   **Goalscoring**

Hartlepool (Division Two 1992-93) both hold the record.
Hartlepool actually went 13 games without scoring. Spanning
over two months, and 1,227 minutes, they failed to score in 11
League games, one FA Cup match and an Autoglass Shield
Trophy tie.

*The British non-scoring record was set by Striling Albion in 1981.
From January 31 to August 8 they went 14 matchs without netting.
That run consisted of 13 Scottish League matches and one Scottish
Cup game. It took them 1,292 minutes to score their next goal.*

Arsenal's Ian Wright became the first player to score in each leg
of each round for a club that reached a European Final. He
achieved the feat in the 1994-95 European Cup-Winner's Cup, but
failed to score in the Final, which Arsenal lost to Real Zaragova.

*The most goals scored by one player in a first-class match was set by
Polish striker Stephan Stanis. He scored 16 goals for Lens against
Aubry-Austuries in a wartime French Cup match on December 13,
1942.*

The record number of goals scored by one player in an
international match is 10 goals, shared by two men, and both
were in Olympic tournaments: Denmark's Sofus Nielsen against
France in the 1908 Olympics and Gottfried Fuchs for Germany
in the 1912 competition against Russia.

ENGLAND'S TOP 10 GOALSCORERS:

Bobby Charlton (49 goals in 106 games)
Gary Lineker (48 in 80)
Jimmy Greaves (44 in 57)
Tom Finney (30 in 76)
Nat Lofthouse (30 in 33)
Vivian Woodward (29 in 23)
Steve Bloomer (28 in 23)
David Platt (27 in 62)
Bryan Robson (26 in 90)
Geoff Hurst (24 in 49)

GOALS BY GOALKEEPERS

Chris MacKenzie
Hereford United's Chris Mackenzie beat his opposite number,
Barnet's Mark Taylor, in last season's Third Division encounter
at Edgar Street.

Goalscoring

Facts

Iain Hesford
Iain Hesford scored Maidstone's winner against Hereford in a
Fourth Division match in November 1991. His clearance beat
visiting keeper Tony Elliot with one bounce.

Ray Charles
East Fife's Ray Charles joined the exclusive list in February
1990. His long ball deceived his opposite number, Stranraer's
Bernard Duffy, in the Scottish Second Division match.

Alan Paterson
The 1989 Roadferry Cup Final in Belfast was brightened up when
Glentoran keeper Alan Paterson embarrassed Linfield's George
Dunlop with a towering clearance.

Andy McLean
On his Irish league debut in August 1988, keeper Andy Mclean
scored for Cliftonville. The hapless goalkeeper at the other end
was once again Linfield's George Dunlop.

Andy Goram
Scotland's international stopper Andy Goram scored once for his old
club Hibernian. It was in the Premier Division in May 1988, the
unlucky opposition keeper was Morton's David Wylie.

Steve Ogrizovic
Coventry stalwart Ogrizovic grabbed his only goal for the Sky
Blues against Sheffield Wednesday in October 1986, his big-boot
beating Martin Hodge in the home goal.

Steve Sherwood
Watford's Steve Sherwood got his name on the score sheet in a First
Division game in 1984. He beat Coventry's Raddy Avramovic in the
match at Highfield Road.

Ray Cashley
The Division Two match between Bristol City and Hull City in
September 1993 produced another moment of goalkeeping
folklore when Bristol's Ray Cashley scored against Jeff
Wealands.

Peter Shilton
In over 900 league games England's Peter Shilton scored once. It was
in 1967 playing for Leicester City, his obliging opposite number was
Southampton's Campbell Forsyth.

CUP FINAL WINNERS

Cup Final Winners

Facts

WALES

1878	Wrexham	1926	Ebbw Vale
1879	Newtown	1927	Cardiff City
1880	Druids	1928	Cardiff City
1881	Druids	1929	Connah's Quay
1882	Druids	1930	Cardiff City
1883	Wrexham	1931	Wrexham
1884	Oswestry	1932	Swansea
1885	Druids	1933	Chester
1886	Druids	1934	Bristol City
1887	Chirk	1935	Tranmere
1888	Chirk	1936	Crewe
1889	Bangor	1937	Crewe
1890	Chirk	1938	Shrewsbury
1891	Shrewsbury	1939	South Liverpool
1892	Chirk	1940	Wellington
1893	Wrexham	1947	Chester
1894	Chirk	1948	Lovells
1895	Newtown	1949	Merthyr
1896	Bangor	1950	Swansea
1897	Wrexham	1951	Merthyr
1898	Druids	1952	Rhyl
1899	Druids	1953	Rhyl
1900	Aberwystwyth	1954	Flint
1901	Oswestry	1955	Barry
1902	Wellington	1956	Cardiff City
1903	Wrexham	1957	Wrexham
1904	Druids	1958	Wrexham
1905	Wrexham	1959	Cardiff City
1906	Wellington	1960	Wrexham
1907	Oswestry	1961	Swansea
1908	Chester	1962	Bangor
1909	Wrexham	1963	Borough
1910	Wrexham	1964	Cardiff City
1911	Wrexham	1965	Cardiff City
1912	Cardiff City	1966	Swansea
1913	Swansea	1967	Cardiff City
1914	Wrexham	1968	Cardiff City
1915	Wrexham	1969	Cardiff City
1920	Cardiff City	1970	Cardiff City
1921	Wrexham	1971	Cardiff City
1922	Cardiff City	1972	Wrexham
1923	Cardiff City	1973	Cardiff City
1924	Wrexham	1974	Cardiff City
1925	Wrexham	1975	Wrexham
		1976	Cardiff City
		1977	Shrewsbury

Facts

Cup Final Winners

1978	Wrexham	1988	Cardiff City
1979	Shrewsbury	1989	Swansea
1980	Newport County	1990	Hereford
1981	Swansea	1991	Swansea
1982	Swansea	1992	Cardiff City
1983	Swansea	1993	Cardiff City
1984	Shrewsbury	1994	Barry Town
1985	Shrewsbury	1995	Wrexham
1986	Wrexham	1996	Llansantffraid
1987	Merthyr	1997	Barry Town

Cup Final Winners

SCOTLAND

1874 Queen's Park
1875 Queen's Park
1876 Queen's Park
  (after a replay)
1877 Vale of Leven
  (after two replays)
1879 Vale of Leven
  (awarded Cup after
  Rangers withdrew)
1880 Queen's Park
1881 Queen's Park
1882 Queen's Park
  (after a replay)
1883 Dumbarton
  (after a replay)
1884 Queen's Park (awarded
  Cup after Vale of Leven
  withdrew from Final)

1885 Renton (after a replay)
1886 Queen's Park
1887 Hibernian
1888 Renton
1889 Third Lanark
1890 Queen's Park
  (after a replay)
1891 Hearts
1892 Celtic
1893 Queen's Park
1894 Rangers
1895 St.Bernard's
1896 Hearts
1897 Rangers
1898 Rangers
1899 Celtic
1900 Celtic
1901 Hearts
1902 Hibernian

 Facts **Cup Final Winners**

1903	Rangers (after two replays)	1931	Celtic (after a replay)
1904	Celtic	1932	Rangers (after a replay)
1905	Third Lanark (after a replay)	1933	Celtic
1906	Hearts	1934	Rangers
1907	Celtic	1935	Rangers
1908	Celtic	1936	Rangers
1910	Dundee (after two replays)	1937	Celtic
1911	Celtic (after a replay)	1938	East Fife (after a replay)
1912	Celtic	1939	Clyde
1913	Falkirk	1947	Aberdeen
1914	Celtic (after a replay)	1948	Rangers (aet; after a replay)
1920	Kilmarnock	1949	Rangers
1921	Partick Thistle	1950	Rangers
1922	Morton	1951	Celtic
1923	Celtic	1952	Motherwell
1924	Airdrieonians	1953	Rangers (after a replay)
1925	Celtic	1954	Celtic
1926	St Mirren	1955	Clyde (after a replay)
1927	Celtic	1956	Hearts
1928	Rangers	1957	Falkirk (aet; after a replay)
1929	Kilmarnock	1958	Clyde
1930	Rangers (after a replay)	1959	St Mirren

Cup Final Winners

 Facts

1960 Rangers
1961 Dunfermline
(after a replay)
1962 Rangers
1963 Rangers (after a replay)
1964 Rangers
1965 Celtic
1966 Rangers (after a replay)
1967 Celtic
1968 Dunfermline
1969 Celtic
1970 Aberdeen
1971 Celtic (after a replay)
1972 Celtic
1973 Rangers
1974 Celtic
1975 Celtic
1976 Rangers
1977 Celtic
1978 Rangers
1979 Rangers
(aet; after two replays)
1980 Celtic (aet)
1981 Rangers (after a replay)
1982 Aberdeen (aet)
1983 Aberdeen (aet)
1984 Aberdeen (aet)
1985 Celtic
1986 Aberdeen
1987 St Mirren (aet)
1988 Celtic
1989 Celtic
1990 Aberdeen
(aet; Aberdeen won 9-8 on penalties)
1991 Motherwell(aet)
1992 Rangers
1993 Rangers
1994 Dundee United
1995 Celtic
1996 Rangers
1997 Kilmarnock

Facts

Cup Final Winners

IRELAND

1881 Moyola Park
1882 Queen's Island
1883 Cliftonville
1884 Distillery
1885 Distillery
1886 Distillery
1887 Ulster
1888 Cliftonville
1889 Distillery
1890 Gordon H.
1891 Linfield
1892 Linfield
1893 Linfield
1894 Distillery
1895 Linfield
1896 Distillery
1897 Cliftonville
1898 Linfield
1899 Linfield
1900 Cliftonville
1901 Cliftonville
1902 Linfield
1903 Distillery
1904 Linfield
1905 Distillery
1906 Shelbourne
1907 Cliftonville
1908 Bohemians
1909 Cliftonville
1910 Distillery
1911 Shelbourne
1912 Linfield
1913 Linfield
1914 Glentoran
1915 Linfield
1916 Linfield
1917 Glentoran
1918 Celtic
1919 Linfield
1920 Shelbourne
1921 Glentoran
1922 Linfield
1923 Linfield

1924 Queen's Island
1925 Distillery
1926 Celtic
1927 Ards
1928 Willowfield
1929 Ballymena
1930 Linfield
1931 Linfield
1932 Glentoran
1933 Glentoran
1934 Linfield
1935 Glentoran
1936 Linfield
1937 Celtic
1938 Celtic
1939 Linfield
1940 Ballymena
1941 Celtic
1942 Linfield
1943 Celtic

Cup Final Winners

1944	Celtic	1971	Distillery
1945	Linfield	1972	Coleraine
1946	Linfield	1973	Glentoran
1947	Celtic	1974	Ards
1948	Linfield	1975	Coleraine
1949	Derry City	1976	Carrick Rangers
1950	Linfield	1977	Coleraine
1951	Glentoran	1978	Linfield
1952	Ards	1979	Cliftonville
1953	Linfield	1980	Linfield
1954	Derry City	1981	Ballymena United
1955	Dundela	1982	Linfield
1956	Distillery	1983	Glentoran
1957	Glenavon	1984	Ballymena United
1958	Ballymena	1985	Glentoran
1959	Glenavon	1986	Glentoran
1960	Linfield	1987	Glentoran
1961	Glenavon	1988	Glentoran
1962	Linfield	1989	Ballymena United
1963	Linfield	1990	Glentoran
1964	Derry City	1991	Portadown
1965	Coleraine	1992	Glenavon
1966	Glentoran	1993	Bangor
1967	Crusaders	1994	Linfield
1968	Crusaders	1995	Linfield
1969	Ards	1996	Glentoran
1970	Linfield	1997	Glenavon

EUROPEAN CLUB TOURNAMENTS

European Club Tournaments

Real Madrid defended the Champions Cup a record five times between 1956 and 1960.

Ajax won and retained the Champions Cup three times in a row from 1971 through to 1973.

Bayern Munich were also thrice consecutive winners, between 1974 and 1976.

Five clubs have won and defended the trophy over two consecutive seasons: Benfica 1961-1962, Internazionale 1964-1965, Liverpool 1977-1978, Nottingham Forest 1979-1980 and AC Milan 1989-1990.

England have bought the Champions Cup home a record six consecutive years, the longest stretch of any one country. The double wins of Liverpool in 19777-1978 and Nottingham Forest in 1979-1980 were followed by Liverpool again in 1981 and Aston Villa in 1982.

Dutch clubs have won the trophy four seasons in a row, starting with Feyenoord in 1970 followed by Ajax until 1974.

The Italian city of Milan has won the Champions Cup over three consecutive seasons first with Milan in 1963 then Inter in 1964 and 1965.

In the first 21 years of the Champions Cup only two clubs won the trophy unbeaten, Internazionale in 1964 and Ajax in 1972.

Since Nottingham Forest in 1979 eight clubs have won the Cup undefeated: Liverpool in 1981 and 1984, Milan in 1989, Red Star Belgrade in 1991, Olympique Marseille in 1993, Milan in 1994 and Ajax in 1995.

Ajax, Liverpool and Milan are the only three teams to have won the trophy unbeaten twice.
Ajax set the record of 20 consecutive matches unbeaten in the Champions Cup before being beaten by Panathinaikos in 1996.

The biggest win in a Champions Cup match was 11 when Dinamo Bucharest beat Crusaders in a first round match in 1973-74.

 **Facts**   **European Club Tournaments**

The most goals scored in a Champions Cup match is 18, this has happened four times: Benfica beat Stade Dudelange 18-0 on aggregate over two legs in a first round match in 1965-66. In the second round of 1968-69 Spartak Trnava beat Reipas (Lahti) 16-2 on aggregate. In the first round of 1969-70 Fyenoord beat KR (Reykjavik) 16-2 on aggregate and in a 1979-80 first round match Ajax beat HJK (Helsinki) 16-2.

The European Champions Cup was the idea of Frenchman Gabriel Hanot, then editor of L'Equipe a daily sports paper. In 1955 Hanot invited representitives to Paris to discuss the idea of creating a championship for the major clubs of Europe. It began the following year.

The European Champions Cup was the first European Cup competition to get underway in Europe.

In the first European Cup only half the clubs that entered were actually the champions of their respective countries.

Not until Celtic won the European Cup in 1967, beating Internazionale 2-1, had a non-Latin team won the competition.

No club has ever managed to successfully defend the European Cup Winners Cup.

Seven clubs who have won the Cup-Winners' Cup: Arsenal, Ajax, Anderlecht, Atletico Madrid, Fiorentina, Milan and Parma went on to reach the Final the following season, only to lose.

European Club Tournaments

The highest aggregate win in a European Cup-Winners' Cup match was in the 1971-72 first round game between Jeunesse Hautcharage and Chelsea. Chelsea won 21-0 over two legs.

The highest win in one leg was Sporting Lisbon 16, APOEL Nicosia 1 in a 1963-64 second round match.

Fiorentina won the first European Cup Winners Cup Final in 1961 in spite of losing the 1960 Italian Cup Final to Juventus.

The 1985 European Cup Final between Liverpool and Juventas resulted in 39 fans, mainly Italians, being crushed to death in the Heysel Stadium disaster. The tragedy was a result of hoolaganism and meant English clubs were banned from all European competitions until 1991.

Real Madrid have won the European Cup a record six times, AC Milan have won the trophy a total of five times and Liverpool and Ajax have won it four times each.

Barcelona have won the European Cup Winners Cup the most, chalking up four victories in 1979, 1982, 1989 and 1997.

Barcelona, tied with Juventus, have won the Fairs/UEFA Cup a record three times. Barcelona in 1958, 1960 and 1966, Juventus in 1977, 1990 and 1993.

In 1955 Ernst Thommen, a Swiss vice-president of UEFA invited representatives to Basle to organise a tournament for clubs from cities that regularly held trade fairs. The International Industries Fairs Inter-Cities Cup (The Fairs Cup) was launched in the autumn of 1955. The competition changed its name to the UEFA Cup in 1971-72.

The Fairs Cup has seen three domestic Finals, all involving Spanish Clubs, Valencia v Barcelona in 1962, Real Zaragoza v Valencia in 1964 and Barcelona v Real Zaragoza in 1966.

There have been five domestic Finals in the UEFA Cup, Tottenham v Wolves in 1972, Eintracht Frankfurt v Borussia Monchengladbach of West Germany in 1980, Juventus v Fiorentina in 1990, Internazionale v Roma in 1991 and Parma v Juventus in 1995 all from Italy.

Only one club has ever successfully defended the UEFA Cup – Real Madrid in 1985 and 1986.

 **Facts**   **European Club Tournaments**

The only country to keep the UEFA Cup for three consecutive seasons is Italy. They did this on two occasions between 1989 and 1991 – with Napoli, Juventus and Internazionale, and between 1993 and 1995 with Juventus, Internazionale and Parma.

Combining the end of the Fairs Cup with the beginning of the UEFA Cup sees English clubs winning the trophy six times in succession with: Leeds in 1968, Newcastle in 1969, Arsenal 1970, Leeds again in 1971, Tottenham 1972, and Liverpool in 1973.

In 1979/80 West Germany had five entrants in the UEFA Cup – four by right, and Borussia Monchengladbach as holders. This led to all German semi-finals and Final. Eintracht Frankfurt were the eventual champions.

English clubs have won the European Cup eight times, just one behind Italy. Manchester United triumphed in 1968, Liverpool won in 1977, 1978, 1981 and 1984, Nottingham Forest in 1979 and 1980 and Aston Villa in 1982.

Due to the ban imposed after Heysel, four English clubs who had never played in a European competition before were once more denied: Norwich City in 1985, Oxford United in 1986 and Wimbledon and Luton Town in 1988.

British clubs currently hold the record for the most wins in the European Cup-Winners' Cup with nine victories. Tottenham won it in 1963, West Ham in 1965, Manchester City in 1970, Chelsea in 1971, Rangers in 1972, Aberdeen in 1983, Everton in 1985, Manchester United in 1991, and Arsenal in 1994.

Only two players have scored a record eight goals in a European tie, over two legs, Jose Altafini for AC Milan v US Luxembourg in a European Cup preliminary round in 1962-63. And Peter Osgood for Chelsea v Jeunesse Hautcharage in the European Cup-Winners' Cup first round in 1971-72.

The heaviest defeat for an English club in the European Cup Winners Cup was Sporting Lisbon's 5-0 victory over Manchester United in a quarter-final match in 1964.

Lothar Emmerich scored a record six goals in one match for Borussia Dortmund v Floriana (Malta) in the 1965-66 Cup-Winners' Cup first round , second leg. Dortmund eventually won 8-0.

European Club Tournaments Facts

Three English clubs have been knocked out of the UEFA Cup after leading 3-0 from the first leg: Ipswich lost 3-4 to Bruges in the 1976 second round and to Barcelona on penalties after drawing 3-3 on aggregate in the 1979 third round. And QPR lost on penalties after drawing 3-3 with AEK Athens in the 1977 quarter-final.

The heaviest defeat suffered by an English club in the Fairs/UEFA Cup was Coventry's 6-1 defeat by Bayern Munich in a second round match in 1970.

In 1992 a 'Champions League' of two divisions was introduced to replace the knockout stages, from the quarter-finals onwards, of the European Cup. However in 1995 the League was expanded to four divisions of four teams, replacing the first and second rounds and the knock-out format was re-instated from the quarter-finals onwards. This format meant more money for clubs as there would no longer be any inconvenient early exits.

Less than half the winners of the European Cup have managed to retain their domestic league title in the same season.

The legendary Alfredo Di Stefano of Real Madrid scored 49 goals in 58 European Cup matches – a record that is not likely to be equalled.

The 1960 European Cup Final between Real Madrid and Eintracht Frankfurt finished 7-3 to Real, the highest scorng final to date. Alfredo Di Stefano scored a hat-trick that day.

Of the 41 European Cup Finals five have been decided on a penalty shoot-out.

Barcelona beat Fortuna Dusseldorf 4-3 in the 1979 European Cup-Winners' Cup Final, the highest scoring final in the competition.

Ian Wright of Arsenal was the top scorer with nine goals in the 1994-95 European Cup-Winners' Cup, scoring in every match except the final.

Anderlecht have appeared in three successive European Cup-Winners' Cup Finals winning the competition in 1976 and 1978, but losing to Hamburg in 1977.

The 1995 European Cup-Winners' Cup Final between Arsenal and Real Zaragoza was memorable for Nayim's spectacular 45-yard lob of David Seaman in the last minute of extra-time. One of the greatest goals of any European final.

 **Facts**   **European Club Tournaments**

From 1989 to 1995 the UEFA Cup was won by an Italian club five times out of a possible six, Ajax spoilt the symmetry in 1992 by beating Torino on the away goal rule after drawing 2-2 on aggregate.

Only two clubs have defended the Fairs Cup successfully – Barcelona won in 1958 and 1960 (there was no Final in 1959) and Valencia in 1962 and 1963.

The away goal rule for European competitions was first introduced in 1967. It replaced the replay system of determining a winner.

In 1971 penalty shoot-outs were introduced into all European competitions, replacing the toss of a coin to determine the victor.

The European Cup Final and the European Cup Winners Cup Final are the only two fixtures not played on a home and away basis. These finals are played in a neutral city.

The infamous 1975 European Cup Final was marred by Leeds United supporters destroying the stadium as their team lost 2-0 to Bayern Munchen.

Not including the 1997 final there have been 41 European Cup Finals won by 20 different clubs.

In the 1974 European Cup semi-final first leg between Atletico Madrid and Celtic. Atletico had three players sent-off and four booked.

European Club Tournaments

Celtic had two players booked. Six of Atletico's players were banned from playing in the return leg and they were fined £14,000 by UEFA. Celtic lost the semi-final 2-0 on aggregate.

That infamous Atletico Madrid team were managed by Juan Carlos Lorenzo, who was in charge of the 1966 Argentinian World Cup squad – the team that Alf Ramsey branded as "animals".

In 1968 Leeds won the Fairs Cup 1-0 on aggregate against Ferencvaros. They disposed of three Scottish clubs: Hibernian, Rangers and Dundee, in successive rounds leading up to the final.

In the first leg of the 1968 final between Leeds and Ferencvaros, Leeds' Johnny Giles had to leave the pitch with concussion, such was the style of the Hungarian's play.

Celtic were the first British club to win the European Cup beating Internazionale 2-1 in Lisbon. Winning against all the odds the team was dubbed the 'Lions of Lisbon'.

Nottingham Forest's first European Cup Final win, 1-0 against Malmo, was won by the most expensive British signing at the time – Trevor Francis, who had cost over £1m.

Bob Paisley manager of Liverpool is the only manager so far to have achieved a hat-trick of European Cup wins: in 1977, 1978 and 1981.

When Aston Villa won the European Cup in 1982 it was Villa manager Tony Barton's first post. Ron Saunders had walked out on the club the previous February leaving the job to Barton, his assistant.

In that 1982 European Cup Final Villa's first choice goalkeeper Jimmy Rimmer had to leave the pitch injured after only eight minutes. Replacement goalkeeper Nigel Spink, aged 23, had played one first team match for Villa before that night, but he became a hero when Villa beat beat Bayern Munich 1-0.

WEMBLEY STADIUM

Wembley Stadium

Facts

Originally named the Empire Stadium, the famous home of English football was opened in 1923.

The original contract between the FA and the British Empire Exhibition was for the FA Cup final to be played there for 21 years.

Wembley was officially named England's national stadium in December 1996. It will cost an estimated £180m for re-development.

Wembley's first FA Cup Final was in 1923 when West Ham met Bolton Wanderers. The official attendance of 126,047 is still a record for the stadium.

The present contract, signed in 1983, by the FA ensured that Wembley will host England's home matches, the FA Cup Final and Charity Shield until 2002.

There have been only two England home games played away from Wembley since January 5, 1966. The two games were at Leeds' Elland Road against Sweden in the Umbro Cup on June 8, 1995 and the friendly against South Africa at Manchester United's Old Trafford on May 24, 1997.

The last 100,000 attendance at Wembley was for the 1985 FA Cup Final between Manchester United and Everton.

The first international played under floodlights at Wembley was on November 20, 1963 for the game between England and Northern Ireland. England won 8-3.

The first Wembley final to be decided on a 'Golden Goal' was the 1995 Auto Windscreens Shield. Paul Tait's goal in the 103rd minute ensured Birmingham beat Carlisle 1-0.

Nottingham Forest became the first club to reach two Wembley Finals in the same season when they reached the League Cup and Simod Cup Finals in 1989.

Three teams have reached both League and FA Cup Finals at Wembley in the same season. Arsenal and Sheffield Wednesday made both Finals in 1993, the first time the same two teams contested both Finals, and Middlesbrough in 1997. Sheffield Wednesday and Middlesbrough lost both games.

 **Facts** **Wembley Stadium**

Three players have scored hat-tricks in major Wembley Finals. They are Stan Mortensen (Blackpool v Bolton, FA Cup Final, 1953), Geoff Hurst (England v West Germany, World Cup Final, 1966) and David Speedie (Chelsea v Manchester City, Full Members Cup Final, 1985).

England's heaviest Wembley defeat to date was also their first in the stadium. They were beaten 3-6 by Hungary in November 1953.

The fastest goal in a Wembley match was scored after 20 seconds by Maurice Cox for Cambridge University against Oxford on December 5, 1979.

The fastest FA Cup Final goal at Wembley was scored by Chelsea's Roberto di Matteo after 42 seconds of the 1997 Final.

Up to June 1997, Wembley has hosted five European Cup Finals (1963,1968,1971,1978,1992). Two English clubs have won in the Wembley Finals. Manchester United in 1968 and Liverpool in 1978. The stadium has also hosted two European Cup-Winners' Cup Finals. Both finals have seen clubs win their first European trophy – West Ham in 1965 and Italian club Parma in 1993.

ONLY 12 PLAYERS HAVE BEEN SENT-OFF IN MAJOR MATCHES AT WEMBLEY. THEY ARE:

Boris Stankovic (Yugoslavia v Sweden, Olympic Games, August 1948)

Antonio Rattin (Argentina v England, World Cup, July 1966)

Billy Bremner (Leeds United v Liverpool, Charity Shield, August 1974)

Kevin Keegan (Liverpool v Leeds United, Charity Shield, August 1974)

Gilbert Dresch (Luxembourg v England, World Cup qual., March 1977)

Kevin Moran (Manchester United v Everton, FA Cup Final, May 1985)

Lee Dixon (Arsenal v Tottenham, FA Cup semi-final, April 1993)

Peter Swan (Port Vale v West Bromwich Albion, Play-off Final, May 1993)

Wembley Stadium

Andrei Kanchelskis (Manchester United v Aston Villa, League Cup Final, April 1994)

Mike Wallace (Stockport County v Burnley, Play-off Final, May 1994)

Chris Beaumont (Stockport County v Burnley, Play-off Final, May 1994)

Tetsuji Hashiratani (Japan v England, Umbro Cup, June 1995)

YOUNGEST
AND OLDEST

Youngest and Oldest Facts

The youngest player to be capped by England was James Prinsep, who played v Scotland in April 1879 at the age of 17 years 252 days.

The youngest player to score a goal in the top-flight was Ipswich schoolboy Jason Dozzell. He scored against Coventry in February 1984 at the age of 16 years, 57 days.

The youngest player to take part in a Carling Premiership match was West Ham's Neil Finn, who played in goals against Coventry in January 1996 when he was only 17 years and three days.

Neil McBain, manager of New Brighton, became the oldest player to figure in a League match when he came on as a goalkeeper in their game with Hartlepool in 1947 at the age of 51 years, 120 days.

Stanley Matthews holds the record as the oldest player to be capped by England, playing his final international against Denmark in May 1957 at the age of 42 years and 104 days.

BRITISH YOUNGEST CAPPED PLAYERS ARE:

Scotland – Denis Law, 18 years, 235 days (v Wales, October 18, 1958)

Northern Ireland – Norman Whiteside, 17 years, 42 days (v Yugoslavia, June 17, 1982)

Wales – Ryan Giggs, 17 years, 332 days (v Germany, October 16, 1991)

Republic of Ireland – Jimmy Holmes, 17 years, 200 days (v Austria, May 30, 1971)

Manchester United's Duncan Edwards became England's youngest capped player this century when he played against Scotland on April 2, 1955. He was 18 years, 183 days.

England's youngest goalscorer record was set by Tommy Lawton who was 19 years, 6 days when he scored a penalty against Wales in Cardiff on October 22, 1938.

Sunderland's goalkeeper Derek Foster became the youngest First Division player when he played against Leicester City on August 22, 1964. He was 15 years, 185 days.

 **Facts** **Youngest and Oldest**

Andrew Cunningham became the oldest player to make hid Football League debut. He was 38 years, 2 days when he turned out for Newcastle United against Leicester City in a First Division match on February 2, 1929.

Walter (Billy) Hampson became the oldest player to play in the FA Cup Final when he appeared for Newcastle United against Aston Villa in 1924. He was 41 years, 8 months.

The record for oldest Carling Premiership player was set by goalkeeper John Burridge on April 29, 1995. Aged 43 years, 4 months, 26 days, he appeared as a half-time substitute for Manchester City against Newcastle United. At the time he was goalkeeper coach for Newcastle.

The record for the youngest England captain was set by Bobby Moore. He captained his country away to Czechoslovakia on May 29, 1963 aged 22 years, 1 month, 17 days.

Tottenham's Andy Turner became the youngest Carling Premiership goalscorer when he scored against Everton on September 5, 1992. He was 17 years, 166 days.

Alan Shearer holds the record for the youngest First Division hat-trick scorer. He was 17 years, 240 days when he scored three for Southampton against Arsenal on April 9, 1988. It was Shearer's full debut.

Chelsea's Jimmy Greaves became the youngest player to score 100 Football League goals when he reached his ton against Manchester City on November 19, 1960 aged 20 years, 261 days.

Arsenal's average age of their 1950 FA Cup winning team was 31 years, 2 months, a record in the competition.

Stanley Matthews became England's oldest goalscorer when, aged 41 years, 248 days, he scored against Northern Ireland in Belfast on October 6, 1956.

The youngest FA Cup player record was set by Andy Awford. He played for Worcester City in a third round qualifying match against Borehamwood on October 10, 1987.

Youngest and Oldest

The youngest player to play in the FA Cup proper was Kettering Town's goalkeeper Scott Endersby. He was 15 years, 279 days when he played against Tilbury in the first round match on November 26, 1977.

The record for youngest goalscorer in an international match was set on April 22, 1995 by Mohamed Kallon of Sierra Leone. He was 15 years, 6 months, 16 days when he netted against Congo in an African Nations Cup match.

The oldest player to make his England debut was Leslie Compton. He was 38 years, 2 months when he played against Wales in Sunderland on November 15, 1950.

The oldest British international player was Wales' Billy Meredith on March 15, 1920. He was 45 years, 8 months when he played against England at Highbury.

The youngest player to score in the Football League was Bristol Rovers' Ronnie Dix. He was 15 years, 180 days when he scored against Norwich City in a Division Three (South) match on March 3, 1928.

David Nish still remains the youngest FA Cup Final captain. Aged 21 years, 7 months, Nish led out Leicester City against Manchester City in 1969.

Two men share the record for youngest Football League players. They are: Albert Geldard (Bradford v Millwall, Division Two, September 16, 1929) and Ken Roberts (Wrexham v Bradford, Division Three (North), September 1, 1951). Both were aged 15 years, 158 days.

Sunderland's Barry Venison became the youngest Wembley Cup Final captain when, at the age of 20 years, 7 months, 8 days, he led the club to the 1985 League Cup Final.

The record for youngest FA Cup-winning captain was set by Bobby Moore in 1964. He was 23 years, 20 days when he led West Ham to victory over Preston North End.

Chesterfield's Kevin Davies became the youngest League Cup player on September 22, 1993. He was 16 years, 180 days when he appeared as a substitute against West Ham in the second round, second leg tie.

 **Facts**   **Youngest and Oldest**

Aside from becoming the youngest England player, James
Prinsep became the youngest FA Cup Final player when he
appeared for Clapham Rovers against Old Etonians in 1879
aged 17 years, 245 days.

*West Ham's Paul Allen has so far come closest to beating Prinsep's
record. He was 11 days older than Prinsep when he played against
Arsenal in 1980, and became the youngest FA Cup finalist this
century.*

The youngest FA Cup Final goalscorer was Manchester United's
Norman Whiteside. He was 18 years, 19 days when he scored
against Brighton and Hove Albion in the 1983 replay.

*Whiteside is also the youngest goalscorer in a Wembley Cup Final.
Aged 17 years, 324 days, he scored for Manchester United against
Liverpool in the 1983 League Cup Final.*

Chris Woods became the youngest Wembley Cup Final
goalkeeper when he appeared for Nottingham Forest aged 18
years, 125 days against Liverpool in the 1978 League Cup Final.

Youngest and Oldest

The record for youngest FA Cup Final goalkeeper was set by Leicester City's Peter Shilton. He was 19 years, 7 months when he played against Manchester City in the the 1969 Final.

The youngest international in a senior match to play at Wembley was Albania's goalkeeper Blendi Nolbani. He was 17 years, 19 days when he faced England on April 26, 1989.

Kevin Howley became the youngest FA Cup Final referee in 1960. He was 35 when he took charge of Wolves-Blackburn Final.

Cameron Campbell Buchanan is the youngest player in senior football when, aged 14 years, 57 days, he played for Wolves against West Bromwich Albion in a war-time league match on September 26, 1942.

The record for the youngest player in peace-time senior football was set by Blackpool's Eamon Collins on September 9, 1980. He was 14 years, 323 days when he played against Kilmarnock in the Anglo-Scottish Cup quarter-final, first leg.

The record for the oldest First Division player was set by Stoke City's Stanley Matthews. He was 50 years, 5 days when he played against Fulham on February 6, 1965.

PLAYER
AWARD WINNERS

Player Award Winners

THE FOOTBALL WRITERS ASSOCIATION
PLAYER OF THE YEAR
1948 Stanley Matthews (Blackpool)
1949 Johnny Carey (Manchester United)
1950 Joe Mercer (Arsenal)
1951 Harry Johnston (Blackpool)
1952 Billy Wright (Wolverhampton Wanderers)
1953 Nat Lofthouse (Bolton)
1954 Tom Finney (Preston North End)
1955 Don Revie (Manchester City)
1956 Bert Trautmann (Manchester City)
1957 Tom Finney (Preston North End)
1958 Danny Blanchflower (Tottenham Hotspur)
1959 Syd Owen (Luton Town)
1960 Bill Slater (Wolverhampton Wanderers)
1961 Danny Blanchflower (Tottenham Hotspur)
1962 Jimmy Adamson (Burnley)
1963 Stanley Matthews (Blackpool)
1964 Bobby Moore (West Ham United)
1965 Bobby Collins (Leeds United)
1966 Bobby Charlton (Manchester United)
1967 Jack Charlton (Leeds United)
1968 George Best (Manchester United)
1969 Tony Book (Manchester City) and Dave Mackay (Derby County)
1970 Billy Bremner (Leeds United)
1971 Frank McLintock (Arsenal)
1972 Gordon Banks (Stoke City)
1973 Pat Jennings (Tottenham Hotspur)
1974 Ian Callaghan (Liverpool)
1975 Alan Mullery (Fulham)
1976 Kevin Keegan (Liverpool)
1977 Emlyn Hughes (Liverpool)
1978 Kenny Burns (Nottingham Forest)
1979 Kenny Dalglish (Liverpool)
1980 Terry McDermott (Liverpool)
1981 Frans Thijssen (Ipswich Town)
1982 Steve Perryman (Tottenham Hotspur)
1983 Kenny Dalglish (Liverpool)
1984 Ian Rush (Liverpool)
1985 Neville Southall (Everton)
1986 Gary Lineker (Everton)
1987 Clive Allen (Tottenham Hotspur)
1988 John Barnes (Liverpool)
1989 Steve Nicol (Liverpool); Special award to Liverpool players for their compassion to Hillsborough families

 **Facts**   **Player Award Winners**

1990 John Barnes (Liverpool)
1991 Gordon Strachan (Leeds United)
1992 Gary Lineker (Tottenham Hotspur)
1993 Chris Waddle (Sheffield Wednesday)
1994 Alan Shearer (Blackburn Rovers)
1995 Jurgen Klinsmann (Tottenham Hotspur)
1996 Eric Cantona (Manchester United)
1997 Gianfranco Zola (Chelsea)

P.F.A. PLAYER OF THE YEAR
1974 Norman Hunter (Leeds United)
1975 Colin Todd (Derby County)
1976 Pat Jennings (Tottenham Hotspur)
1977 Andy Gray (Aston Villa)
1978 Peter Shilton (Nottingham Forest)
1979 Liam Brady (Arsenal)
1980 Terry McDermott (Liverpool)
1981 John Wark (Ipswich Town)
1982 Kevin Keegan (Southampton)
1983 Kenny Dalglish (Liverpool)
1984 Ian Rush (Liverpool)
1985 Peter Reid (Everton)
1986 Gary Lineker (Everton)
1987 Clive Allen (Tottenham Hotspur)
1988 John Barnes (Liverpool)
1989 Mark Hughes (Manchester United)
1990 David Platt (Aston Villa)
1991 Mark Hughes (Manchester United)
1992 Gary Pallister (Manchester United)
1993 Paul McGrath (Aston Villa)
1994 Eric Cantona (Manchester United)
1995 Alan Shearer (Blackburn Rovers)
1996 Les Ferdinand (Newcastle United)
1997 Alan Shearer (Newcastle United)

P.F.A. YOUNG PLAYER OF THE YEAR
1974 Kevin Beattie (Ipswich Town)
1975 Mervyn Day (West Ham United)
1976 Peter Barnes (Manchester City)
1977 Andy Gray (Aston Villa)
1978 Tony Woodcock (Nottingham Forest)
1979 Cyrille Regis (West Bromwich Albion)
1980 Glenn Hoddle (Tottenham Hotspur)
1981 Gary Shaw (Aston Villa)
1982 Steve Moran (Southampton)
1983 Ian Rush (Liverpool)

Player Award Winners

1984 Paul Walsh (Luton Town)
1985 Mark Hughes (Manchester United)
1986 Tony Cottee (West Ham United)
1987 Tony Adams (Arsenal)
1988 Paul Gascoigne (Newcastle United)
1989 Paul Merson (Arsenal)
1990 Matthew Le Tissier (Southampton)
1991 Lee Sharpe (Manchester United)
1992 Ryan Giggs (Manchester United)
1993 Ryan Giggs (Manchester United)
1994 Andy Cole (Newcastle United)
1995 Robbie Fowler (Liverpool)
1996 Robbie Fowler (Liverpool)
1997 David Beckham (Manchester United)

SCOTTISH FOOTBALL WRITERS ASSOCIATION
PLAYER OF THE YEAR
1965 Billy McNeill (Celtic)
1966 John Greig (Rangers)
1967 Ronnie Simpson (Celtic)
1968 Gordon Wallace (Raith Rovers)
1969 Bobby Murdoch (Celtic)
1970 Pat Stanton (Hibernian)
1971 Martin Buchan (Aberdeen)
1972 David Smith (Rangers)
1973 George Connelly (Celtic)
1974 Scotland's World Cup squad
1975 Dandy jardine (Rangers)
1976 John Greig (Rangers)
1977 Danny McGrain (Celtic)
1978 Derek Johnstone (Rangers)
1979 Andy Ritchie (Morton)
1980 Gordon Strachan (Aberdeen)
1981 Alan Rough (Partick Thistle)
1982 Paul Sturrock (Dundee United)
1983 Charlie Nicholas (Celtic)
1984 Willie Miller (Aberdeen)
1985 Hamish McAlpine (Dundee United)
1986 Sandy Jardine (Heart of Midlothian)
1987 Brian McClair (Celtic)
1988 Paul McStay (Celtic)
1989 Richard Gough (Rangers)
1990 Alex McLeish (Aberdeen)
1991 Maurice Malpas (Dundee United)
1992 Ally McCoist (Rangers)
1993 Andy Goram (Rangers)

Facts   **Player Award Winners**

1994 Mark Hateley (Rangers)
1995 Brian Laudrup (Rangers)
1996 Paul Gascoigne (Rangers)
1997 Brian Laudrup (Rangers)

SCOTTISH P.F.A. PLAYER OF THE YEAR
1978 Derek Johnstone (Rangers)
1979 Paul Hegarty (Dundee United)
1980 Davie Provan (Celtic)
1981 Mark McGee (Aberdeen)
1982 Sandy Clarke (Aidrieonians)
1983 Charlie Nicholas (Celtic)
1984 Willie Miller (Aberdeen)
1985 Jim Duffy (Morton)
1986 Richard Gough (Dundee United)
1987 Brian McClair (Celtic)
1988 Paul McStay (Celtic)
1989 Theo Snelders (Aberdeen)
1990 Jim Bett (Aberdeen)
1991 Paul Elliott (Celtic)
1992 Ally McCoist (Rangers)
1993 Andy Goram (Rangers)
1994 Mark Hateley (Rangers)
1995 Brian Laudrup (Rangers)
1996 Paul Gascoigne (Rangers)
1997 Paolo di Canio (Celtic)

SCOTTISH P.F.A. YOUNG PLAYER OF THE YEAR
1978 Graeme Payne (Dundee United)
1979 Ray Stewart (Dundee United)
1980 John McDonald (Rangers)
1981 Charlie Nicholas (Celtic)
1982 Frank McAvennie (St. Mirren)
1983 Paul McStay (Cektic)
1984 John Robertson (Heart of Midlothian)
1985 Craig Levein (Heart of Midlothian)
1986 Craig Levein (Heart of Midlothian)
1987 Robert Fleck (Rangers)
1988 John Collins (Hibernian)
1989 Billy McKinlay (Dundee United)
1990 Scott Crabbe (Heart of Midlothian)
1991 Eoin Jess (Aberdeen)
1992 Phil O'Donnell (Motherwell)
1993 Eoin Jess (Aberdeen)
1994 Phil O'Donnell (Motherwell)
1995 Charlie Miller (Rangers)

Player Award Winners

 Facts

1996 Jack McNamara (Celtic)
1997 Robbie Winters (Dundee United)

EUROPEAN FOOTBALLER OF THE YEAR
1956 Stanley Matthews (Blackpool)
1957 Alfredo di Stefano (Real Madrid)
1958 Raymond Kopa (Real Madrid)
1959 Alfredo di Stefano (Real Madrid)
1960 Luis Suarez (Barcelona)
1961 Omar Sivori (Juventus)
1962 Josef Masopust (Dukla Prague)
1963 Lev Yashin (Moscow Dynamo)
1964 Denis Law (Manchester United)
1965 Eusebio (Benfica)
1966 Bobby Charlton (Manchester United)
1967 Florian Albert (Ferencvaros)
1968 George Best (Manchester United)
1969 Gianni Rivera (AC Milan)
1970 Gerd Muller (Bayern Munich)
1971 Johan Cruyff (Ajax)
1972 Franz Beckenbauer (Bayern Munich)
1973 Johan Cruyff (Barcelona)
1974 Johan Cruyff (Barcelona)
1975 Oleg Blokhin (Dynamo Kiev)
1976 Franz Beckenbauer (Bayern Munich)
1977 Allan Simonsen (Borussia Moenchengladbach)
1978 Kevin Keegan (SV Hamburg)
1979 Kevin Keegan (SV Hamburg)
1980 Karl-Heinz Rummenigge (Bayern Munich)
1981 Karl-Heinz Rummenigge (Bayern Munich)
1982 Paolo Rossi (Juventus)
1983 Michel Platini (Juventus)
1984 Michel Platini (Juventus)
1985 Michel Platini (Juventus)
1986 Igor Belanov (Dynamo Kiev)
1987 Ruud Gullit (AC Milan)
1988 Marco Van Basten (AC Milan)
1989 Marco Van Basten (AC Milan)
1990 Lothar Matthaus (Inter Milan)
1991 Jean-Pierre Papin (Marseille)
1992 Marco Van Basten (AC Milan)
1993 Roberto Baggio (Juventus)
1994 Hristo Stoichkov (Barcelona)
1995 George Weah (AC Milan)
1996 Matthias Sammer (Borussia Dortmund)

THE ULTIMATE FACT AND QUIZ BOOK

SCOTTISH RECORDS

Scottish Records

Scotland's record international defeat came in April 1961 when they lost 9-3 to England at Wembley.

The highest number of goals scored in a Scottish Premier League fixture was 11 in January 1987, when Celtic beat Hamilton 8-3.

In December 1894 Airdrieonians beat Dundee Wanderers 15-1 to set a long-standing record for Scottish League Division Two scoring.

The biggest British score this century came in December 1984 when Stirling Albion beat Selkirk 20-0 in the Scottish Cup. Davie Thompson scored seven goals.

Five players have scored eight goals in a Scottish League fixture – Jimmy McGrory (Celtic), Owen McNally (Arthurlie), Jim Dyet (King's Park), John Calder (Morton) and Norman Haywood (Raith Rovers).

A last-minute goal for Aberdeen on the last day of the 1967-68 ruined Rangers' unbeaten record and gave the title to rivals Celtic.

In November 1984 Paul Sturrock set a Scottish Premiership scoring record when he netted five goals for Dundee United against Morton.

In 1986-87 Brian McClair set a Scottish Premiership scoring record when he hit the target 36 times for Celtic.

A Scottish First Division scoring record was set in 1931-32 by William McFayden, who scored 53 goals for Motherwell.

The British record for League goals in a season is held by Ayr's Jimmy Smith, who scored 66 goals in 38 appearances in the 1927-28 season.

John Petrie of Arbroath holds the record for Scottish Cup goals in one game when he scored 13 goals in their record victory over Bon Accord in September 1885.

Jim Forrest of Rangers became the second player to score five goals in a Scottish League Cup fixture when they played Stirling Albion in August 1966. The first was Ayr's Jim Fraser in August 1952.

 **Facts**   **Scottish Records**

St Mirren's Gerry Baker set a post-match Scottish Cup record with ten goals against Glasgow University in Janusry 1960. A year later his brother Joe came close to equalling his record when he scored nine for Hibs against Peebles Rovers.

The highest League scorer in Scottish football history is Jimmy McGory, who scored 410 goals for Celtic and Clydebank between 1922 and 1938.

Jimmy McGory scored a total of 550 goals in his first-class career – playing for Celtic, Clydebank and Scotland.

In Rangers' title-winning season of 191-92 they set a record by scoring 101 goals in their 44 games.

The highest number of goals scored in a season by a Scottish League club is 142 in 34 games, scored by Raith Rovers in 1937-38. That is an average of more than four goals a game.

Morton have the dubious honour of conceding 100 goals in a Scottish Premier League season twice, in 1984-85 and 1987-88.

Scottish Records

Facts

In 1931-32 Edinburgh City leaked 146 goals in 38 games – a Scottish League record. Almost four goals a game flew past the City goalkeeper.

In 1989-90 Rangers conceded only 19 goals in 36 games to become the meanest defence in Scottish Premier League history.

The fastest hat-trick in Scottish football was scored by Ian St. John in August 1959. He took just two and a half minutes to net three against Hibernian while playing for Motherwell.

Nine Stirling Albion players scored in their 20-0 win over Selkirk in the 1984-85 Scottish Cup.

Chris Woods holds the record for the longest clean sheet in British football history. While playing for Rangers he played 1,196 minutes between November 1986 and January 1987 without conceding a goal.

In 1989-90 Stirling were ordered to play their Scottish FA Cup games on other grounds because their artificial pitch was not allowed in the competition.

The British record for the longest sequence without a goal is held by Stirling Albion, who played 14 matches and 1,292 minutes in 1981 without scoring a goal.

The biggest crowd for a Scottish League game came in January 1939, when a masive total of 118,567 people watched Rangers play Celtic.

146,433 spectators watched the Scottish FA Cup Final of 1937 between Celtic and Aberdeen. It is estimated that another 20,000 were shut outside Hampden Park.

In 1965 the Scottish League Cup Final attracted its highest-ever crowd, 107,609 people watching the game between Celtic and Rangers.

When Scotland played Austria in May 1963 a total of 94,596 spectators saw only 79 minutes of football, the game being called off after two players were sent off and one was carried off.

Scotland's smallest international crowd at Hampden Park came in May 1969, when only 7,843 turned out to watch them play Northern Ireland.

 **Facts**   **Scottish Records**

On March 26 1986 Kenny Dalglish became Scotland's first 100-cap player against Romania. He played two more games before retiring from international football.

The most dismissals for one club in a Scottish League game came in December 1994, when four Stranraer players were sent off at Airdrie.

Willie Johnston holds the record for the most sendings-off in a career, being dismissed 21 times in his time with Rangers, West Brom, Vancouver Whitecaps, Hearts and Scotland.

In September 1994 Hearts players Grame Hogg and Craig Levein are suspended by the Scottish FA for fighting each other in a friendly against Raith.

The longest ban issued to a Scottish player was eight and a half months, Stenhousemuir striker Billy McLafferty being punished in April 1992 for failing to turn up at a disciplinary hearing. He was also fined £250.

Scotland's longest-serving manager was Jim McLean, who took control at Dundee United in November 1971 and stayed until his resignation in 1993.

The first major Scottish match to be decided by penalties was the 1987 League Cup Final, when Rangers beat Aberdeen 5-3.

The first Scottish FA Cup Final to be decided by penalties came in 1990, when Aberdeen beat Celtic 9-8 after the score was goalless at full-time.

Rangers hold the world record for national titles, claiming their 47th in 1997.

In 1898-99 Rangers set a record by winning every game in a Scottish League season.

Rangers have completed the domestic treble a record five times, in 1948-49, 1963-64, 1975-76, 1977-78 and 1992-93.

Celtic's 1966-67 season is the most successful by any British club, when they won the Scottish League, FA Cup and League Cup, the Glasgow Cup and the European Cup.

Scottish Records

Facts

Hearts captain Walter Kidd became the third player to be sent off in a Scottish FA Cup final in 1986. The two previous dismissals were Jock Buchanan (Rangers) and Roy Aitken (Celtic).

Celtic hold the record for the longest unbeaten run in Scottish League football. Between November 1915 and April 1917 they played 62 matches without defeat.

In 1964 Greenock Morton clinched promotion as early as February 29 in a season when they won 67 points out of 72 and scored 135 goals.

Queen's Park did not concede a single goal in the first seven years of their existence between 1867 and 1874.

Between August 1992 and April 1994 Cowdenbeath disappointed their supporters by not winning a single game at home.

In December 1992 Ally McCoist became the first player to score 200 Scottish Premier goals when he scored Rangers' winner against Falkirk.

Rangers' Alan Morton won a record nine Scottish Championship medals between 1921 and 1931.

In 1909 there was no Scottish FA Cup awarded, the SFA withholding the cup and medals after Rangers and Celtic played out two draws. Spectators, unsurprisingly, rioted.

Ally McCoist was inducted into the Scottish Hall of Fame when he received his 50th cap against Australia in March 1996.

The first president of the Scottish Football League was William McGregor, who worked as a draper in Birmingham.

The first British club to play in the European Cup was Hibernian, who reached the semi-finals in 1956.

The first British winners of the European Cup were Celtic, who took the trophy in 1967.

Dundee United were relegated from the Scottish Premier Division in 1995 for the first time since 1932. They were replaced by Raith Rovers.

 **Facts** **Scottish Records**

When Scotland played England at the West of Scotland cricket ground in Partick in November 1872 it was the world's first recorded international.

The Scottish League Cup was first held in 1945-46. It would be another 15 years before Alan Hardaker launched the English equivalent.

In May 1990 Rangers' boss Graeme Souness was fined a record £5,000 for breaking his touchline ban. His ban was extended another two years.

In the 1992-93 season two Scottish teams were fined by UEFA for crowd misconduct. Hibs were fined £5,730 while Rangers were fined £8,000.

In August 1993 Airdrie were fined £10,000 and Aberdeen £5,000 for poor disciplinary conduct during the previous season.

Rangers' coach John McGregor was banned from the touchline until the year 2000 and fined £3,000 after using foul and abusive language at a reserve match in 1994.

Celtic were fined a record £100,000 in August 1994 after poaching manager Tommy Burns from Kilmarnock.

In November 1994 Celtic manager Tommy Burns and assistant Billy Stark were both fined £2,000 for leaving Kilmarnock to join the Glasgow club.

Celtic did not qualify for Europe after the 1989-90 season, the first time they had failed to qualify in nine years.

In 1996 Rangers recorded their 14th Scottish League and Cup double.

The youngest player to pull on a Scotland jersey was Denis Law, who was only 18 years and 235 days when he played against Wales in October 1958.

The youngest player to appear in a Scottish League fixture was legendary goalkeeper Ronnie Simpson, who was only 15 when he made his debut for Queens Park.

Scottish Records

Facts

The youngest player to appear for the Scotland Under-21 team was Christian Dailly, who played against Rumania in September 1990 at the age of 16 years and 11 months.

The first Scottish club to play on plastic were Stirling Albion, who began the 1987-88 on artificial turf.

On February 16 1993 goalkeeper Scott Howie played in Scotland's 3-0 U-21 game against Malta and played for Clyde against Queen of the South on the same day.

In August 1993 Ally McCoist had a testimonial match, Rangers playing Newcastle United. The game raised £500,000, setting a British record.

In 1964 Kilmarnock won a UEFA Cup tie against Eintracht Frankfurt despite being three goals down from the first leg, winning the second leg 5-1.

Willie Miller is Aberdeen's most faithful servant, playing in 556 games between 1973 and 1990.

Aberdeen's record defeat came at the hands of Celtic, who beat them 8-0 in January 1965.

The nickname of Albion Rovers is the Wee Rovers, while Arbroath are known as the Red Lichties.

 Facts **Scottish Records**

Ayr's nickname is the Honest Men, while Clyde's is the Bully Wee.

Neither Brechin or Berwick Rangers have ever provided a player capped by an international team.

Celtic's record defeat came in April 1937 at the hands of Motherwell, who put eight past the League Champions.

Jim Fallon played 620 games for Clydebank between 1968 and 1986.

Dundee's record defeat came in October 1895 against Celtic. The Bhoys put 11 goals past the Dee.

Dave Narey of Dundee United holds the Scottish record for number of appearances in European ties. He has played a total of 76 games.

East Stirling's record attendance came back in February 1921, when they attracted a massive 12,000 spectators to see their Cup game against Partick Thistle.

Falkirk's previous grounds include Randyford and Blinkbonny Grounds, before the Bairns settled at Hope Street.

Forfar Athletic's nickname is the Loons, and they once attracted 10,780 spectators to watch them play Rangers.

Hibs recorded a 22-1 victory over 42nd Highlanders in September 1881, their record win.

Montrose's nickname is the Gable Endies, while Partick Thistle are knows as the Jags and Queen of the South's moniker is the Doonhammers.

Queen's Park still retain their amateur status.

St Mirren's nickname is the Buddies, and their most capped player is the Icelandic Gudmundor Torfason.

The record for lowest goals in a Scottish League season belongs to Stirling Albion, who scored only 18 goals in 39 games in 1980-81.

In 1954-55 Stirling Albion set a record for the fewest number of points accumulated in a season when they accrued only six points.

Scottish Records

Facts

One Scottish team played a whole season without winning a League game. Vale of Leven won no games in 22 attempts in 1891-92.

In 1993-94 Aberdeen drew 21 of their 44 games, a Scottish Premier Division record.

Morton hold the record for the longest winning sequence in a season, recording 23 consecutive victories in 1963-64.

John Reid Smith was the first Scot to score at Wembley, and the first to win and score in Cup finals at Hampden Park and Wembley, while playing for Kilmarnock and then Bolton Wanderers.

In the 1937 English FA Cup Final there were 12 Scots on the field – seven with Preston and five with Sunderland.

In the 1950s a referee operating in Scotland was called Charlie Faultless.

In 1921-22 Wee Willie Crilley (5ft 1in) scored 49 of Alloa's 81 League goals. In one game against King's Park he wriggled through the legs of the opposing defender.

In March 1991 Mo Johnston missed a gilt-edged opportunity for Rangers against Aberdeen. He picked up a piece of mud and threw it down in annoyance, cricking his back and ruling himself out for the next game.

In 1971-72 Rangers won the European Cup-Winners' Cup despite being beaten in a penalty shoot-out in the second round. They won the tie on away goals, but the referee did not realise and Sporting Lisbon won on penalties. His decision was later revoked.

In 1909 Cowdenbeath were saved from extinction by a whippet race at their ground to raise funds. They were also helped by railway officials who allowed them on the trains to away games without tickets.

The first Scottish League Championship in 1890-91 was given to two clubs, Rangers finishing level with Dunbarton. They drew in a play-off and so the title was shared.

In 1904-05 Rangers finished the season level on points with Celtic, but lost the play-off and the title went to the Bhoys.

 **Facts** **Scottish Records**

Rangers' first fixture in the Scottish Cup came against Oxford, who they played in 1874.

In 1879 Vale of Leven won the Scottish Cup despite the game ending 1-1. Rangers protested that they had scored another goal and refused to replay.

The highest-ever attendance for a European Championship game came in a qualifier between Scotland and England at Hampden Park in 1968 when 134,461 turned up to watch the great rivals play.

Queen's Park competed in early English FA Cup competitions, and it was on a journey back from England that the club's players discussed the idea of a Scottish Cup.

Queen's Park won the Scottish FA Cup for the first three years.

Renton, one of the original members of the Scottish League, were expelled after five games. They had played Edinburgh Saints, a team described as professional by the Scottish FA.

Of the 11 clubs who formed the original Scottish League only five are still League teams – Rangers, Celtic, Dumbarton, Hearts and St Mirren.

Rangers entered the English FA Cup in 1885, and pulled out of the game rather than play a professional club (Rawtenstall). They were fined ten shillings.

In 1886 Rangers reached the English FA Cup semi-finals, success which prompted the Scottish FA to ban its member from playing in the competition.

When Scotland met England in April 1902 at Ibrox Park a section of terracing collapsed, killing 25 people and injuring 500.

Third Lanark won the Scottish League in 1904, the last time for 28 years that it would be won by anybody other than Rangers or Celtic.

Dundee could have won the Scottish FA Cup in five matches, but in 1909-1910 they took ten matches. Both the semi-final and the final went to two replays.

Scottish Records

Facts

Rangers' man James Gordon is Scotland's most versatile footballer. During 20 years with the club between 1910 and 1930 he played in every position, including in goal.

In 1912-13 every player who appeared for Morton in their Scottish League campaign scored a goal, including their goalkeeper.

In 1925-26 the Scottish Third Division was abandoned in mid-season because half the clubs could not afford to continue playing.

When Rangers won the Scottish FA Cup in 1928 it was at the sixth attempt, losing five finals to prompt talk of a Cup curse on the club.

In May 1930 Scotland played their first official international abroad, beating France 2-0 in Paris.

In Rangers' title-winning side of 1932-33 they boasted 13 international players – ten Scots and three Irishmen.

Scotland's first home international against a team outside of the British Isles was a 2-2 draw with Austria in November 1933.

When East Fife beat Kilmarnock in the Scottish Cup Final of 1938 they had to borrow Danny McKerrall, a Falkirk reserve, because they did not have enough fit players.

In the 1937-38 season Brechin were beaten 10-0 on three occasions, beaten by Airdrie, Albion Rovers and Cowdenbeath.

Hibs won the Scottish League title for the first time in 1947-48, but their manager Willie McCartney died in January before they completed the honour.

Rangers completed their first treble in 1948-49, their success based around their 'Iron Curtain' defence, with George Young at its heart.

Rangers completed the Double in 1952-53 despite defender George Young playing in goals for 20 minutes in the Cup Final.

In 1954-55 Aberdeen won the Scottish Championship, Hearts the League Cup and Clyde the Scottish FA Cup. It was only the second time in history that neither of the Old Firm clubs had won a medal.

Facts   Scottish Records

When Hearts beat Celtic in the Scottish Cup Final in 1956 it was their first trophy for 50 years.

Scotland's record international victory came against Ireland back in February 1901 when the Scots scored 11 goals without any reply.

Falkirk's victory over Kilmarnock in the 1957 Scottish FA Cup Final was so unexpected that Kilmarnock had already laid on a civic reception for their triumph.

When Celtic beat Rangers 7-1 in the Scottish League Cup Final of 1958 it was the largest score in any British final in history.

Hearts' convincing title win of 1957-58 when they lost only one League match and scored a record 132 goals was their first Championship of the century.

Joe Baker of Hibs became the first player at a Scottish club to represent England when he played against Northern Ireland in November 1959.

In March 1960 Jock Stein took his first management position with Dunfermline. The team win their last six games of the season to avoid relegation. The next season he leads them to the Scottish FA Cup.

The Scottish League were beaten 2-0 by the Italian League in November 1961, with Denis Law, John Charles and Gerry Hitchens helping the Italians.

In 1962 Scotland beat England 2-0 at Hampden Park, inflicting their first defeat at the ground in 25 years.

Rangers lost only two matches in their Scottish League Championship win of 1962-63, thanks to their strike duo of Jimmy Millar and Ralph Brand – known as 'a dose of M & B'.

Hearts lost the 1964-65 Championship on goal average – Kilmarnock winning by 0.042 goals. This prompted the Scottish FA to adopt the goal difference rule.

In 1965-66 Jock Stein became the first Celtic manager to have a completely free hand on team selection.

Scottish Records

Facts

In January 1967 Rangers were dealt the most embarassing defeat of their history when they were beaten by lowly Berwick in the first round of the Scottish FA Cup. Their strike duo of Jim Forrest and George McLean never played for Rangers again.

Celtic had four players sent off when they played Racing Club in Argentina for the World Club Championship. But Celtic played on with eight rather than seven players, as no-one knew who had been sent off.

Rangers broke the Scottish transfer record in October 1968 when they bought Colin Stein from Hibs for £100,000.

The 0-0 draw betwen England and Scotland in April 1970 was the first goalless draw in this fixture since their inaugural game in 1872.

Rangers' Scottish League Cup victory of 1970 brought their first silverware in five years.

Partick Thistle's Scottish League Cup victory of 1971-72 brought their first trophy in over 50 years. They did it in style, putting four past Celtic in the first 37 minutes.

On September 12 1971 Tommy Docherty was appointed Scotland manager.

The biggest away win in Scottish League history came in October 1959, when Hibs travelled to Airdrie and won 11-1.

After a pitch battle in the 1972 Final of the European Cup-Winners' Cup Rangers were banned from European football for two years – later commuted to a year.

 **Facts**   **Scottish Records**

In 1972-73 the Scottish women's team played their first international. They were beaten 3-2 by England at Morton.

Meadowbank were admitted to the Scottish League in 1975 as a reshuffle separates the teams into three divisions.

Billy Bremner and four other Scottish players were banned from playing for their country for life after incidents in a nighclub and hotel.

A friendle between Rangers and Aston Villa in October 1976 was abandoned when fans threw bottles onto the pitch and fought with police.

In 1976-77 Hearts were relegated for the first time in their 103-year history.

In 1977 Alfie Conn became the first player to win Scottish Cup Finals with both Old Firm teams, wining with Celtic four years after winning with Rangers.

In October 1976 Rangers announced that they would begin to sign players regardless of their religion.

Scotland were the only team from the British Isles to qualify for the 1978 World Cup.

The Scottish Cup fixture between Inverness Thistle and Falkirk in 1979 was postponed a record 29 times. It was scheduled for January 6 but was not played until February 22.

When Alex Ferguson led Aberdeen to the Scottish title in 1979-80 it was the first time the chamoionship had gone outside Glasgow since 1965.

The Glasgow Cup Final of 1980 was postponed after supporters of the Old Firm teams clashed after the Scottish FA Cup Final.

The 1980-81 Scottish League Cup Final was the first time that the two Dundee sides had met in a major final. The honours went to United.

In 1980-81 alcohol was banned at all Scottish football matches and on trains taking supporters to games.

In June 1981 Stranraer finally became the last Scottish League club to install floodlights.

Scottish Records

St Johnstone's John Pelosi was banned for six months in November 1981 after breaking the leg of Dunfermline's Jim Brown. Rangers' Gregor Stevens was also banned for six months after breaking the leg of a Kilmarnock player.

Celtic's 2-1 win at Rangers on January 1 1983 was their first New Year's Day victory away from home for 62 years.

Celtic's Roy Aitken became the first player to be sent off in a Scottish Cup Final since 1929 when he lunged at Mark McGhee in the 1984 final.

Celtic's European Cup-Winners' Cup second round replay against Rapid Vienna was played at Old Trafford when they were ordered to play at least 100 miles away from Parkhead to avoid crowd trouble.

Selkirk goalkeeper Richard Taylor was given the match ball as a souvenir after his side had been beaten 20-0 by Stirling Albion in the 1984-85 Scottish Cup.

When Dundee United beat Aberdeen at Pittodrie in December 1984 it was the Dons' first home defeat since September 1983, when their conquerors had also been Dundee United.

In 1984-85 Rangers signed a 14-year-old Catholic schoolboy – John Spencer.

Ken Wright scored three goals in four minutes when Raith beat Stenhousemuir 9-2 in November 1985.

Rangers broke the Scottish transfer record when they bought Terry Butcher for £725,000 in July 1986.

In July 1986 Andy Roxburgh was announced as the new Scotland manager, although he was yet to manage a club.

Graeme Souness was sent off in his first game in charge of Rangers in August 1986.

By the end of Graeme Souness' first year in charge of Rangers he had signed a record eight Englishmen.

Celtic built the first press box at a British ground at Celtic Park in 1894.

 **Facts**   **Scottish Records**

Dundee United were the first Scottish team to reach the final of the UEFA Cup when they lost to Gothenburg in 1986-87.

Two Scottish internationals have scored 30 goals for their country – Denis Law and Kenny Dalglish. Law scored his 30 in only 55 games, but Dalglish played 102 games for Scotland.

The beginning of the 1994-95 season saw the Scottish League structure change once again, as the system was extended to four leagues. It also took up the 'three points for a win' system.

Berwick physiotherapist Bobby Gordon had to play in goal for six minutes in their 1987-88 clash with Albion Rovers because the goalkeeper's car had broken down on the way to the match.

In July 1989 Rangers signed their first Catholic player – Mo Johnston. Some fans burnt their programmes and tickets. Johnston had been set to rejoin Celtic after a spell in France.

Rangers were just one game away from the treble in 1988-89 when Gary Stevens played a backpass which gave Celtic's Joe Miller the only goal of the Scotish Cup Final.

In January 1989 Rangers' first team played Gretna to raise money for the Lockerbie disaster fund. gretna won 2-1.

In 1989-90 Hearts made an audacious bid to buy out Hibs in an attempt to end the Glasgow duopoly on Scottish football. Protests from fans put an end to the plan.

Ally MCoist became the first player to win Europe's Golden Boot in 1991-92, when he formed a terrific strike partnership with Mark Hateley.

In February 1993 Ian Durrant of Rangers reached an out of court settlement of approximately £200,000 with Aberdeen's Neil Simpson after a tackle which almost ended Simpson's career.

Dundee United's shock victory over Rangers in the 1994 Scottish Cup Final followed six Cup Final defeats.

Brian Laudrup became the first foreigner to pick up the Scottish Player of the Year award in 1995.

Dundee hold the record for the least number of goals conceded in a Scottish League season, letting in only 12 goals in 1902-

Scottish Records

Facts

*03.*SCOTTISH LEAGUE CUP
WINNERS

1946 Aberdeen
1947 Rangers
1948 East Fife
1949 Rangers
1950 East Fife
1951 Motherwell
1952 Dundee
1953 Dundee
1954 East Fife
1955 Hearts
1956 Aberdeen
1957 Celtic
1958 Celtic
1959 Hearts
1960 Hearts
1961 Rangers
1962 Rangers
1963 Hearts
1964 Rangers
1965 Rangers
1966 Celtic
1967 Celtic
1968 Celtic
1969 Celtic
1970 Celtic
1971 Rangers
1972 Partick Thistle
1973 Hibernian
1974 Dundee
1975 Celtic
1976 Rangers
1977 Aberdeen
1978 Rangers
1979 Rangers
1980 Dundee United
1981 Dundee United
1982 Rangers
1983 Celtic
1984 Rangers

SKOL CUP

1985 Rangers
1986 Aberdeen
1987 Rangers
1988 Rangers
1989 Rangers
1990 Aberdeen
1991 Rangers
1992 Hibernian
1993 Rangers
1994 Rangers

COCA-COLA CUP

1995 Raith Rovers
1996 Aberdeen
1997 Rangers

SCOTTISH LEAGUE
CHAMPIONS

1891 Dumbarton/Rangers
1892 Dumbarton
1893 Celtic
1894 Celtic
1895 Hearts
1896 Celtic
1897 Hearts
1898 Celtic
1899 Rangers
1900 Rangers
1901 Rangers
1902 Rangers
1903 Hibernian
1904 Third Lanark
1905 Celtic
1906 Celtic
1907 Celtic
1908 Celtic
1909 Celtic
1910 Celtic
1911 Rangers
1912 Rangers
1913 Rangers
1914 Celtic

Facts   **Scottish Records**

1915 Celtic	1938 Celtic
1916 Celtic	1939 Rangers
1917 Celtic	1947 Rangers
1918 Rangers	1948 Hibernian
1919 Celtic	1949 Rangers
1920 Rangers	1950 Rangers
1921 Rangers	1951 Hibernian
1922 Celtic	1952 Hibernian
1923 Rangers	1953 Rangers
1924 Rangers	1954 Celtic
1925 Rangers	1955 Aberdeen
1926 Celtic	1956 Rangers
1927 Rangers	1957 Rangers
1928 Rangers	1958 Hearts
1929 Rangers	1959 Rangers
1930 Rangers	1960 Hearts
1931 Rangers	1961 Rangers
1932 Motherwell	1962 Dundee
1933 Rangers	1963 Rangers
1934 Rangers	1964 Rangers
1935 Rangers	1965 Kilmarnock
1936 Celtic	1966 Celtic
1937 Rangers	1967 Celtic

Scottish Records

1968 Celtic
1969 Celtic
1970 Celtic
1971 Celtic
1972 Celtic
1973 Celtic
1974 Celtic
1975 Rangers
1976 Partick Thistle
1977 St Mirren
1978 Morton
1979 Dundee
1980 Hearts
1981 Hibernian
1982 Motherwell
1983 St. Johnstone
1984 Morton
1985 Motherwell
1986 Hamilton Academicals
1987 Morton
1988 Hamilton
1989 Dunfermline
1990 St. Johnstone
1991 Falkirk
1992 Dundee
1993 Raith Rovers
1994 Falkirk
1995 Raith Rovers
1996 Dunfermline
1997 St. Johnstone

SCOTTISH PREMIER DIVISION

1976 Rangers
1977 Celtic
1978 Rangers
1979 Celtic
1980 Aberdeen
1981 Celtic
1982 Celtic
1983 Dundee United
1984 Aberdeen
1985 Aberdeen
1986 Celtic
1987 Rangers
1988 Celtic
1989 Rangers
1990 Rangers
1991 Rangers
1992 Rangers
1993 Rangers
1994 Rangers
1995 Rangers
1996 Rangers
1997 Rangers

INTERNATIONAL RECORDS

International Records

Facts

Peter Shilton became Britain's most-capped player when he won his 125th England cap against Italy in the 1990 World Cup.

Shilton overcame Pat Jennings' record, who played 119 times for Northern Ireland.

Up to the end of the 1996-97 season, four England players have gained more than a hundred caps – Peter Shilton (125), Bobby Moore (108), Bobby Charlton (106) and Billy Wright (105).

Kenny Dalglish is so far the only Scotland player to register 100 caps for his country. He won 102 in total.

The most consecutive international appearances involving a British player is set by Billy Wright who played for England for 70 straight games between October 1951 and May 1959.

Bobby Moore and Billy Wright both share the record for captaining England a record number of times – 90 each.

Billy Wright played in 105 of England's first 108 post-war matches.

Currently the most capped player in the world is Saudi Arabia's Majid Abdullah, who played 147 times for his country.

Sir Alf Ramsey fielded the same eleven England players in six consecutive matches – and England record. The same team played in the 1966 World Cup quarter-final, semi-final and final and the first three games of the next season.

Brazil hold the record for the longest unbeaten international sequence – 37 matches from December 1993 to January 1996. They had won 30 and drawn seven.

The previous record of unbeaten matches was 32, set by Hungary.

 **Facts**   **International Records**

The first all-seated attendance for a full international in Britain was 30,000 On May 31, 1989 for the game between Wales and West Germany at Cardiff Arms Park. The crowd was low because the terracing was closed.

England's first all-seated international at Wembley was against Yugoslavia on December 13, 1989.

England's first black player was Viv Anderson against Czechoslovakia on November 29, 1978.

The first British black player to be capped at international level was Eddie Parris for Wales against Northern Ireland in Belfast on December 5, 1931.

England's first black captin was Ugo Ehiogu who captained the Under-21 side against Holland on April 27, 1993.

Paul Ince became the first black player to captain England in a full international on June 9, 1993 against U.S.A.

Johnny Carey looks likely to be the last man to play for two British countries at full international level. Carey played 29 times for the Republic of Ireland and won seven caps for Northern Ireland.

Ryan Wilson played for England U-18's but went on to play international football with Wales under his more famous name of Ryan Giggs.

Many players have played for more than one country. They include: Ferenc Puskas – Hungary (84 caps, Spain 4) and Alfredo di Stefano – Argentina (7 caps, Spain 31).

Ladislav Kubala is the only player to have played for three different countries at international level. He played for Hungary three times, Czechoslovakia eleven times and Spain on 19 occasions.

The only player to have played for England and another country is John Reynolds. He also won caps for Ireland in the 1890's.

On only one occasion has a father and son played for the same international team inthe same match. Iceland's Arnor Gudjohnsen started the match against Estonia and was replaced by his 17-year-old son Eidur later in the match.

International Records

Facts

Up to July 1997, Marco Van Basten is the last player to score a hat-trick against England. He scored all three goals for Holland in the European Championship victory on June 15, 1988.

BRITISH INTERNATIONAL RECORDS

FIFA, the world governing body, was started in 1904 with seven founder members: Belgium, Denmark, France, Holland, Spain, Sweden and Switzerland.

ENGLAND V SCOTLAND
(England score first)

Year Res. Venue
1872 0-0 (Glasgow)
1873 4-2 (The Oval)
1874 1-2 (Glasgow)
1875 2-2 (The Oval)
1876 0-3 (Glasgow)
1877 1-3 (The Oval)
1878 2-7 (Glasgow)
1879 5-4 (The Oval)
1880 4-5 (Glasgow)
1881 1-6 (The Oval)
1882 1-5 (Glasgow)
1883 2-3 (Sheffield)
1884 0-1 (Glasgow)
1885 1-1 (The Oval)
1886 1-1 (Glasgow)
1887 2-3 (Blackburn)
1888 5-0 (Glasgow)
1889 2-3 (The Oval)
1890 1-1 (Glasgow)
1891 2-1 (Blackburn)
1892 4-1 (Glasgow)
1893 5-2 (Richmond)
1894 2-2 (Glasgow)
1895 3-0 (Goodison Park)
1896 1-2 (Glasgow)

1897 1-2 (Crystal Palace)
1898 3-1 (Glasgow)
1899 2-1 (Birmingham)
1900 1-4 (Glasgow)
1901 2-2 (Crystal Palace)
1902 2-2 (Birmingham)
1903 1-2 (Sheffield)
1904 1-0 (Glasgow)
1905 1-0 (Crystal Palace)
1906 1-2 (Glasgow)
1907 1-1 (Newcastle)
1908 1-1 (Glasgow)
1909 2-0 (Crystal Palace)
1910 0-2 (Glasgow)
1911 1-1 (Goodison Park)
1912 1-1 (Glasgow)
1913 1-0 (Stamford Bridge)
1914 1-3 (Glasgow)
1920 5-4 (Sheffield)
1921 0-3 (Glasgow)
1922 0-1 (Birmingham)
1923 2-2 (Glasgow)
1924 1-1 (Wembley)
1925 0-2 (Glasgow)
1926 0-1 (Manchester)
1927 2-1 (Glasgow)
1928 1-5 (Wembley)
1929 0-1 (Glasgow)
1930 5-2 (Wembley)
1931 0-2 (Glasgow)
1932 3-0 (Wembley)
1933 1-2 (Glasgow)
1934 3-0 (Wembley)
1935 0-2 (Glasgow)
1936 1-1 (Wembley)
1937 1-3 (Glasgow)
1938 0-1 (Wembley)
1939 2-1 (Glasgow)
1947 1-1 (Wembley)
1948 2-0 (Glasgow)

Facts   **International Records**

1949 1-3 (Wembley)	*SUMMARY:*
1950 1-0 (Glasgow) (WC)	*Played: 108.*
1951 2-3 (Wembley)	*England wins: 44.*
1952 2-1 (Glasgow)	*Scotland wins: 40.*
1953 2-2 (Wembley)	*Draws: 24.*
1954 4-2 (Glasgow) (WC)	
1955 7-2 (Wembley)	*GOALS:*
1956 1-1 (Glasgow)	*England 190,*
1957 2-1 (Wembley)	*Scotland 168.*
1958 4-0 (Glasgow)	
1959 1-0 (Wembley)	**ENGLAND V WALES**
1960 1-1 (Glasgow)	*(England score first)*
1961 9-3 (Wembley)	
1962 0-2 (Glasgow)	*Year Res. Venue*
1963 1-2 (Wembley)	1879 2-1 (The Oval)
1964 0-1 (Glasgow)	1880 3-2 (Wrexham)
1965 2-2 (Wembley)	1881 0-1 (Blackburn)
1966 4-3 (Glasgow)	1882 3-5 (Wrexham)
1967 2-3 (Wembley) (EC)	1883 5-0 (The Oval)
1968 1-1 (Glasgow) (EC)	1884 4-0 (Wrexham)
1969 4-1 (Wembley)	1885 1-1 (Blackburn)
1970 0-0 (Glasgow)	1886 3-1 (Wrexham)
1971 3-1 (Wembley)	1887 4-0 (The Oval)
1972 1-0 (Glasgow)	1888 5-1 (Crewe)
1973 5-0 (Glasgow)	1889 4-1 (Stoke)
1973 1-0 (Wembley)	1890 3-1 (Wrexham)
1974 0-2 (Glasgow)	1891 4-1 (Sunderland)
1975 5-1 (Wembley)	1892 2-0 (Wrexham)
1976 1-2 (Glasgow)	1893 6-0 (Stoke)
1977 1-2 (Wembley)	1894 5-1 (Wrexham)
1978 1-0 (Glasgow)	1895 1-1 (London)
1979 3-1 (Wembley)	1896 9-1 (Cardiff)
1980 2-0 (Glasgow)	1897 4-0 (Sheffield)
1981 0-1 (Wembley)	1898 3-0 (Wrexham)
1982 1-0 (Glasgow)	1899 4-0 (Bristol)
1983 2-0 (Wembley)	1900 1-1 (Cardiff)
1984 1-1 (Glasgow)	1901 6-0 (Newcastle)
1985 0-1 (Glasgow)	1902 0-0 (Wrexham)
1986 2-1 (Wembley)	1903 2-1 (Portsmouth)
1987 0-0 (Glasgow)	1904 2-2 (Wrexham)
1988 1-0 (Wembley)	1905 3-1 (Anfield)
1989 2-0 (Glasgow)	1906 1-0 (Cardiff)
1996 2-0 (Wembley) (EC)	1907 1-1 (Fulham)
	1908 7-1 (Wrexham)
	1909 2-0 (NOttingham)
	1910 1-0 (Cardiff)

International Records

1911 3-0 (Millwall)
1912 2-0 (Wrexham)
1913 4-3 (Bristol)
1914 2-0 (Cardiff)
1920 1-2 (Highbury)
1921 0-0 (Cardiff)
1922 1-0 (Anfield)
1923 2-2 (Cardiff)
1924 1-2 (Blackburn)
1925 2-1 (Swansea)
1926 1-3 (Selhurst Park)
1927 3-3 (Wrexham)
1927 1-2 (Burnley)
1928 3-2 (Swansea)
1929 6-0 (Stamford Bridge)
1930 4-0 (Wrexham)
1931 3-1 (Anfield)
1932 0-0 (Wrexham)
1933 1-2 (Newcastle)
1934 4-0 (Cardiff)
1935 1-2 (Wolverhampton)
1936 1-2 (Cardiff)
1937 2-1 (Middlesbrough)
1938 2-4 (Cardiff)
1946 3-0 (Manchester)
1947 3-0 (Cardiff)
1948 1-0 (Villa Park)
1949 4-1 (Cardiff) (WC)
1950 4-2 (Sunderland)
1951 1-1 (Cardiff)
1952 5-2 (Wembley)
1953 4-1 (Cardiff) (WC)
1954 3-2 (Wembley)
1955 1-2 (Cardiff)
1956 3-1 (Wembley)
1957 4-0 (Cardiff)
1958 2-2 (Birmingham)
1959 1-1 (Cardiff)
1960 5-1 (Wembley)
1961 1-1 (Cardiff)
1962 4-0 (Wembley)
1963 4-0 (Cardiff)
1964 2-1 (Wembley)
1965 0-0 (Cardiff)
1966 5-1 (Wembley) (EC)
1967 3-0 (Cardiff) (EC)

1969 2-1 (Wembley)
1970 1-1 (Cardiff)
1971 0-0 (Wembley)
1972 3-0 (Cardiff)
1972 1-0 (Cardiff) (WC)
1973 1-1 (Wembley) (WC)
1973 3-0 (Wembley)
1974 2-0 (Cardiff)
1975 2-2 (Wembley)
1976 2-1 (Wrexham)
1976 1-0 (Cardiff)
1977 0-1 (Wembley)
1978 3-1 (Cardiff)
1979 0-0 (Wembley)
1980 1-4 (Wrexham)
1981 0-0 (Wembley)
1982 1-0 (Cardiff)
1983 2-1 (Wembley)
1984 0-1 (Wrexham)

SUMMARY:
Played: 97.
England wins: 62.
Welsh wins: 14.
Draws: 21.

GOALS:
England 239,
Wales 90.

ENGLAND V IRELAND
(England score first)

Year Res. Venue
1882 13-0 (Belfast)
1883 7-0 (Liverpool)
1884 8-1 (Belfast)
1885 4-0 (Manchester)
1886 6-1 (Belfast)
1887 7-0 (Sheffield)
1888 5-1 (Belfast)
1889 6-1 (Goodison Park)
1890 9-1 (Belfast)
1891 6-1 (Wolverhampton)
1892 2-0 (Belfast)
1893 6-1 (Birmingham)

Facts

International Records

1894 2-2 (Belfast)	1907 1-0 (Goodison Park)
1895 9-0 (Derby)	1908 3-1 (Belfast)
1896 2-0 (Belfast)	1909 4-0 (Bradford Park
1897 6-0 (Nottingham)	Avenue)
1898 3-2 (Belfast)	1910 1-1 (Belfast)
1899 13-2 (Sunderland)	1911 2-1 (Derby)
1900 2-0 (Dublin)	1912 6-1 (Dublin)
1901 3-0 (Southampton)	1913 1-2 (Belfast)
1902 1-0 (Belfast)	1914 0-3 (Middlesbrough)
1903 4-0 (Wolverhampton)	1919 1-1 (Belfast)
1904 3-1 (Belfast)	1920 2-0 (Sunderland)
1905 1-1 (Middlesbrough)	1921 1-1 (Belfast)
1906 5-0 (Belfast)	1922 2-0 (West Bromwich)

International Records

Facts

1923 1-2 (Belfast)	1974 1-0 (Wembley)
1924 3-1 (Goodison Park)	1975 0-0 (Belfast)
1925 0-0 (Belfast)	1976 4-0 (Wembley)
1926 3-3 (Anfield)	1977 2-1 (Belfast)
1927 0-2 (Belfast)	1978 1-0 (Wembley)
1928 2-1 (Goodison Park)	1979 4-0 (Wembley) (EC)
1929 3-0 (Belfast)	1979 2-0 (Belfast)
1930 5-1 (Sheffield)	1979 5-1 (Belfast) (EC)
1931 6-2 (Belfast)	1980 1-1 (Wembley)
1932 1-0 (Blackpool)	1982 4-0 (Wembley)
1933 3-0 (Belfast)	1983 0-0 (Belfast)
1935 2-1 (Goodison Park)	1984 1-0 (Wembley)
1935 3-1 (Belfast)	1985 1-0 (Belfast) (WC)
1936 3-1 (Stoke)	1985 0-0 (Wembley) (WC)
1937 5-1 (Belfast)	1986 3-0 (Wembley (EC)
1938 7-0 (Manchester)	1987 2-0 (Belfast) (EC)
1946 7-2 (Belfast)	
1947 2-2 (Goodison Park)	*SUMMARY:*
1948 6-2 (Belfast)	*Played: 96.*
1949 9-2 (Manchester) (WC)	*England wins: 74.*
1950 4-1 (Belfast)	*Ireland wins: 6.*
1951 2-0 (Birmingham)	*Draws: 16*
1952 2-2 (Belfast)	
1953 3-1 (Goodison Park)	*GOALS:*
(WC)	*England: 319,*
1954 2-0 (Belfast)	*Ireland 80.*
1955 3-0 (Wembley)	
1956 1-1 (Belfast)	**SCOTLAND V WALES**
1957 2-3 (Wembley)	**(Scotland score first)**
1958 3-3 (Belfast)	
1959 2-1 (Wembley)	*Year Res. Venue*
1960 5-2 (Belfast)	1876 4-0 (Glasgow)
1961 1-1 (Wembley)	1877 2-0 (Wrexham)
1962 3-1 (Belfast)	1878 9-0 (Glasgow)
1963 8-3 (Wembley)	1879 3-0 (Wrexham)
1964 4-3 (Belfast)	1880 5-1 (Glasgow)
1965 2-1 (Wembley)	1881 5-1 (Wrexham)
1966 2-0 (Belfast) (EC)	1882 5-0 (Glasgow)
1967 2-0 (Wembley) (EC)	1883 4-1 (Wrexham)
1969 3-1 (Belfast)	1884 4-1 (Glasgow)
1970 3-1 (Wembley)	1885 8-1 (Wrexham)
1971 1-0 (Belfast)	1886 4-1 (Glasgow)
1972 0-1 (Wembley)	1887 2-0 (Wrexham)
1973 2-1 (Goodison Park) –	1888 5-1 (Edinburgh)
venue changed from	1889 0-0 (Wrexham)
Belfast because of	1890 5-0 (Paisley)
political situation.	1891 4-3 (Wrexham)

Facts

International Records

1892 6-2 (Edinburgh)	1949 2-0 (Glasgow)
1893 8-0 (Wrexham)	1950 3-1 (Cardiff)
1894 5-2 (Kilmarnock)	1951 0-1 (Glasgow)
1895 2-2 (Wrexham)	1952 2-1 (Cardiff) (WC)
1896 4-0 (Dundee)	1953 3-3 (Glasgow)
1897 2-2 (Wrexham)	1954 1-0 (Cardiff)
1898 5-2 (Motherwell)	1955 2-0 (Glasgow)
1899 6-0 (Wrexham)	1956 2-2 (Cardiff)
1900 5-2 (Aberdeen)	1957 1-1 (Glasgow)
1901 1-1 (Wrexham)	1958 3-0 (Cardiff)
1902 5-2 (Greenock)	1959 1-1 (Glasgow)
1903 1-0 (Cardiff)	1960 0-2 (Cardiff)
1904 1-1 (Dundee)	1961 2-0 (Glasgow)
1905 1-3 (Wrexham)	1962 3-2 (Cardiff)
1906 0-2 (Edinburgh)	1963 2-1 (Glasgow)
1907 0-1 (Wrexham)	1964 2-3 (Cardiff)
1908 2-1 (Dundee)	1965 4-1 (Glasgow) (EC)
1909 2-3 (Wrexham)	1966 1-1 (Cardiff) (EC)
1910 1-0 (Kilmarnock)	1967 3-2 (Glasgow)
1911 2-2 (Cardiff)	1969 5-3 (Wrexham)
1912 1-0 (Tynecastle)	1970 0-0 (Glasgow)
1913 0-0 (Newcastle)	1971 0-0 (Cardiff)
1914 0-0 (Glasgow)	1972 1-0 (Glasgow)
1920 1-1 (Cardiff)	1973 2-0 (Wrexham)
1921 2-1 (Aberdeen)	1974 2-0 (Glasgow)
1922 1-2 (Wrexham)	1975 2-2 (Cardiff)
1923 2-0 (Paisley)	1976 3-1 (Glasgow)
1924 0-2 (Cardiff)	1977 1-0 (Glasgow) (WC)
1925 3-1 (Tynecastle)	1977 0-0 (Wrexham)
1926 3-0 (Cardiff)	1977 2-0 (Anfield) (WC)
1927 3-0 (Glasgow)	1978 1-1 (Glasgow)
1928 2-2 (Wrexham)	1979 0-3 (Cardiff)
1929 4-2 (Glasgow)	1980 1-0 (Glasgow)
1930 4-2 (Cardiff)	1981 0-2 (Swansea)
1931 1-1 (Glasgow)	1982 1-0 (Glasgow)
1932 3-2 (Wrexham)	1983 2-0 (Cardiff)
1933 2-5 (Edingburgh)	1984 2-1 (Glasgow)
1934 2-2 (Cardiff)	1985 0-1 (Glasgow) (WC)
1935 3-2 (Aberdeen)	1985 1-1 (Cardiff) (WC)
1936 1-1 (Cardiff)	1997 0-1 (Kilmarnock)
1937 1-2 (Dundee)	
1938 1-2 (Cardiff)	*SUMMARY:*
1939 3-2 (Edinburgh)	*Played: 102.*
1946 1-3 (Wrexham)	*Scotland wins: 60.*
1947 1-2 (Glasgow)	*Welsh wins: 19.*
1948 3-1 (Cardiff) (WC)	*Draws: 23.*

International Records

GOALS:
Scotland 238,
Wales 113.

SCOTLAND V IRELAND
(Scotland score first)

Year Res. Venue
1884 5-0 (Belfast)
1885 8-2 (Glasgow)
1886 7-2 (Belfast)
1887 4-1 (Belfast)
1888 10-2 (Belfast)
1889 7-0 (Glasgow)
1890 4-1 (Belfast)
1891 2-1 (Glasgow)
1892 3-2 (Belfast)
1893 6-1 (Glasgow)
1894 2-1 (Belfast)
1895 3-1 (Glasgow)
1896 3-3 (Belfast)
1897 5-1 (Glasgow)
1898 3-0 (Belfast)
1899 9-1 (Glasgow)
1900 3-0 (Belfast)
1901 11-0 (Glasgow)
1902 5-1 (Belfast)
1903 0-2 (Glasgow)
1904 1-1 (Dublin)
1905 4-0 (Glasgow)
1906 1-0 (Dublin)
1907 3-0 (Glasgow)
1908 5-0 (Dublin)
1909 5-0 (Glasgow)
1910 0-1 (Belfast)
1911 2-0 (Glasgow)
1912 4-1 (Belfast)
1913 2-1 (Dublin)
1914 1-1 (Belfast)
1920 3-0 (Glasgow)
1921 2-0 (Belfast)
1922 2-1 (Glasgow)
1923 1-0 (Belfast)
1924 2-0 (Glasgow)
1925 3-0 (Belfast)
1926 4-0 (Glasgow)

1927 2-0 (Belfast)
1928 0-1 (Glasgow)
1929 7-3 (Belfast)
1930 3-1 (Glasgow)
1931 0-0 (Belfast)
1932 3-1 (Glasgow)
1933 4-0 (Belfast)
1934 1-2 (Glasgow)
1935 1-2 (Belfast)
1936 2-1 (Edinburgh)
1937 3-1 (Belfast)
1938 1-1 (Aberdeen)
1939 2-0 (Belfast)
1946 0-0 (Glasgow)
1947 0-2 (Belfast)
1948 3-2 (Glasgow)
1949 8-2 (Belfast)
1950 6-1 (Glasgow)
1951 3-0 (Belfast)
1952 1-1 (Glasgow)
1953 3-1 (Belfast)
1954 2-2 (Glasgow)
1955 1-2 (Belfast)
1956 1-0 (Glasgow)
1957 1-1 (Belfast)
1958 2-2 (Glasgow)
1959 4-0 (Belfast)
1960 5-1 (Glasgow)
1961 6-1 (Belfast)
1962 5-1 (Glasgow)
1963 1-2 (Belfast)
1964 3-2 (Glasgow)
1965 2-3 (Belfast)
1966 2-1 (Glasgow)
1967 0-1 (Belfast)
1969 1-1 (Glasgow)
1970 1-0 (Belfast)
1971 0-1 (Glasgow)
1972 2-0 (Glasgow)
1973 1-2 (Glasgow)
1974 0-1 (Glasgow)
1975 3-0 (Glasgow)
1976 3-0 (Glasgow)
1977 3-0 (Glasgow)
1978 1-1 (Glasgow)
1979 1-0 (Glasgow)

Facts — **International Records**

1980 0-1 (Belfast)
1981 1-1 (Glasgow) (WC)
1981 2-0 (Glasgow)
1981 0-0 (Belfast) (WC)
1982 1-1 (Belfast)
1983 0-0 (Glasgow)
1984 0-2 (Belfast)
1992 1-0 (Glasgow)

SUMMARY:
Played: 92.
Scotland wins: 61.
Ireland wins: 15.
Draws: 16.

GOALS:
Scotland 254,
Ireland 81.

WALES V IRELAND
(Wales score first)

Year Res. Venue
1882 7-1 (Wrexham)
1883 1-1 (Belfast)
1884 6-0 (Wrexham)
1885 8-2 (Belfast)
1886 5-0 (Wrexham)
1887 1-4 (Belfast)
1888 11-0 (Wrexham)
1889 3-1 (Belfast)
1890 5-2 (Shrewsbury)
1891 2-7 (Belfast)
1892 1-1 (Bangor)
1893 3-4 (Belfast)
1894 4-1 (Swansea)
1895 2-2 (Belfast)
1896 6-2 (Wrexham)
1897 3-4 (Belfast)
1898 0-1 (Llandudno)
1899 0-1 (Belfast)
1900 2-0 (Llandudno)
1901 1-0 (Belfast)
1902 0-3 (Cardiff)
1903 0-2 (Belfast)
1904 0-1 (Bangor)

1905 2-2 (Belfast)
1906 4-4 (Wrexham)
1907 3-2 (Belfast)
1908 0-1 (Aberdare)
1909 3-2 (Belfast)
1910 4-1 (Wrexham)
1911 2-1 (Belfast)
1912 2-3 (Cardiff)
1913 1-0 (Belfast)
1914 1-2 (Wrexham)
1920 2-2 (Belfast)
1921 2-1 (Swansea)
1922 1-1 (Belfast)
1923 0-3 (Wrexham)
1924 1-0 (Belfast)
1925 0-0 (Wrexham)
1926 0-3 (Belfast)
1927 2-2 (Cardiff)
1928 2-1 (Belfast)
1929 2-2 (Wrexham)
1930 0-7 (Belfast)
1931 3-2 (Wrexham)
1932 0-4 (Belfast)
1933 4-1 (Wrexham)
1934 1-1 (Belfast)
1935 3-1 (Wrexham)
1936 2-3 (Belfast)
1937 4-1 (Wrexham)
1938 0-1 (Belfast)
1939 3-1 (Wrexham)
1947 1-2 (Belfast)
1948 2-0 (Wrexham)
1949 2-0 (Belfast)
1950 0-0 (Wrexham) (WC)
1951 2-1 (Belfast)
1952 3-0 (Swansea)
1953 3-2 (Belfast)
1954 1-2 (Wrexham) (WC)
1955 3-2 (Belfast)
1956 1-1 (Cardiff)
1957 0-0 (Belfast)
1958 1-1 (Cardiff)
1959 1-4 (Belfast)
1960 3-2 (Wrexham)
1961 5-1 (Belfast)
1962 4-0 (Cardiff)

International Records

1963 4-1 (Belfast)
1964 2-3 (Swansea)
1965 5-0 (Belfast)
1966 1-4 (Cardiff)
1967 0-0 (Belfast) (EC)
1968 2-0 (Wrexham) (EC)
1969 0-0 (Belfast)
1970 1-0 (Swansea)
1971 0-1 (Belfast)
1972 0-0 (Wrexham)
1973 0-1 (Goddison Park)
    venue changed from
    Belfast because of
    political situation
1974 1-0 (Wrexham)
1975 0-1 (Belfast)
1976 1-0 (Swansea)

1977 1-1 (Belfast)
1978 1-0 (Wrexham)
1979 1-1 (Belfast)
1980 0-1 (cardiff)
1982 3-0 (Wrexham)
1983 1-0 (Belfast)
1984 1-1 (Swansea)

SUMMARY:
Played: 90.
Welsh wins: 42.
Ireland wins: 27.
Draws: 21.

GOALS:
Wales 182,
Ireland 127.

LEAGUE CUP

League Cup

Facts

The League Cup was founded by Alan Hardaker in 1960. The former League secretary is still part of the competition, his name is given to the Final's Man of the Match trophy.

Aston Villa became the first winners of the League Cup in 1961, when they beat Rotherham United 3-2 on aggregate.

The first six League Cup Finals were played over two legs.

The first League Cup Final to be played at Wembley was in 1967. QPR beat West Bromwich Albion 3-2.

That year also saw the first year of qualification for Europe for the League Cup winners.

Aston Villa became the first team to win the trophy for the second time, when they defeated Norwich City 2-1 in 1975.

Nottingham Forest were the first side to successfully defend the trophy when they beat Liverpool and Southampton in 1978 and 1979 respectively.

In 1982 the League Cup became the Milk Cup and the sponsorship of the Cup began.

Liverpool stamped their authority on League Cup history when they won the competition four times in succession in the early 1980's.

Liverpool's reign was ended in the 1984-85 competition, when eventual winners' Sunderland beat them in the fourth round. Liverpool's undefeated run in the League Cup lasted 41 games.

Everton are the only team out of the original "big five" not to have won the League Cup. They have appeared in two finals, in 1977 and 1984.

Before the start of the 1997-98 season, Aston Villa and Liverpool are the most successful teams in League Cup history. Both have won the trophy five times.

The largest margin of victory in a League Cup Final is currently three goals, shared by Oxford United (1986) and Aston Villa (1996). Both were 3-0 victors.

 **Facts**   **League Cup**

Before the 1997-98 season, Manchester United have lost three of their four League Cup Finals. Their only victory came in 1992.

In 1987 the Milk Cup became the Littlewoods Cup. The first winners' of the newly named trophy were Arsenal, beating Liverpool 2-1.

Arsenal created another piece of history in the 1987 Final. Liverpool had never lost a game when Ian Rush had scored the first goal, but two goals from Arsenal's Charlie Nicholas put paid to that record.

Luton reached consecutive finals in 1988 and 1989, but failed to retain the trophy they won in 1988 when Nottingham Forest defeated them 3-1.

The name of the Cup changed for the third time in 1991 when it was renamed the Rumbelows Cup. The first winners of the newly sponsored Cup was Sheffield Wednesday when they defeated Manchester United 1- 0

Before the 1997-98 season, the last time a League Cup Final went to extra-time was in 1984, when Liverpool beat Everton after a replay.

The top score by a team in a League Cup tie was set by West Ham. They beat Bury 10-0 in the second round, second leg on October 25, 1983. That scoreline was matched by Liverpool in the second round, first leg against Fulham on September 23, 1986.

The record aggregate score was also set by Liverpool in their 13-2 defeat over Fulham in 1986. Other 11-goal aggregate wins: West Ham 12, Bury 1 in 1983 and Liverpool 11, Exeter 0 in 1981.

Oldham Athletic's Frank Bunn set an individual scoring record in the competition when he scored six goals against Scarborough in the 1989 third round.

The 1,987 attendance at the Wimbledon-Bolton second round, second leg tie in 1992 was the lowest for a League Cup tie played at a top division club's ground.

The first £1m gate receipts for a League Cup Final was in 1987 for the Arsenal-Liverpool match.

League Cup

Up to the start of the 1997-98 season, the League Cup has had four sponsors – Milk Cup 1981-86, Littlewoods Cup 1987-90, Rumbelows Cup 1991-92 and Coca-Cola Cup since 1993.

Geoff Hurst set the record for individual League Cup goals. He scored 49 goals (43 for West Ham, 6 for Stoke City) between 1960 and 1975. At the start of the 1997-98 season, Ian Rush was just one goal behind, scoring all his 48 goals for Liverpool.

Clive Allen's 12 goals for Tottenham in 1986-87 was a record by an individual player in a League Cup season.

Kenny Dalglish and Ian Rush have both made six League Cup Final appearances for Liverpool. Rush has won the most winners medals, five.

Port Vale and Nothampton Town both had two players sent-off when they met in a first round, first leg tie on August 18, 1987 to set a League Cup record.

Andrei Kanchelskis became the first player to be sent-off in a Wembley League Cup Final when he was shown the red card for Manchester United against Aston Villa in 1994.

Up to the start of the 1997-98 season, two players have missed League Cup Final penalties at Wembley. Clive Walker (Sunderland) missed in 1985 and Nigel Winterburn (Arsenal) had his saved by Luton's Andy Dibble in 1988.

Aston Villa's Ray Graydon also had his penalty saved by Norwich's Kevin Keelan in the 1975 Final, but he scored from the rebound.

Andy Blair set a League Cup record when he scored a hat-trick of penalties for Sheffield Wednesday against Luton in the fourth round on November 20, 1984.

 **Facts**   **League Cup**

LEAGUE CUP FINALS

(1961-66 over two legs)
1961 Aston Villa 3, Rotherham United 2 (aet) (0-2a, 3-0h)
1962 Norwich 4, Rochdale 0 (3-0a, 1-0h)
1963 Birmingham City 3, Aston Villa 1 (3-1h, 0-0a)
1964 Leicester City 4, Stoke City 3 (1-1a, 3-2h)
1965 Chelsea 3, Leicester City 2 (3-2h, 0-0a)
1966 West Bromwich Albion 5, West Ham United 3 (1-2a, 4-1h)

AT WEMBLEY

1967 **Queens Park Rangers 3, West Browmich Albion 2**
1968 **Leeds United 1, Arsenal 0**
1969 **Swindon Town 3, Arsenal 1 (aet)**
1970 **Manchester City 2, West Bromwich Albion 1 (aet)**
1971 **Tottenham Hotspur 2, Aston Villa 0**
1972 **Stoke City 2, Chelsea 1**
1973 **Tottenham Hotspur 1, Norwich City 0**
1974 **Wolverhampton Wanderers 2, Manchester City 1**
1975 **Aston Villla 1, Norwich City 0**
1976 **Manchester City 2, Newcastle United 1**

League Cup

1977 Aston Villa 0, Everton 0 (aet) (Replay at Sheffield
Wednesday's Hillsborough: 1-1 (aet). Second replay at
manchester United's Old Trafford: 3-2)
1978 Nottingham Forest 0, Liverpool 0 (Replay at Manchester
United's Old Trafford: 1-0)
1979 Nottingham Forest 3, Southampton 2
1980 Wolverhampton Wanderers 1, Nottingham Forest 0
1981 Liverpool 1, West Ham United 1 (Replay at Aston Villa's
Villa Park: 2-1)

MILK CUP

1982 Liverpool 3, Tottenham Hotspur 1 (aet)
1983 Liverpool 2, Manchester United 1 (aet)
*1984 Liverpool 0, Everton 0 (aet) (Replay at Manchester City's
Maine Road: 1-0)*
1985 Norwich City 1, Sunderland 0
1986 Oxford United 3, Queens Park Rangers 0

LITTLEWOODS CUP

1987 Arsenal 2, Liverpool 1
1988 Luton Town 3, Arsenal 2
1989 Nottingham Forest 3, Luton Town 1
1990 Nottingham Forest 1, Oldham Athletic 0

RUMBELOWS CUP

1991 Sheffield Wednesday 1, Manchester United 0
1992 Manchester United 1, Nottingham Forest 0

COCA-COLA CUP

1993 Arsenal 2, Sheffield Wednesday 1
1994 Aston Villa 3, Manchester United 1
1995 Liverpool 2, Bolton Wanderers 1
1996 Aston Villa 3, Leeds United 0
1997 Leicester City 1, Middlesbrough 1 (aet) (Replay at
Sheffield Wednesday's Hillsborough: 1-0)

EUROPEAN CHAMPIONSHIP

European Championship Facts

EUROPEAN CHAMPIONSHIP FINALS

1960 USSR 2, Yugoslavia 1 (aet) (Paris, France)
1964 Spain 2, USSR 1 (Madrid, Spain)
1968 Italy 1, Yugoslavia 1 (Rome, Italy) (replay: 2-0)
1972 West Germany 3, USSR 0 (Brussels, Belgium)
1976 Czechoslovakia 2, West Germany 2 (aet) (Czechoslovakia won 5-3 on penalties) (Belgrade, Yugoslavia)
1980 West Germany 2, Belgium 1 (Rome, Italy)
1984 France 2, Spain 0 (Paris, France)
1988 Holland 2, USSR 0 (Munich, West Germany)
1992 Denmark 2, Germany 0 (Gothenburg, Sweden)
1996 Germany 2, Czech Republic 1 (in overtime) (London, England)
The USSR were the first European champions. They beat Yugoslavia 2-1 after extra-time in 1960.

Euro 96 was the 10th European Championship. There have been nine different winners. West Germany won the title in 1972 and 1980, and a united Germany succeded in 1996.

The list of winners are: 1960 – USSR, 1964 – Spain, 1968 – Italy, 1972 – West Germany, 1976 – Czechoslovakia, 1980 – West Germany, 1984 – France, 1988 – Holland, 1992 – Denmark, 1996 – Germany.

West Germany made three successive appearances in the Final, from 1972.

Michel Platini currently holds the record for most goals in the finals. He scored nine in 1984, scoring in every match.

For the first time in the competition's history, the 2000 Championship will be co-hosted. Holland and Belgium were the only applicants and will share the matches.

The trophy is officially named the Henri Delaunay Cup, which is named after the Frenchman who founded the competition.

Seven players were sent-off in Euro 96, equalling the total of dismissals in all of the previous nine finals.

Holland's 1988 semi-final victory over West Germany was particulary special for manager Rinus Michels – he had been in charge of the Dutch when they lost the World Cup Final to the Germans 14 years earlier.

 **Facts** — **European Championship**

Since winning the first tournament in 1960, the USSR have appeared in three more European Championship Finals – and lost them all.

Up to the 2000 qualifying tournament, three men top the goalscoring charts in the competition's history with 16 goals. Gerd Muller of West Germany scored 12 in qualifying matches and four in the finals, Holland's Marco Van Basten has 11 goals in qualifying and five in finals, and Davor Suker scored once for Yugoslavia in qualifying and 12 for Croatia, plus three in the finals.

Although England were beaten in the 1996 semi-finals, they did win one award – the Fair Play trophy.

Alan Shearer was top goalscorer in the 1996 Championship. He scored five goals in five games. Marco Van Basten is the only other player to score five times in one tournament, in 1988.

West Germany went 32 European Championship matches without defeat (including qualifiers) from October 7, 1967 to November 17, 1982.

The highest score in the tournament was set by Spain on December 21, 1983. They beat Malta 12-1 in a qualifier.

Before Euro 2000 qualifying, only three England players have scored hat-tricks in the Championship, and all in qualifiers – Luther Blissett v Luxembourg in 1984, Gary Lineker in 1988 against Turkey. Malcolm Macdonald scored five goals against Cyprus in 1976.

Germany's Oliver Bierhoff became the first player to score a 'golden goal' in a major Final. His goal five minutes into sudden death gave his country victory over the Czech Republic in 1996.

The USSR reached the 1960 semi-finals after being awarded a walkover against Spain because General Franco refused his team to play in Communist Moscow.

England first entered the tournament in 1964.

Seventeen teams entered the first tournament in 1960. It was called the European Nations Cup until 1966.

The 1960 Final was played at the Parc des Princes in Paris, which was watched by only 17,966.

European Championship  Facts

England failed to qualify for the 1984 Championship after losing to Denmark 1-0. That goal is the only one the Danes have scored against England at Wembley in five matches.

England scored only two goals in the 1988 Championship in West Germany. Bryan Robson scored in the 1-3 defeat by Holland and Tony Adams netted against USSR, but England suffered the same scoreline as the Dutch game.

Up to the start of the 2000 Championship, no British country have made a Final appearance.

The eight stadiums that hosted matches during Euro 96 were: Wembley, Villa Park (Aston Villa), St James' Park (Newcastle), Elland Road (Leeds), Hillsborough (Sheffield Wednesday), City Ground (Nottingham Forest), Anfield (Liverpool) and Old Trafford (Manchester United).

Holland were the last nation to qualify for Euro 96. They beat the Republic of Ireland in a play-off at Anfield in December 1995.

Royal Mail issued special commemorative stamps for the 1996 Championship. Five football legends were featured: Dixie Dean, Bobby Moore, Duncan Edwards, Billy Wright and Danny Blanchflower.

The first European Championship match was a qualifier between Ireland and Czechoslovakia on April 5, 1958.

England were awarded to host the 1996 Championship because their bid was the only to be registered by the closing date of November 1991.

The Queen presented the trophy to Jurgen Klinsmann after the 1996 Final. The last time she handed over a trophy at Wembley was the World Cup to Bobby Moore in 1966.

For the 1996 European Championship, all the previous winners of the trophy qualified.

England's victory over Scotland in Euro 96 was their first win in the finals since 1980.

San Marino's European qualifying record is abysmal. They have lost all 18 matches.

 **Facts**   **European Championship**

*For the first time in the competition's history, the holders
(Denmark) did not have to qualify for the 1996 finals*

**Denmark caused the biggest shock of the tournament's history
when they won in 1992, despite not qualifying. They received a
late entry after Yugoslavia were ejected as civil war broke out
in the country.**

*England manager Glenn Hoddle's last playing appearance for his
country was in the 1-3 defeat by USSR in the 1988 Championship.*

**Euro 96 was the biggest tournament in the competition's
history. 16 teams competed in the finals for the first time.**

*Despite being the second highest England goalscorer, Gary Lineker
failed to score in his six finals appearances.*

**Berti Vogts became the first
man to win the European
Championship as both
player and as a
manger. He played
for the victorious
West Germans in
1972 and managed
Germany to victory
in 1996.**

European Championship

Euro 96 was the first top-class tournament to introduce the "Golden Goal" rule.

In 1968 Scotland faced England at Hampden Park in the tournament. 134,000 packed into Hampden Park.

Euro 96 had four countries competiting in their first European Championship – Switzerland, Croatia, Turkey and the Czech Republic.

The referee for the first European Championship Final in 1960 was Englishman Arthur Ellis, who later became a presenter on TV game show It's A Knockout.

Germany's Euro 96 captain Jurgen Klinsmann was suspended for the first game of the tournament after picking up a yellow card in his country's final qualifying match.

The official mascot for Euro 96 was a lion named Goaliath.

FOOTBALL LEAGUE MILESTONES

Football League Milestones Facts

The first code of football rules were compiled at Cambridge University in 1848.

The oldest Football League club, Notts County, were formed in 1862.

The Football Association was founded in 1863. The FA Cup was introduced eight years later.

The first football international match took place in 1872. Scotland and England drew 0-0.

Shinguards were introduced into football in 1874. A year later the crossbar replaced tape as part of the goal frame.

The Footbal League was founded by Wm. McGregor in 1888 with the first match taking place on September 8.

Goal-nets were introduced in 1891, as well as the penalty-kick.

The Football League opened a Second Division in 1892. Promotion and relegation was introduced six years later.

FIFA was founded by the seven member countries in 1904.

Transfer deadline day was introduced in 1911.

The Football League was extended to 44 clubs in 1919.

The Third Division (South) was formed in 1920. The North version came a year later.

England and Scotland met in the first Wembley International in 1924. The game ended 1-1.

Also in 1924, the Rules were changed to allow goals to be scored direct from corner-kicks.

The new offside law came into effect from 1925.

The first Football League match to be broadcast on radio was on January 22, 1927, for the match between Arsenal and Sheffield United. Other firsts in 1927: The FA Cup Final was broadcast on radio and Charles Clegg, president of the FA became the first knight of foootball.

 **Facts**   **Football League Milestones**

Britain's representatives withdrew from FIFA in 1928. They rejoined in 1946.

The Football League celebrate their 50th Jubilee. An arc on the edge of the penalty-area was introduced. FA secretary, Stanley Rous, re-drafts the Laws of the Game.

The numbering of players' shirts in Football League matches became compulsory in 1939.

Stanley Rous is knighted in 1949.

The Football League was extended from 88 clubs to 92 in 1950.

The last occasion of Football League matches played on Christmas Day was in 1957.

The Football League was re-structured into four divisions in 1958.

The Football League Cup was introduced in 1960.

The first Match of the Day was televised on August 22, 1964. The first match to be covered was the League match between Liverpool and Arsenal. Liverpool won 3-2.

Substitutes were allowed in Football League matches in 1965.

The Football League introduced the loan system in 1967. Originally two loan transfers a season were allowed to clubs.

League football was played for the first time on a Sunday on January 20, 1974.

Transfer Tribunal was formed by the Football League in 1978.

The Football League increase the points for a win to three instead of two in 1981. Queens Park Rangers become the first Football League club to install an artifical pitch in the same year. Also in the same year, referee's yellow and red cards are scrapped by the Football League. They were re-introduced in 1987.

The Football League Cup becomes a sponsored event when it is re-named the Milk Cup in 1982.

The Football League gains sponsorship and becomes the Canon Football League at the start of the 1983-84 season.

Football League Milestones

Charlton and Crystal Palace become the first clubs to share a ground (Palace's Selhurst Park) in the Football League's history in 1985.

Football League clubs are banned from European competition in 1985 after the Heysel disaster before the Liverpool-Juventus European Cup Final.

The Football League announced a new sponsor in 1986 when the Today newspaper put it's name to the competition.

The Football League introduce play-off matches to decide the final promotion/relegation places in 1987.

The Football League acquired their third sponsor, Barclays Bank, in 1987.

Football League clubs are allowed back into European competition after a five-year exile in 1990.

The Football League is reduced to three divisions, and 71 clubs, after the introduction of the FA Carling Premiership in the 1992-93 season.

Barclays Bank ended their sponsorship with the Football League in 1993. Endsleigh Insurance replace them.

For the start of the 1996-97 season, Nationwide Building Society were the new sponsors of the Football League.

In 1961 Fulham's Johnny Haynes became the first player to earn £100 a week wages.

EUROPEAN CLUB CUP FINALS

European Club Cup Finals

EUROPEAN CUP FINALS

1956 Real Madrid 4, Rheims 3 (Paris)
1957 Real Madrid 2, Fiorentina 0 (Madrid)
1958 Real Madrid 3, AC Milan 2 (aet) (Brussels)
1959 Real Madrid 2, Rheims 0 (Stuttgart)
1960 Real Madrid 7, Eintracht Frankfurt 3 (Glasgow)
1961 Benfica 3, Barcelona 2 (Berne)
1962 Benfica 5, Real Madrid 3 (Amsterdam)
1963 AC Milan 2, Benfica 1 (Wembley)
1964 Inter Milan 3, Real Madrid 1 (Vienna)
1965 Inter Milan 1, Benfica 0 (Milan)
1966 Real Madrid 2, Partizan Belgrade 1 (Brussels)
1967 Celtic 2, Inter Milan 1 (Lisbon)
1968 Manchester United 4, Benfica 1 (aet) (Wembley)
1969 AC Milan 4, Ajax 1 (Madrid)
1970 Feyenoord 2, Celtic 1 (aet) (Milan)
1971 Ajax 2, Panathinaikos 0 (Wembley)
1972 Ajax 2, Inter Milan 0 (Rotterdam)
1973 Ajax 1, Juventus 0 (Belgrade)
1974 Bayern Munich 1, Atletico Madrid 1 (Brussels; replay: 4-0)
1975 Bayern Munich 2, Leeds United 0 (Paris)
1976 Bayern Munich 1, St. Etienne 0 (Glasgow)
1977 Liverpool 3, Borussia Moenchengladbach 1 (Rome)
1978 Liverpool 1, Brugge (Wembley)
1979 Nottingham Forest 1, Malmo 0 (Munich)
1980 Nottingham Forest 1, Hamburg 0 (Madrid)
1981 Liverpool 1, Real Madrid 0 (Paris)
1982 Aston Villa 1, Bayern Munich 0 (Rotterdam)
1983 Hamburg 1, Juventus 0 (Athens)
1984 Liverpool 1, Roma 1
       (aet; Liverpool won 4-2 on penalties) (Rome)
1985 Juventus 1, Liverpool 0 (Brussels)
1986 Steaua Bucharest 0, Barcelona 0
       (aet; Steaua won 2-0 on penalties) (Seville)
1987 Porto 2, Bayern Munich 1 (Vienna)
1988 PSV Eindhoven 0, Benfica 0
       (aet; PSV won 6-5 on penalties) (Stuttgart)
1989 AC Milan 4, Steaua Bucharest 0 (Barcelona)
1990 AC Milan 1, Benfica 0 (Vienna)
1991 Red Star Belgrade 0, Marseille 0
       (aet; Red Star won 5-3 on penalties) (Bari)
1992 Barcelona 1, Sampdoria 0 (Wembley)
1993 Marseille 1, AC Milan 0 (Munich)
1994 AC Milan 4, Barcelona 0 (Athens)
1995 Ajax 1, AC Milan 0 (Vienna)

 **Facts**   **European Club Cup Finals**

1996   Juventus 1, Ajax 1
       (aet; Juventus won 4-2 on penalties) (Rome)
1997   Borussia Dortmund 3, Juventus 1 (Munich)

EUROPEAN CUP-WINNERS' CUP FINALS

(First Final played over two legs. Aggregate score shown)
1961 Fiorentina 4, Rangers 1
1962 Atletico Madrid 1, Fiorentina 1
      (Glasgow; replay at Stuttgart: 3-0)
1963 Tottenham Hotspur 5, Atletico Madrid 1 (Rotterdam)
1964 Sporting Lisbon 3, MTK Budapest 3
      (Brussels; replay at Antwerp: 1-0)
1965 West Ham United 2, 1860 Munich 0 (Wembley)
1966 Borussia Dortmund 2, Liverpool 1 (aet) (Glasgow)
1967 Bayern Munich 1, Rangers 0 (aet) (Nuremberg)
1968 AC Milan 2, Hamburg 0 (Rotterdam)
1969 Slovan Bratislava 3, Barcelona 2 (Basle)
1970 Manchester City 2, Gornik Zabrze 1 (Vienna)
1971 Chelsea 1, Real Madrid 1 (aet) (Athens; replay 2-1)
1972 Rangers 3, Moscow Dynamo 2 (Barcelona)
1973 AC Milan 1, Leeds United 0 (Salonika)
1974 Magdeburg 2, AC Milan 0 (Rotterdam)
1975 Dynamo Kiev 3, Ferencvaros 0 (Basle)
1976 Anderlecht 4, West Ham United 2 (Brussels)
1977 Hamburg 2, Anderlecht 0 (Amsterdam)
1978 Anderlecht 4, Austria Wacker 0 (Paris)
1979 Barcelona 4, Fortuna Dusseldorf 3 (aet) (Basle)
1980 Valencia 0, Arsenal 0 (aet; Valencia won 5-4 on penalties)
1981 Dynamo Tbilisi 2, Carl Zeiss Jena 1 (Dusseldorf)
1982 Barcelona 2, Standard Liege 1 (Barcelona)
1983 Aberdeen 2, Real Madrid 1 (aet) (Gothenburg)
1984 Juventus 2, Porto 1 (Basle)
1985 Everton 3, Rapid Vienna 1 (Rotterdam)
1986 Dynamo Kiev 3, Atletico Madrid 0 (Lyon)
1987 Ajax 1, Lokomotiv Leipzig 0 (Athens)
1988 Mechelen 1, Ajax 0 (Strasbourg)
1989 Barcelona 2, Sampdoria 0 (Berne)
1990 Sampdoria 2, Anderlecht 0 (Gothenburg)
1991 Manchester United 2, Barcelona 1 (Rotterdam)
1992 Werder Bremen 2, Monaco 0 (Lisbon)
1993 Parma 3, Royal Antwerp 1 (Wembley)
1994 Arsenal 1, Parma 0 (Copenhagen)
1995 Real Zaragoza 2, Arsenal 1 (aet) (Paris)
1996 Paris St. Germain 1, Rapid Vienna 0 (Brussels)
1997 Barcelona 1, Paris St. Germain 0 (Rotterdam)

European Club Cup Finals Facts

FAIRS CUP FINALS

(Played over two legs – except 1964 & 1965)
1958 Barcelona 8, London 2 (2-2a,6-0h)
1960 Barcelona 4, Birmingham 1 (0-0a,4-1h)
1961 Roma 4, Birmingham City 2 (2-2a,2-0h)
1962 Valencia 7, Barcelona 3 (6-2h,1-1a)
1963 Valencia 4, Dynamo Zagreb 1 (2-1a,2-0h)
1964 Real Zaragoza 2, Valencia 1 (Barcelona)
1965 Ferencvaros 1, Juventus 0 (Turin)
1966 Barcelona 4, Real Zaragoza 3 (0-1h,4-2a)
1967 Dynamo Zagreb 2, Leeds United 0 (2-0h,0-0a)
1968 Leeds United 1, Ferencvaros 0 (1-0h,0-0a)
1969 Newcastle United 6, Ujpest Dozsa 2 (3-0h,3-2a)
1970 Arsenal 4, Anderlecht 3 (1-3a,3-0h)
1971 Leeds United 3, Juventus 3
(2-2a,1-1h; Leeds won on away goals)

UEFA CUP FINALS

1972 Tottenham Hotspur 3, Wolverhampton Wanderers 2 (2-1a,1-1h)
1973 Liverpool 3, Borussia Moenchengladbach 2 (3-0h,0-2a)
1974 Feyenoord 4, Tottenham Hotspur 2 (2-2a,2-0h)
1975 Borussia Moenchengladbach 5, Twente Enschede 1 (0-0h,5-1a)
1976 Liverpool 4, Brugge 3 (3-2h,1-1a)
1977 Juventus 2, Atletico Bilbao 2 (1-0h,1-2a; Juventus won on
*   away goals)*
1978 PSV Eindhoven 3, Bastia 0 (0-0a,3-0h)
1979 Borussia Moenchengladbach 2, Red Star Belgrade 1 (1-1a,1-0h)
1980 Eintracht Frankfurt 3, Borussia Moenchengladbach 3 (2-3a,1-
*   0h; Frankfurt won away goals)*
1981 Ipswich Town 5, AZ 67 Alkmaar 4 (3-0h,2-4a)
1982 Gothenburg 4, Hamburg 0 (1-0h,3-0a)
1983 Anderlecht 2, Benfica 1 (1-0h,1-1a)
1984 Tottenham Hotspur 2, Anderlecht 2 (1-1a,1-1h; Tottenham won
*   4-3 on penalties)*
1985 Real Madrid 3, Videoton 1 (3-0a,0-1h)
1986 Real Madrid 5, Cologne 3 (5-1h,0-2a)
1987 Gothenburg 2, Dundee United 1 (1-0h,1-1a)
1988 Bayer Leverkusen 3, Espanol 3 (0-3a,3-0h; Leverkusen won 3-
*   2 on penalties)*
1989 Napoli 5, Stuttgart 4 (2-1h,3-3a)
1990 Juventus 3, Fiorentina 1 (3-1h,0-0a)
1991 Inter Milan 2, Roma 1 (2-0h,0-1a)
1992 Ajax 2, Torino 2 (2-2a,0-0h; Ajax won on away goals)
1993 Juventus 6, Borussia Dortmund 1 (3-1a,3-0h)

Facts   **European Club Cup Finals**

1994 Inter Milan 2, Salzburg 0
      (1-0a,1-0h)
1995 Parma 2, Juventus 1 (1-
      0h,1-1a)
1996 Bayern Munich 5,
      Bordeaux 1 (2-0h,3-1a)
1997 Schalke 04 1, Inter Milan
      1 (1-0h,0-1a; Schalke won
      4-1 on penalties)

EUROPEAN CUP

6 - Real Madrid
5 - AC Milan
4 - Ajax, Liverpool
3 - Bayern Munich
2 - Benfica
2 - Inter Milan
2 - Juventus
2 - Nottingham Forest
1 - Aston Villa
1 - Barcelona
1 - Borussia Dortmund
1 - Celtic
1 - Feyenoord
1 - Hamburg
1 - Manchester United
1 - Marseille
1 - PSV Eindhoven
1 - FC Porto
1 - Red Star Belgrade
1 - Steaua Bucharest

*EUROPEAN CUP-WINNERS'
CUP*

4 - Barcelona
2 - Anderlecht
2 - Dynamo Kiev
2 - AC Milan
1 - Aberdeen
1 - Ajax
1 - Arsenal
1 - Atletico Madrid
1 - Bayern Munich
1 - Borussia Dortmund

1 - Chelsea
1 - Dynamo Tbilisi
1 - Everton
1 - Fiorentina
1 - Hamburg
1 - Juventus
1 - Magdeburg
1 - Manchester City
1 - Manchester United
1 - Mechelen
1 - Paris St Germain
1 - Parma
1 - Rangers
1 - Real Zaragoza
1 - Sampdoria
1 - Slovan Bratislava
1 - Sporting Lisbon
1 - Tottenham
1 - Valencia
1 - Werder Bremen
1 - West Ham

UEFA CUP

3 - Barcelona
3 - Juventus
2 - Borussia
Moenchengladbach
2 - IFK Gothenburg
2 - Inter Milan
2 - Leeds United
2 - Liverpool
2 - Real Madrid
2 - Tottenham
2 - Valencia
1 - Ajax
1 - Anderlecht
1 - Arsenal
1 - Bayer Leverkusen
1 - Bayern Munich
1 - Dynamo Zagreb
1 - Eintracht Frankfurt
1 - PSV Eindhoven
1 - Ferencvaros
1 - Feyenoord
1 - Ipswich Town1 - Napoli

European Club Cup Finals

1 - Newcastle United
1 - Parma
1 - Real Zaragoza
1 - Roma
1 - Schalke

EUROPEAN CUP

1967 - Celtic
1968 - Manchester United
1977 - Liverpool
1978 - Liverpool
1979 - Nottingham Forest
1980 - Nottingham Forest
1981 - Liverpool
1982 - Aston Villa
1984 - Liverpool

EUROPEAN CUP-WINNERS' CUP

1963 - Tottenham
1965 - West Ham United
1970 - Manchester City
1971 - Chelsea
1972 - Rangers
1983 - Aberdeen
1985 - Everton
1991 - Manchester United
1994 - Arsenal

FAIRS/UEFA CUP

1968 - Leeds United
1969 - Newcastle United
1970 - Arsenal
1971 - Leeds United
1972 - Tottenham
1973 - Liverpool
1976 - Liverpool
1981 - Ipswich Town
1984 - Tottenham

STRANGE GOALS IN FOOTBALL

Strange Goals in Football

DENNIS EVANS (ARSENAL) v BLACKPOOL 12.56 – Hearing what he thought was the final whistle, Evans turned to celebrate Arsenal's 4-0 victory by whacking the ball into his own net. Unfortunately, the whistle had come from the crowd.

CHRIS MACKENZIE (HEREFORD) v BARNET 08.95 – Hereford keeper Mackenzie beat his opposite number, Barnet's Maik Taylor, who was making his League debut, when his wind-assisted kick sailed over Taylor's head.

GEOFF HURST (ENGLAND) v WEST GERMANY 06.66 – The most famous World Cup final goal ever. The scores stood 2-2 in extra-time when Hurst turned and thudded a shot against the German bar. The ball rebounded down onto the line and the referee awarded a goal, although television evidence suggests it did not cross the line.

GARY CROSBY (NOTTINGHAM FOREST) v MANCHESTER CITY 03.90 – City keeper Andy Dibble was balancing the ball on his palm when Crosby nipped in from behind him, headed the ball off Dibble's hand and turned it into the net.

PETER HUNT (CHARLTON) v OLDHAM 10.72 – Hunt was credited with his first goal for Charlton although his shot clearly hit the side netting before the ball rebounded into the advertising hoardings.

SAM CHEDGZOY (EVERTON) v SPURS 04.24 – A loophole in the law allowed Chedgzoy to take a corner to himself and dribble past the Tottenham defence before scoring. The law was subsequently changed.

MARCUS BROWNING (BRISTOL ROVERS) v BRENTFORD 10.96 – Brentford keeper Kevin Dearden, hearing a whistle in the crowd, placed the ball for a free-kick and then watched Browning knock the ball into the empty net.

JOHAN CRUYFF (AJAX) v HELMOND SPORTS 1982-83 – Awarded a penalty, Cruyff decided not to take a direct shot at goal, instead playing a one-two with Jesper Olsen before scoring.

DIEGO MARADONA (ARGENTINA) v ENGLAND 06.86 – Maradona used the 'Hand of God' to steer the ball past England keeper Peter Shilton in the 1986 World Cup quarter-final in Mexico City.

 **Facts**   **Strange Goals in Football**

JIM FRYATT (BRADFORD PA) v TRANMERE 04.64 – Fryatt scored the quickest goal in British football history when he put Bradford Park Avenue ahead after only four seconds.

GARY SPRAKE (LEEDS) v LIVERPOOL 12.67 – Leeds goalkeeper Sprake decided at the last minute not to throw the ball out to a colleague. However, the momentum took the ball out of his hand and it ended up in his own net.

GARY SPRAKE (LEEDS) v CHELSEA, 05.70 – Another howler from the Welsh international, who allowed Peter Houseman's speculative long-range effort to creep beneath his diving body on a boggy Wembley pitch for the equaliser. Chelsea won the replay.

ANDY GORAM (HIBERNIAN) v MORTON 05.88 – One keeper who scored at the right end was Scotland international Goram whose Premier Division effort beat Morton's David Wylie.

TOMMY HUTCHISON (MANCHESTER CITY) v TOTTENHAM 05.81 – With eight minutes left of the FA Cup final, Hutchison, having earlier put City in front, deflected Glenn Hoddle's free-kick into his own net for the equaliser.

PETER SCHMEICHEL (MANCHESTER UNITED) v ROTOR VOLGOGRAD 09.95 – With his side trailing 2-1 in the final minute, United keeper Schmeichel went up for a corner and hammered his side level.

LARS RICKEN (BORUSSIA DORTMUND) v JUVENTUS 05.97 – The Dortmund substitute made his entrance into the 1997 European Cup final with Dortmund holding on to a 2-1 lead and within seconds chipped Juventus keeper Angelo Peruzzi with his first touch.

PAT JENNINGS (TOTTENHAM) v MANCHESTER UNITED 08.67 – The Spurs keeper launched a huge kick out of his hands in the 1967 Charity Shield. The ball bounced once over the head of his opposite number Alex Stepney and ended up in the net.

DAVID BECKHAM v WIMBLEDON 08.96 – Spotting Neil Sullivan off his line, Beckham hammered the ball over the Dons' keeper from inside his own half on the opening day of the 1996-97 season.

DAVID BATTY v WIMBLEDON 08.96 – Four days later, Sullivan was beaten with another long-distance effort as Batty chipped him from 35 yards.

Strange Goals in Football

NAYIM (REAL ZARAGOZA) v ARSENAL 05.95 – Instead of playing out time at the end of 90 minutes in the European Cup Winners' Cup final, Nayim beat Arsenal keeper David Seaman with a looping shot from 40 yards to win the cup for Zaragoza.

SHAUN SMITH (CREWE) v BRENTFORD 04.97 – With a howling gale at his back, Smith caught Bees' keeper Kevin Dearden unaware by striking a free-kick from inside his own half straight into the net.

SCOTT MINTO (CHARLTON) v DERBY 10.92 – Charlton defenders Darren Pitcher and Scott Minto contrived to turn possession on the half-way line into a spectacular own goal. Pitcher sliced the ball 30 yards back to Minto, who headed past his own keeper.

ROD WALLACE (LEEDS) v ARSENAL 01.97 – Wallace lobbed keeper David Seaman, sending the ball towards the Arsenal goal. Martin Keown came across to clear but, expecting it to roll out for a goal-kick, left it. Instead, the ball struck the post and rebounded for Wallace to smash it home, while Keown also ended up in the net.

RONNIE BOYCE (WEST HAM) v MANCHESTER CITY – City keeper Joe Corrigan drop-kicked the ball out of his hands, but watched in horror as Boyce promptly volleyed it back past him.

RONNIE BOYCE (WEST HAM) v PRESTON 04.64 – Boyce deserves a second mention for his 30-yard chip in the 1964 FA Cup final, which struck the crossbar, came out and struck the diving body of Preston keeper Alan before rebounding into the net.

RAY CASHLEY (BRISTOL CITY) v HULL CITY 09.93 – The Division Two match produced another moment of goalkeeping folklore when City's Cashley scored against Jeff Wealands.

STAN COLLYMORE (LIVERPOOL) v BLACKBURN 02.95 – Collymore struck a shot from outside the area but was so convinced that Tim Flowers had it covered, he missed seeing the ball strike a divot and bounce over the stranded Rovers keeper.

ROBERTO RIVELINO (CORINTHIANS) v RIO PRETO – Goalkeeper Isadore Irandir was still on his knees saying his pre-match prayers when Rivelino hammered the ball home from the half-way line after only three seconds.

 **Facts**   **Strange Goals in Football**

ROBERTO RIVELINO (BRAZIL) v EAST GERMANY 06.74 –
More Brazilian magic when Rivelino scored one of the greatest
free-kicks of all time. The Brazilians placed a man in the East
German wall, who ducked his head at the last moment to allow
Rivelino's shot to pass untouched into the net.

*PAUL PARKER (ENGLAND) v WEST GERMANY 07.90 – England's
World Cup hopes appeared to be in tatters when Andreas Brehme's
free-kick cannoned off Parker's shoulder and looped over stranded
keeper Peter Shilton.*

DES WALKER (NOTTINGHAM FOREST) v LUTON 01.91 –
Walker's only goal in a Football League career which stretches
to 416 games came in the dying seconds against Luton. Walker
strode forward to hammer the ball into the roof of
the net but his manager Brian Clough didn't
see it, having already left for the
dressing room.

Strange Goals in Football

Facts

DES WALKER (NOTTINGHAM FOREST) v TOTTENHAM 05.91 By contrast, Walker earned notoriety for the wrong reason in the 1991 FA Cup final with a spectacular diving header which handed Spurs a 2-1 victory.

HAROLD PHIPPS (CHARLTON) v ARSENAL 11.48 – Phipps beat keeper Ted Platt, playing his first game for two years, with a 45-yard free-kick in Charlton's 4-3 win.

BRYAN ROBSON (ENGLAND) v NORWAY 09.81 – Robson admitted his first international goal involved the use of a hand on the blind side of the referee before he belted the ball into the Norwegian net.

ESKANDARIAN (IRAN) v SCOTLAND 06.78 – Scotland needed a freak own goal to avoid an embarrassing World Cup defeat by Iran. Eskandarian's back-pass ended up in his own net after his keeper and a fellow defender collided with each other.

DENIS LAW (MANCHESTER CITY) v MANCHESTER UNITED 04.74 – In front of 56,996 United fans who used to adore him, Law produced an instinctive backheel to give City a 1-0 derby win over his former club. The goal sent United down to Division Two and Law, realising what he had done, left the field in tears.

IAIN HESFORD (MAIDSTONE) v HEREFORD 11.91 – Hesford scored Maidstone's winner against Hereford in a Fourth Division match. His clearance beat visiting keeper Tony Elliot with one bounce.

STAN MILBURN and JACK FROGGATT (LEICESTER) v CHELSEA 1954 – The only recorded instance of a shared own goal. Milburn and Froggatt owned up to getting simultaneous touches to the ball on its way past their own keeper.

TOMMY WRIGHT (EVERTON) v LIVERPOOL 03.72 – The England full-back scored one of the fastest League own goals in history after 33 seconds of the Merseyside derby.

TOMMY WRIGHT (EVERTON) v MANCHESTER CITY 03.72 – A week later he went one second better when he put through his own net after just 32 seconds.

RAY CHARLES (EAST FIFE) v STRANRAER 02.90 – Charles joined the exclusive list of goalkeepers who have scored when his long ball deceived Stranraer's Bernard Duffy in a Scottish Second Division match.

 # Facts   **Strange Goals in Football**

BENNY SMITH (NORWICH) v METROGAS 12.21 – The Norwich full-back struck such a fierce penalty that Metrogas keeper Leach was instantly knocked out, allowing Smith to hit the rebound into the unguarded net. The hapless Leach was carried off.

PETER ALDIS (ASTON VILLA) v SUNDERLAND 09.52 – Aldis scored what was thought to be the longest headed goal ever in the Football League from 35 yards.

GARRY JONES (BOLTON) v ROTHERHAM 11.72 – Rotherham keeper Jim McDonagh placed the ball for a goal-kick not realising the ball was still in play. Jones nipped in to score.

SANDY BROWN (EVERTON) v LIVERPOOL 02.70 – The Merseyside derby is the last match in which to score an own goal but Brown's searing header from a Liverpool corner would have been acknowledged as brilliant even if it had gone in at the right end.

WILLIE DONACHIE (SCOTLAND) v WALES 05.78 – A week before Scotland's departure for the 1978 World Cup finals, defender Donachie hit a low backpass, without looking, towards his keeper Jim Blyth, who was on the other side of his area and could only watch the ball roll into the net.

PAT KRUSE (TORQUAY) v CAMBRIDGE 1977 – Kruse holds the unenviable record of scoring the quickest own goal in Football League history with a header in just six seconds.

DAN LEWIS (ARSENAL) v CARDIFF 04.27 – Probably the worst FA Cup Final blunder ever. Arsenal keeper Lewis allowed a weak 25-yarder from Hugh Ferguson to slip from his grasp and under his left arm. In an effort to retrieve the ball, he knocked it gently over the goalline with an elbow.

JOHNNY SUMMERS (CHARLTON) v MIDDLESBROUGH 10.60 – With Charlton trailing 5-6 in the 89th minute, striker Stuart Leary stood on goalkeeper Peter Taylor's foot so that Summers could score direct from the corner to make the score 6-6.

GEOFF NULTY (BURNLEY) v IPSWICH 03.71 – Nulty is credited with the latest Football League goal ever. He equalised for Burnley with a goal officially timed at one second from the end.

Strange Goals in Football

SAM LAWRIE (CHARLTON) v LIVERPOOL 11.60 – A month later, The Valley witnessed another bizarre goal when winger Lawrie's back-pass from the half-way line caught his keeper Frank Reed looking the other way.

NAT LOFTHOUSE (BOLTON) v MANCHESTER UNITED 05.58 – Wanderers centre forward Lofthouse set up his side's FA Cup final victory when he charged United keeper Harry Gregg and the ball into the Wembley net.

ANDY GRAY (EVERTON) v WATFORD 05.84 – Twenty six years later, Watford keeper Steve Sherwood felt sympathy with Gregg when he caught a cross only for Gray to head the ball through his hands into the net.

 **Facts**   **Strange Goals in Football**

ANDY GRAY (EVERTON) v NOTTS COUNTY 03.85 – Always renowned for his heading ability, Gray stooped to conquer with a diving header only inches off the ground when it would have been easier to reach it with his foot.

BRIAN GAYLE (SHEFFIELD UNITED) v LEEDS 04.92 – Gayle's cock-up gave Leeds their first championship in 25 years. With the score tied at 2-2, Gayle reached a through ball ahead of his outrushing keeper and promptly headed it into his own net.

STEVE OGRIZOVIC (COVENTRY) v SHEFFIELD WEDNESDAY 10.86 – Coventry stalwart keeper Ogrizovic grabbed his only goal for the Sky Blues when his big-boot beat Martin Hodge in the home goal.

STEVE SHERWOOD (WATFORD) v COVENTRY 01.84 – It was a Coventry keeper's turn to be on the wrong end of a goal from his opposite number when Raddy Avramovic was beaten by Sherwood.

JACK ALLEN (NEWCASTLE) v ARSENAL 04.32 – Newcastle inside-forward Jimmy Richardson chased a long ball which crossed the by-line before he centred it. Eddie Hapgood and his fellow Arsenal defenders didn't bother to intercept it, allowing Allen to turn it home.

ANDY HINCHCLIFFE (EVERTON) v LEICESTER 11.96 – With the Leicester players still protesting about the referee's decision to award a free-kick against them, Everton's Nick Barmby snatched the ball out of Kasey Keller's hands and quickly placed it for Hinchcliffe to strike the ball into the empty net.

BARRY DAINES (TOTTENHAM) v BRISTOL ROVERS 03.78 – In a goalmouth melee following a Rovers corner, Daines tripped over when attempting to clear the ball only to volley it into the roof of his own net.

DAVE SYRETT (MANSFIELD) v TOTTENHAM 03.78 – The same month, Daines experienced another calamitous moment when he raced out of his area to clear the ball. It took a strange bounce on the muddy pitch and the keeper connected only with fresh air, leaving Syrett an easy tap-in.

EDDIE KELLY (ARSENAL) v LIVERPOOL 05.71 – With Arsenal trailing 1-0 in the FA Cup final, Kelly slipped the ball forward to George Graham, who appeared to flick it past keeper Ray Clemence. Graham wheeled away in triumph to claim the goal only for television replays to give it back to Kelly.

Strange Goals in Football

KENNY DALGLISH (SCOTLAND) v ENGLAND 05.76 – England keeper Ray Clemence produced a Hampden Park howler when he allowed Dalglish's tame shot to trickle through his legs and gift Scotland a 2-1 win.

OLMO (BARCELONA) v TOTTENHAM 04.82 – Clemence assured himself another piece of unwanted fame when he allowed Olmo's long-range shot to swerve past him despite having a clear view of it for over 30 yards.

JIMMY GREENHOFF (MANCHESTER UNITED) v LIVERPOOL 05.77 – A crazy FA Cup final winner when Jimmy Greenhoff inadvertently deflected Lou Macari's mishit shot past the stranded Ray Clemence. Greenhoff was actually trying to get out of the way.

BILLY BONDS (CHARLTON) v PORTSMOUTH 12.65 – Bonds always claimed the fastest goal he ever scored was the one he headed past his own 18-year-old debutant keeper Les Surman, who was stranded on an icy Fratton Park pitch after just 18 seconds.

PETER SHILTON (LEICESTER) v SOUTHAMPTON 1967 – In over 1000 league games, England's Peter Shilton scored only once. It was in 1967 playing for Leicester City, when his obliging opposite number was Southampton's Campbell Forsyth.

ROBERTO BAGGIO (ITALY) v ENGLAND 07.90 – Shilton figures again, this time for the wrong reason. In his 125th and final game for England, he was trying to dribble the ball to the edge of the area when Baggio dispossessed him and slid the ball home.

RONNIE WHELAN (LIVERPOOL) v MANCHESTER UNITED 03.90 – Whelan sent a superb 30-yard chip, which dipped just under the crossbar. The trouble was it was past his own keeper Bruce Grobbelaar.

STEVE McMANAMAN (LIVERPOOL) v TOTTENHAM 12.97 – A weak shot from McManaman appeared to be rolling straight to Ian Walker but, as the Spurs keeper got down to the ball, a sudden bobble took it over his hands and into the back of the net.

ALAN MULLERY (FULHAM) v SHEFFIELD WEDNESDAY 01.61 – Wednesday scored the easiest goal in their history when Mullery contrived to score an own goal past his own keeper without a Sheffield player touching the ball.

 **Facts**   **Strange Goals in Football**

JOHN BARNES (LIVERPOOL) v SOUTHAMPTON 12.96 –
Southampton keeper Dave Beasant attempted to clear his area but
succeeded only in finding Barnes whose shot just beat Beasant into
the corner of the net.

ERNIE HUNT (COVENTRY) v EVERTON 10.70 – Awarded a
free-kick on the edge of the box, Coventry's Willie Carr held
the ball between his heels and flicked the ball up for Hunt to
blast the ball home. The move was later outlawed.

CHARLIE DYKE (CHELSEA) v CHARLTON 11.50 – Dyke scored
direct from a corner when legendary Charlton keeper Sam Bartram
caught the ball but staggered over the goal-line.

ALAN PATERSON (GLENTORAN) v LINFIELD 04.89 – The 1989
Roadferry Cup Final in Belfast was brightened up when
Glentoran keeper Paterson embarrassed Linfield's George
Dunlop with a towering clearance.

ANDY McLEAN (CLIFTONVILLE) v LINFIELD 08.88 –
Unfortunately for the hapless Dunlop, Paterson's goal was not a new
experience for him. Eight months earlier he had been beaten in
similar fashion by McLean, who was making his Irish League debut.

PAUL INCE (MANCHESTER UNITED) v IPSWICH 03.95 –
Shellshocked Ipswich keeper Craig Forrest was on the edge of
his area protesting to the referee about the award of a United
free kick when the quick-thinking Ince stepped up to chip into
an empty goal. It stood to give United a Carling Premiership
record 9-0 win.

ROGER MILLA (CAMEROON) v COLOMBIA 06.90 – With Colombia
1-0 down to Cameroon in the 1990 World Cup, keeper Rene Higuita
decided to help out by dribbling the ball out of his area.
Unfortunately he was tackled by Milla, who stroked it into an empty
net.

RENE HIGUITA (ATLETICO NACIONAL) v RIVER PLATE 09.95
– The legendary Colombian keeper scored at the right end in a
Copa Libertadores match. When his side were awarded a free-
kick, Higuita raced from his goal to smack home the only goal
of the game.

LEE DIXON (ARSENAL) v IPSWICH 03.94 – Dixon, possibly feeling
sorry for Ipswich, sent an unstoppable header whistling into the roof
of his own net, but Arsenal won 5-1.

Strange Goals in Football

Facts

LEE DIXON (ARSENAL) v COVENTRY 09.91 – The feeling was nothing new for the England full-back, who has made a habit of scoring spectacular own goals. Against Coventry, he lobbed his own keeper from outside the area after just 54 seconds.

IAIN DOWIE (WEST HAM) v STOCKPORT 12.96 – Dowie's classic downward header into the bottom corner was far too good for his own keeper Ludek Miklosko. It helped Stockport to a Coca-Cola Cup shock and to make matters worse for Dowie, he limped off soon afterwards with a broken bone in his leg.

CHRIS NICHOLL (ASTON VILLA) v LEICESTER 03.76 – To score one own goal in a match is unlucky. To do it twice smacks of carelessness, but that was Nicholl's fate in a League match. However, he made up for his errors by scoring both of Villa's goals as well in a 2-2 draw.

BARROW v PLYMOUTH 1968 – A Barrow shot was sailing harmlessly wide when it struck referee Ivan Robinson and was deflected into the net for the only goal of the game.

MIKE MILLIGAN (NORWICH) v ASTON VILLA 10.94 – The greatest goalmouth scramble ever? Darren Eadie headed against the post, Mike Sheron's follow-up hit the bar, Eadie's second effort was then cleared off the line before Milligan finally headed home.

ROBERTO DI MATTEO (CHELSEA) v MIDDLESBROUGH 05.97 – Chelsea's Italian star scored the quickest FA Cup final goal ever when his long-range effort sailed over Ben Roberts' hand after only 42 seconds.

 **Facts**   **Strange Goals in Football**

BRUCE GROBBELAAR (LIVERPOOL) v WIMBLEDON 08.88 – In a mad goalmouth scramble, Liverpool keeper Grobbelaar lay on the ground when the ball was kicked off the line behind him, struck his head and ricocheted into the net.

JOHN LUKIC (LEEDS) v GLASGOW RANGERS 10.92 – English champions Leeds were leading their Scottish counterparts in a European Cup tie at Ibrox when their keeper Lukic punched a harmless-looking corner into his own net.

GARY MABBUTT (TOTTENHAM) v COVENTRY 05.87 – Dave Bennett's extra-time cross deflected off the left knee of Spurs skipper Mabbutt and looped over Ray Clemence to win the 1987 FA Cup final for the Sky Blues.

DENNIS TUEART (MANCHESTER CITY) v NEWCASTLE 03.76 Tueart had kids up and down the country practising overhead kicks after his spectacular bicycle effort won the League Cup final for City.

TREVOR SINCLAIR (QPR) v BARNSLEY 01.97 – Sinclair brought off the bicycle kick to end them all when he volleyed home a cross which was drifting behind him into the top corner.

ALEX STEPNEY (MANCHESTER UNITED) v LEICESTER 09.94 – United's keeper charged upfield when his side were awarded a penalty, grabbed the ball and fired home the spot-kick. To prove it was no fluke, he did it again five weeks later.

MADJER (FC PORTO) v BAYERN MUNICH 05.87 – With his back to goal in the area, the Algerian international produced a moment of European Cup magic when he cleverly backheeled the ball into the Bayern net.

ERIC VISCAAL (AA GENT) v LOKEREN 1994 – Outfield player Viscaal was forced to take over in goal when Gent's keeper was sent off in the last five minutes. His first act was to save a penalty and then, in the dying seconds when Gent were awarded a spot-kick, he went up the other end and scored.

ANDRE BAL (SOVIET UNION) v BRAZIL 06.82 – Brazilian keeper Valdir Peres still has nightmares about the World Cup match in which he caught Bal's shot and then dropped it over his line.

Strange Goals in Football

NICK CUSACK (FULHAM) v SCARBOROUGH 01.96 – Borough keeper Ian Ironside dropped a horrendous clanger by trying to keep a back-pass in play. Knocking the ball high in the air he failed to grab it three times when it dropped, allowing Cusack to side-foot it home.

JOHN PEMBERTON (SHEFFIELD UNITED) v MANCHESTER CITY 04.93 – Desperately stretching to intercept David White's cross, Pemberton succeeded only in volleying the ball low into his own net.

MARK CROSSLEY (NOTTINGHAM FOREST) v BLACKBURN 09.92 – Blackburn defender Colin Hendry powered in a header from a corner. Crossley initially caught the ball only to throw it over his own line as he fell to the ground.

NACIONAL v PENAROL 1932 – A Nacional player's shot missed the post but struck a cameraman's briefcase, which had been left close to the by-line. The ball rebounded to another Nacional player, who turned it home.

ANDRES ESCOBAR (COLOMBIA) v USA 06.94 – The most tragic own goal of all time. Escobar's outstretched leg deflected the ball past his own keeper and ended Colombia's hopes in the 1994 World Cup. Just 72 hours after returning to Colombia, Escobar was gunned down outside a restaurant in his home town of Medelin, the assassin allegedly shouting: "That's for the own goal."

THE GREAT TEAMS

The Great Teams

There have been many great matches over the years. Here are just some of the teams that have taken part in those memorable games:

Italy and Brazil provided the most exciting match of the 1982 World Cup. Brazil were favourites to lift the trophy but were beaten by eventual winners Italy 3-2 in the second round. Italy's team on that glorious day: Zoff, Collovati (Bergomi), Gentile, Scirea, Cabrini, Oriali, Antognoni, Tardelli (Marini), Conti, Graziani, Rossi. Scorer: Rossi (3).

Celtic's eleven men that helped them become the first British club to win the European Cup, when they defeated Inter Milan 2-1 in 1967: Simpson, Craig, Gemmell, Murdoch, McNeill, Clark, Johnstone, Wallace, Chalmers, Auld, Lennox. Scorers: Gemmell, Chalmers.

Hungary's famous team that overwhelmed England 6-3 in 1953, inflicting England's first Wembley defeat: Grosics, Buzansky, Lantos, Bozsik, Lorant, Zakarias, Budai, Kocsis, Hidegkuti, Puskas, Czibor. Scorers: Hidegkuti (3), Bozsik, Puskas (2).

England's World Cup Final team that beat West Germany 4-2 in 1966: Banks, Cohen, Wilson, Stiles, J.Charlton, Moore, Ball, Hurst, Hunt, R.Charlton, Peters. Scorers: Hurst (3), Peters.

The Everton side that won the 1985 European Cup-Winners' Cup Final 3-1 against Rapid Vienna: Southall, Stevens, Ratcliffe, Mountfield, Van den Hauwe, Steven, Reid, Bracewell, Sheedy, Sharp, Gray. Scorers: Gray, Steven, Sheedy.

Scotland's 1978 side that beat Holland 3-2 in the World Cup finals: Rough, Kennedy, Donachie, Rioch, Forsyth, Buchan, Dalglish, Hartford, Jordan, Gemmill, Souness. Scorers: Dalglish, Gemmill (2, 1pen).

Manchester United became the first English club to win the European Cup in 1968. The side that beat Benfica 4-1 in the Final was: Stepney, Brennan, Foulkes, Stiles, Dunne, Crerand, Charlton, Sadler, Kidd, Best, Aston. **Scorers: Charlton (2), Kidd, Best.**

The Republic of Ireland team that pulled off a famous 1-0 victory over Italy in their first match of their 1994 World Cup: Bonner, Irwin, Babb, McGrath, Phelan, Houghton (McAteer), Sheridan, Keane, Townsend, Staunton, Coyne (Aldridge). Scorer: Houghton.

 **Facts**   **The Great Teams**

AC Milan's brilliant side that beat Steaua Bucharest 4-0 in the 1989 European Cup Final: G.Galli, Tassotti, Costacurta (F.Galli), Baresi, Maldini, Colombo, Rijkaard, Donadoni, Van Basten, Gullit (Virdis), Ancellotti. Scorers: Gullit (2), Van Basten (2).

The U.S.A team that shocked the world when they beat England 1-0 in the 1950 World Cup: Borghi, Keough, Maca, McIlvenny, Colombo, Bahr, Wallace, Pariani, Gaetjens, J.Souza, E.Souza. Scorer: Gaetjens.

One of Wales' greatest victories came over Germany in 1991 in a European Championship qualifier. Their team who played in that 1-0 win was: Southall, Phillips, Melville, Aizlewood, Ratcliffe, Bodin, Nicholas, Saunders (Speed), Horne, Hughes, Rush. Scorer: Rush.

Brazil's side that beat Italy 4-0 to win the 1970 World Cup Final, a record third success: Felix, Carlos Alberto, Brito, Piazza, Everaldo, Clodoaldo, Gerson, Rivelino, Jairzinho, Tostao, Pele. Scorers: Pele, Jairzinho, Gerson, Carlos Alberto.

Real Madrid's legendary team that beat Eintracht Frankfurt 7-3 to win the 1960 European Cup: Dominguez, Marquitos, Pachin, Vidal, Santamaria, Zarraga, Canario, Del Sol, di Stefano, Puskas, Gento. Scorers: Puskas (4, 1 pen), di Stefano (3).

Northern Ireland upset the odds when they beat Spain, the hosts, 1-0 in the 1982 World Cup finals. Their side that day was: Jennings, J.Nicholl, C.Nicholl, McClelland, Donaghy, O'Neill, McCreery, McIlroy (Cassidy), Armstrong, Hamilton, Whiteside (Nelson). Scorer: Armstrong.

This century has seen five 'Double' winning teams. All completed the feat with victory in the FA Cup Finals. Those teams were: Tottenham Hotspur (1961) 2-0 v Leicester City: Brown, Baker, Henry, Blanchflower, Norman, Mackay, Jones, White, Smith, Allen, Dyson. Scorers: Smith, Dyson.

The Sutton United team that pulled off one of the greatest shocks in FA Cup history when they beat First Division Coventry City 2-0 in the 1989 third round: Roffey, Jones, Rains, Golley, Pratt, Rogers, Stephens, Dawson, Dennis, McKinnon, Hanlan. Scorers: Rains, Hanlan.

The Great Teams

Arsenal (1971) 2-1 (aet) v Liverpool: Wilson, Rice, McNab, Story (Kelly), McLintock, Simpson, Armstrong, Graham, Radford, Kennedy, George. Scorers: Kelly, George.

Liverpool (1986) 3-1 v Everton: Grobbelaar, Lawrenson, Beglin, Nicol, Whelan, Hansen, Dalglish, Johnston, Rush, Molby, MacDonald. Scorers: Rush (2), Johnston.

Manchester United (1994) 4-0 v Chelsea: Schmeichel, Parker, Bruce, Pallister, Irwin (Sharpe), Kanchelskis (McClair), Keane, Ince, Giggs, Cantona, Hughes. Scorers: Cantona (2, 2 pens), Hughes, McClair.

Manchester United (1996) 1-0 Liverpool – Schmeichel, Irwin, May, Pallister, P.Neville, Beckham (G.Neville), Keane, Butt, Giggs, Cantona, Cole (Scholes). Scorer: Cantona.

One of the greatest nail-biting matches ever seen in Football League history occurred on the final day of the 1989 season when Arsenal beat Liverpool 2-0 at Anfield to beat them to the First Division title. The Arsenal team that day was: Lukic, Dixon, O'Leary, Adams, Bould (Groves), Winterburn, Thomas, Rocastle, Richardson, Smith, Merson (Hayes). Scorers: Smith, Thomas.

Because of Yugoslavia's exclusion from the 1992 European Championship, Denmark were awarded a late place in the competition. They went on to surprise everybody by beating Germany 2-0 in the Final. Their team that day was: Schmeichel, Sivebeck (Christiansen), Nielsen, Olsen, Christofte, Jensen, Povlsen, Laudrup, Piechnik, Larsen, Vilfort. Scorers: Jensen, Vilfort.

The first World Cup winners were Uruguay. The side that beat Brazil in the final game to win the trophy was: Ballesteros, Nasazzi, Mascheroni, Andrade, Gestido, Fernandez, Dorado, Scarone, Castro, Cea, Iriarte. Scorers: Dorado, Cea, Iriarte, Castro.

The mighty Real Madrid were beaten 2-1 in the 1983 European Cup-Winners' Cup Final by Scottish club Aberdeen. Alex Ferguson's team that night was: Leighton, Rougvie, Miller, McLeish, McMaster, Cooper, Strachan, Simpson, Weir, McGhee, Black (Hewitt). Scorers: Black, Hewitt.

Probably the best match of the 1996 European Championship was England's 4-1 defeat of Holland at Wembley. The English side that night: Seaman, G.Neville, Southgate, Adams, Pearce, McManaman, Ince (Platt), Gascoigne, Anderton, Shearer (Barmby), Sheringham (Fowler). Scorers: Shearer (2), Sheringham (2).

 **Facts**

The Great Teams

One of the most memorable matches of World Cup history occurred on the opening day of the 1990 finals in Italy. Reigning champions Argentina were beaten 1-0 by Cameroon, despite the Africans having two men sent-off. The Cameroon hero's that day were: N'Kono, Ebwelle, Massing, Kunde, Akem N'Dip, Tataw, M'Bouh, Kana Biyik, Makanaky (Milla), M'Fede (Libih), Omam Biyik. Scorer: Omam Biyik.

The first official international match took place on November 30, 1872 between Scotland and England at the West of Scotland Cricket Club, Partick. The Scotland side in that 0-0 draw: Gardner, Thomson, Ker, Weir, Taylor, Leckie, McKinnon, Rhind, Wotherspoon, J.Smith, R.Smith.

The Great Teams

And England's eleven: Barker, Greenhalgh, Welch, Chappell, Ottaway, Brockbank, Chenery, Clegg, Kirke-Smith, Morice, Maynard.

Brazil became the first country to win the World Cup outside their continent when they beat Sweden 5-2 in the 1958 Final. Their side that day: Gilmar, D.Santos, Zito, N.Santos, Bellini, Orlando, Garrincha, Didi, Vava, Pele, Zagalo. Scorers: Vava (2), Pele (2), Zagalo.

The first winners of the FA Cup in the twentieth century were Bury. Their team in the 4-0 win over Southampton was: Thompson, Darrock, Davidson, Pray, Leeming, Ross, Richards, Wood, McLuckie, Sagar, Plant. Scorers: McLuckie (2), Wood, Plant.

England's record victory over Scotland came in April 1961. The team that played in that 9-3 win: Springett, Armfield, McNeil, Robson, Swan, Flowers, Douglas, Greaves, Smith, Haynes, Charlton. Scorers: Greaves (3), Smith (2), Haynes (2), Robson, Douglas.

Ipswich Town upset the odds when they beat Arsenal in the 1978 FA Cup Final. Their team in that 1-0 victory was: Cooper, Burley, Mills, Talbot, Hunter, Beattie, Osborne (Lambert), Wark, Mariner, Geddis, Woods. Scorer: Osborne.

MIXED BAG

Mixed Bag

The first recorded use of a substitute came in 1889 when Wales faced Scotland. Welsh goalkeeper Sam Gillam arrived late, and Alf Pugh was allowed to take his place until his arrival.

Fulham's Johnny Haynes became the first British player to earn over £100 a week.

Hudersfield Town are the only team to score six goals in a League match and still lose the game. In December 1957 they were leading ten-men Charlton 5-1 with 28 minutes remaining, but ended the game as 7-6 losers.

On February 9, 1963 the weather led to a fixture programme so reduced that only seven Football League games took place, and there were no games at all in Scotland.

The world's largest stadium is the Maracana in Rio de Janeiro, a ground which holds 165,000 spectators.

Preston were the last League club to play football on an artificial pitch, converting back to grass in the summer of 1994.

There is only one recorded case of a Football League game in which no corners were awarded, a match between Newcastle United and Portsmouth in December 1931. The final score was, unsurprisingly, was 0-0.

In a Carling Premiership game between Nottingham Forest and Southampton in November 1992 Forest had 22 corners compared to two for the Saints. But they still lost the game 2-1.

Leyton Orient's Terry Howard gave such a bad first-half performance when he played against Blackpool in February 1995 that he was sacked at half-time. Howard was fined two weeks' wages and given a free transfer to Wycombe Wanderers. It was his 397th appearance for the club.

Jack Kelsey and Danny Clapton played for Arsenal against Juventus on the evening of November 26, 1958. But earlier that same day they had played against each other in a 2-2 draw between Wales and England.

In November 1987 Mark Hughes played for Wales against Czechoslavakia in Prague, got on a plane, and played for Bayern Munich in Germany all on the same day.

 **Mixed Bag**

In 1939 the minimum admission for a Football League game was one shilling.

Arsenal are the longest-serving members of the top flight. They have successfully avoided relegation since 1919.

When Andy Walker moved from Bolton to Celtic in June 1994 Bolton optimistically asked for £2.2m and Celtic offered £250,000. The tribunal decided the striker was worth £550,000.

Andy Legg claims to have the longest throw-in in football, measured in 1994 at 41 metres (45 yards).

Alf Common was the first British player to attract a four-figure fee, when he moved from Sunderland to Middlesbrough in 1905.

The first British six-figure transfer was Denis Law, who moved from Manchester City to Torino in June 1961.

In 1875 the crossbar was introduced to football, replacing the tape previously used.

In 1908 worries of ever-increasing transfer fees prompted a ceiling to be placed at £350. The rule only stood for three months.

In 1964 the first televised 'Match of the Day' was broadcast, featuring a 3-2 win for Liverpool over Arsenal.

In 1978 Viv Anderson became the first black player to don an England shirt.

The smallest FA Cup-winning captain was Sunderland's Bobby Kerr. He was 5ft. 4in. when he lifted the trophy in 1973.

Stanley Matthews holds the longest Football League playing career. Playing for Stoke City, Blackpool and then resigning for Stoke, Matthews spanned 32 years, 10 months from march 19, 1932 to February 6, 1965.

The record number of successive national League Championship is nine. That record is shared by MTK Budapest (Hungary 1917-25), CSKA Sofia (Bulgaria 1954-62), Celtic (Scotland 1966-74) and Rangers (Scotland 1989-96). Rangers will surpass that record if they win the 1997-98 Scottish Premier Division.

Mixed Bag

The record number of unbeaten minutes for a goalkeeper was set by Abel Resino of Atletico Madrid. He kept a clean sheet for 1275 minutes.

The international unbeaten goalkeeping record is 1142 minutes, set by Italy's Dino Zoff, from September 1972 to June 1974.

The British club record in all matches was set by Glasgow Rangers' Chris Woods. The run lasted 1196 minutes from November 26, 1996 to January 31, 1987.

Saudi Arabia's Majed Abdullah Mohammed made a world record 147 international appearances between 1978 and 1994.

One of the 'biggest' characters in British football was England goalkeeper Bill 'Fatty' Foulkes, who weighed 22st 3lb.

Ricardinho Neves of Brazil juggled a football for 19 hours, 5 minutes and 31 seconds non-stop to record a new world record on July 15-16, 1994.

The headed juggling record was set by Tomas Lundman of Sweden on November 26, 1994. The time stands at 7 hours and 16 minutes.

For the 1990 Prague City Marathon local-born Jan Skorkovsky juggled a football while running the distance of 26.2 miles. His time was recorded at 7 hours, 18 minutes and 55 seconds.

British youngest capped players are:

Scotland	Denis Law, 18 years, 235 days (v Wales, October 18, 1958)
Northern Ireland	Norman Whiteside, 17 years, 42 days (v Yugoslavia, June 17, 1982)
Wales	Ryan Giggs, 17 years, 332 days (v Germany, October 16, 1991)
Republic of Ireland	Jimmy Holmes, 17 years, 200 days (v Austria, May 30, 1971)

 Facts   **Mixed Bag**

Manchester United's Duncan Edwards became England's youngest capped player this century when he played against Scotland on April 2, 1955. He was 18 years, 183 days.

England's youngest goalscorer record was set by Tommy Lawton who was 19 years, 6 days when he scored a penalty against Wales in Cardiff on October 22, 1938.

Sunderland's goalkeeper Derek Foster became the youngest First Division player when he played against Leicester City on August 22, 1964. He was 15 years, 185 days.

Andrew Cunningham became the oldest player to make hid Football League debut. He was 38 years, 2 days when he turned out for Newcastle United against Leicester City in a First Division match on February 2, 1929.

Walter (Billy) Hampson became the oldest player to play in the FA Cup Final when he appeared for Newcastle United against Aston Villa in 1924. He was 41 years, 8 months.

The record for oldest Carling Premiership player was set by goalkeeper John Burridge on April 29, 1995. Aged 43 years, 4 months, 26 days, he appeared as a half-time substitute for Manchester City against Newcastle United. At the time he was goalkeeper coach for Newcastle.

The record for the youngest England captain was set by Bobby Moore. He captained his country away to Czechoslovakia on May 29, 1963 aged 22 years, 1 month, 17 days.

Tottenham's Andy Turner became the youngest Carling Premiership goalscorer when he scored against Everton on September 5, 1992. He was 17 years, 166 days.

Alan Shearer holds the record for the youngest First Division hat-trick scorer. He was 17 years, 240 days when he scored three for Southampton against Arsenal on April 9, 1988. It was Shearer's full debut.

Chelsea's Jimmy Greaves became the youngest player to score 100 Football League goals when he reached his ton against Manchester City on November 19, 1960 aged 20 years, 261 days.

Arsenal's average age of their 1950 FA Cup winning team was 31 years, 2 months, a record in the competition.

Mixed Bag

Facts

Stanley Matthews became England's oldest goalscorer when, aged 41 years, 248 days, he scored against Northern Ireland in Belfast on October 6, 1956.

The youngest FA Cup player record was set by Andy Awford. He played for Worcester City in a third round qualifying match against Borehamwood on October 10, 1987.

The youngest player to play in the FA Cup proper was Kettering Town's goalkeeper Scott Endersby. He was 15 years, 279 days when he played against Tilbury in the first round match on November 26, 1977.

The record for youngest goalscorer in an international match was set on April 22, 1995 by Mohamed Kallon of Sierra Leone. He was 15 years, 6 months, 16 days when he netted against Congo in an African Nations Cup match.

The oldest player to make his England debut was Leslie Compton. He was 38 years, 2 months when he played against Wales in Sunderland on November 15, 1950.

The oldest British international player was Wales' Billy Meredith on March 15, 1920. He was 45 years, 8 months when he played against England at Highbury.

The youngest player to score in the Football League was Bristol Rovers' Ronnie Dix. He was 15 years, 180 days when he scored against Norwich City in a Division Three (South) match on March 3, 1928.

David Nish still remains the youngest FA Cup Final captain. Aged 21 years, 7 months, Nish led out Leicester City against Manchester City in 1969.

Two men share the record for youngest Football League players. They are: Albert Geldard (Bradford v Millwall, Division Two, September 16, 1929) and Ken Roberts (Wrexham v Bradford, Division Three (North), September 1, 1951). Both were aged 15 years, 158 days.

Sunderland's Barry Venison became the youngest Wembley Cup Final captain when, at the age of 20 years, 7 months, 8 days, he led the club to the 1985 League Cup Final.

 **Facts**

Mixed Bag

The record for youngest FA Cup-winning captain was set by Bobby Moore in 1964. He was 23 years, 20 days when he led West Ham to victory over Preston North End.

Chesterfield's Kevin Davies became the youngest League Cup player on September 22, 1993. He was 16 years, 180 days when he appeared as a substitute against West Ham in the second round, second leg tie.

Aside from becoming the youngest England player, James Prinsep became the youngest FA Cup Final player when he appeared for Clapham Rovers against Old Etonians in 1879 aged 17 years, 245 days.

West Ham's Paul Allen has so far come closest to beating Prinsep's record. He was 11 days older than Prinsep when he played against Arsenal in 1980, and became the youngest FA Cup finalist this century.

The youngest FA Cup Final goalscorer was Manchester United's Norman Whiteside. He was 18 years, 19 days when he scored against Brighton and Hove Albion in the 1983 replay.

Whiteside is also the youngest goalscorer in a Wembley Cup Final. Aged 17 years, 324 days, he scored for Manchester United against Liverpool in the 1983 League Cup Final.

Chris Woods became the youngest Wembley Cup Final goalkeeper when he appeared for Nottingham Forest aged 18 years, 125 days against Liverpool in the 1978 League Cup Final.

The record for youngest FA Cup Final goalkeeper was set by Leicester City's Peter Shilton. He was 19 years, 7 months when he played against Manchester City in the the 1969 Final.

Mixed Bag

The youngest international in a senior match to play at Wembley was Albania's goalkeeper Blendi Nolbani. He was 17 years, 19 days when he faced England on April 26, 1989.

the youngest FA Cup Final referee in 1960. He was 35 when he took charge of Wolves-Blackburn Final.

Cameron Campbell Buchanan is the youngest player in senior football when, aged 14 years, 57 days, he played for Wolves against West Bromwich Albion in a war-time league match on September 26, 1942.

The record for the youngest player in peace-time senior football was set by Blackpool's Eamon Collins on September 9, 1980. He was 14 years, 323 days when he played against Kilmarnock in the Anglo-Scottish Cup quarter-final, first leg.

The record for the oldest First Division player was set by Stoke City's Stanley Matthews. He was 50 years, 5 days when he played against Fulham on February 6, 1965.

STRANGE BUT TRUE

Strange but True

Facts

With an injury crisis at the club, non-league Tring Town were forced to name their 37-year-old chairman, David Lane, as one of the substitutes for the game against Berkhamsted in the 1990-91 season. Lane was put on, but was sent-off before kicking the ball.

With his Brazilian side San Lorenzo 2-1 up over Estudiantes in the final minutes, defender Siminiota picked up the ball thinking it had already gone out of play. To his amazement the referee, Humberto Dellacasa, awarded a penalty. The spot-kick was converted and two players were sent-off for manhandling the referee who had to be escorted from the pitch by riot police.

One of the easiest spot-the-ball competition's came in Welsh newspaper The Western Mail in January 1993. Instead of publishing that week's competition the newspaper showed the previous week's answer. One thousand copies of the paper were run off before the mistake was realised.

When they entered their first Scottish Cup in 1873 Kilmarnock were more accustomed to playing rugby than football. As they tried to brush up on their football knowledge, opponents Renton were constantly awarded free-kicks after the Kilmarnock players had used their hands rather than their feet. To no-one's surprise Renton won the match 3-0.

Despite losing 10-0 to Liverpool in the 1986 League Cup first round, first leg, Fulham still printed details of what would happen if the tie should finish as a draw. Unfortunately they managed only two goal, with Liverpool scoring three.

Brazilian Roberto Rivelino scored some fantastic goals for club and country, but surely the one he scored against Rio Preto will remain one of the strangest. Rio Preto goalkeeper, Isadore Irandir, always prayed in his goalmouth before every game. When Corinthians kicked off, Irandir took up his praying position only to look up and see Rivelino's half-way line shot sail past him en route to the net.

Nat Lofthouse became one of England's best strikers, but it was not always like that. As a schoolboy in Bolton, Lofthouse played his first football match in goal. His team lost 7-1.

 **Facts**

It's not only players that can score world-class goals, one
referee also got in on the act. In a Sunday League fixture in
Southampton, the referee told the two teams that he would
abandon the match if the persistent fouling continued in the
second period. With the message not seeming to get through to
the players the ref had had enough. With the ball in play on the
edge of the penalty area, he produced an unstoppable shot that
flew into the net. "That is how you are supposed to play the
game," he said as he handed his whistle to his linesman and
walked off the pitch.

Leicester Fosse were already relegated from the First Division
in 1909 before playing Nottingham Forest in a match that

Strange but True

Forest needed to win to stay up. The day before the game one of the Leicester players was getting married so his team-mates decided to celebrate in style. They lost the game 12-0 and a Football League inquiry was launched to find out the secret for the then-Football League record victory. They found that the large defeat was due to the fact that the Leicester players were stil hung over from their wedding celebrations.

Despite losing all their 26 matches in the 1992-93 Darlington and District League, Barton Athletic still managed to pick up a trophy - the League's fair-play award. A club official said: "We've always been a very popular club - particularly with our opponents."

Raith Rovers' first overseas tour was not a happy one. Travelling to the Canary Islands in 1930, the Scottish club found themselves ship-wrecked after their boat had capsized. Fortunately all players and officials were rescued, but a decision to play friendlies closer to home was quickly announced.

Bognor's Paul Pullen became involved in a difference of opinion with the referee during a Diadora League match. The referee, however, called twin brother Mick over to him and sent him off. Despite protesting his innocence Mick, Bognor's player-manager at the time, was ordered off, with his brother laughing loudly in the background.

In a desperate bid to stave off relegation a French team laced the opposing team's drink with knock-out drops. The scene's were hilarious as players started to collapse during the match. The authorities became aware, and when they unearthed the reason for the bizarre behaviour the condemned the offending club to relegation.

When two teams of referees met for a friendly game in Spain it should have boasted 22 of the best-behaved players. But when the match official sent off one of the players he was approached and hit by the player's father, who also happened to be a referee.

Former England goalkeeper Dave Beasant presented one of the more bizarre injury excuses when he missed out on the start of the 1993-94 season with a foot injury. The cause of the injury? He dropped a jar of salad cream and tried to stop it smashing on the floor with his foot, severing a tendon.

 **Facts**　　　　　　　　　　　　　**Strange but True**

Cardiff City received a bumper pay-out when they entertained QPR in a third round FA Cup tie in 1990. Record receipts of £50,000 were taken, but soon discovered that thieves had stolen the money.

When Milwall opened their new stadium, The Den, in 1910 Lord Kinnaird, President of the FA, was asked to to conduct the ceremony. Unfortunately, Lord Kinnaird went to the opposing end of the ground and while club officials were waiting he was being pushed over the wall and then ran across the pitch to perform the dignitaries.

Kidderminster were ecstatic when their protest of their 3-1 FA Cup defeat to Darwen was approved and the match was to be replayed. Joy quickly turned to tragedy when Darwen beat them 13-0 to record the highest score in the competition.

Goalkeeper Jonathan Gould suffered ill-effects on hearing his was to play for the Coventry City first team against Southampton in 1993. Within two hours of the news, his car was pranged twice.

It was the proudest moment in West Ham's Jimmy Barrett's career when he was picked to make his England debut against Northern Ireland on October 19, 1929. But after only eight minutes he was injured and carried off. He never played for England again and holds the record for shortest England career.

After watching their side lose 2-0 in a Uefa Cup tie in September 1992, two Celtic fans were drowning their sorrows in a bar in Cologne. When they hailed a taxi to take them to their hotel they could not remember the name of the digs, or even what town it was located. After consulting each other they decided on Dortmund which was 90 miles away. After the £70 fare they remembered it was Dusseldorf, which was another 70 miles away.

QPR chairman was so anxious to find out the latest news on his club that he rang the Clubcall line on his carphone. Unfortunately he did not replace the handset correctly and only discovered his mistake the next morning when he was hit with a £335 phone bill.

Strange but True

Billy Abercrombie created history in 1986 by being sent-off three times in the same match. The St. Mirren captain was shown the red card from referee Louis Thow for an offence, then another for talking back and then a third one for dissent. He was banned for 12 matches by the Scottish League.

Stockport United FC of the Stockport Football League created the unenviable record of losing 39 consecutive League and Cup matches from September 1976 to February 1978.

Peruvian broadcaster Mario Sanchez received a terrible shock when he asked the striker Corina why he had missed three easy heading chances and how could that part of his game be improved. Corina answer was a swift head-butt to Sanchez, who was knocked unconscious by the blow. Corina was later arrested by the police.

Reaching your local Cup Final is a dream for thousands of footballers across the country, but for one team their success back-fired. After winning their semi-final Lags XI, a prison team from Stockton, Cleveland, were thrown out of the competition because they could only play home matches.

IT'S A
FUNNY OLD GAME

It's a Funny Old Game

Facts

A Danish league match in April 1960 produced a remarkable and controversial finish. With Norager leading 4-3 in the final minute against Ebeltoft, referee Henning Erikstrup was on the verge of blowing the final whistle when his dentures fell out. While he was looking for them, Ebeltoft equalised. To protestations from the Ebeltoft team, Mr Erikstrup disallowed the goal and blew for full-time with the result standing at 4-3.

When Exeter City were beaten 5-1 at Millwall in 1982 manager Brian Godfrey decided to keep the team in London and play Millwall reserves the next day. It didn't get any better for Godfrey, Millwall reserves won 1-0.

Hearts director Douglas Park was so infuriated by the refereeing of David Symes after the game with Rangers in 1988 he locked the Symes in the dressing room for 18 minutes after the game and left with the key. Park was fined £1,000 by the Scottish League for his actions.

Stephen Gould thought he could play in goal for his strugling works side, Little Aston in Staffordshire. As he began his warm-up on his debut he jumped up to touch the crossbar, only for the bar to fall on his head. He was carried back to the dressing room before the start of the match.

Nottingham Forest secured promotion to the First Division in 1977 thanks to an own goal from Millwall's Jon Moore. Later that evening Forest supporters voted Moore their Player of the Year.

Bernie Marsh of Mid Sussex League side Balcombe Reserves suffered the uneviable honour of being tackled by a Ford Sierra. With the ball on the half-way line a spectator decided to reverse his car onto the pitch so he could turn round to leave the playing fields. But then came a long shot toward Marsh's goal. Without looking behind him Marsh began moving towards his goal to stop the shot. He tipped the ball over the crossbar but his momentum sent him crashing into the car and knocking him straight out.

Because of bad weather Inverness Thistle's Scottish Cup tie against Falkirk in 1979 was postponed a record 29 times. The game was not exactly worth the wait – Thistle lost the match 4-0.

When Scottish club Greenock Morton won their first game with their new mascot, Toby the sheep, the celebrations were cut short when Toby was left in the changing room and drowned in the players' bath.

 **Facts** It's a Funny Old Game

In 1924 Cardiff City had the opportunity to become the first, and only, Welsh club to win the Football League Championship. Needing a victory to take the title, City were awarded a penalty in the final game of the season against Birmingham. But Len Davies missed the kick and Huddersfield won the title on goal avaerage.

It's a Funny Old Game

There was no place to hide for Chelsea defender John Sillett when, hearing a whistle, caught the ball in his penalty area thinking the referee had blown up. Unfortunately the whistle came from a spectator and Chelsea's opponents, Sheffield Wednesday, were awarded one of the bizaare penalties in history.

Derby County's Andy Comyn made an immediate impact when he came on as a substitute against Bristol City in September 1992. The defender arrived onto the field to face a City free-kick. He rose to head the ball away but only succeded in putting the ball past stand-in goalkeeper Paul Williams to give Bristol City a goal within 10 seconds of coming on.

Denis Law could even injure himself watching a match on the substitutes bench. In Manchester United's 1968 European Cup semi-final against Real Madrid, Law got so carried away when Bill Foulkes scored that he went to punch the air but smashed his fist through the roof of the dug-out and suffered a broken bone in his hand.

FOOTBALL'S FAMOUS QUOTES

Football's Famous Quotes

"A lot of hard work went into this defeat."
Malcolm Allison

"I went down to pass on some technical information to the team - like the fact the game had started."
Aston Villa manager Ron Atkinson, explaining why he had taken his seat in the dugout early in a match against Sheffield United.

Gordon Lee: *"Well, what business has anyone got naming him Eamon O'Keefe if he isn't Irish?*
Billy Bingham: *"Probably the same business they have naming you Lee when you're not Chinese."*

"Matt (Busby) always believed Manchester United would be one of the greatest clubs in the world. He was the eternal optimist. In 1968 he still hoped Glenn Miller was just missing."
Pat Crerand

"The game in Romania was a game we should have won. We lost it because we thought we were going to win it. But then again, I thought there was no way we were going to get a result there."
Republic of Ireland manager Jack Charlton in 1987

"The first thing that went wrong was half-time. We could have done without that."
England manager Graham Taylor in 1988.

"In terms of the Richter scale, this defeat was a force 8 gale."
John Lyall

"He's my man mountain - he would head aeroplanes away if it helped Birmingham City."
Barry Fry on Liam Daish

"Very few players have the courage of my convictions."
Brian Clough

"The last player to score a hat-trick in an FA Cup Final was Stan Mortensen. He even had a Final named after him - the Matthews Final."
Lawrie McMenemy

"I do want to play the long ball, and I do want to play the short ball. I think long and short balls is what football is all about."
Bobby Robson

"Certain players are for me, certain players are pro me."
Terry Venables

"Before the match I told my players they will be playing against 11 guys ready to fight for each other for 90 minutes...... but I didn't expect it to be with each other."
Spartak Moscow coach Oleg Romantsev after the infamous brawl between Blackburn's Graeme le Saux and David Batty.

"I don't drop players - I make changes."
Bill Shankly

 **Facts**   **Football's Famous Quotes**

"Women run everything. The only thing that I have done within my house in the last 20 years is to recognise Angola as an independent state."
Brian Clough

"Of course I didn't take my wife to see Rochdale as an anniversary present. It was her birthday, Would I have got married during the football season? And, anyway, it wasn't Rochdale, it was Rochdale reserves."
Bill Shankly

"A fan is a person who, when you have made an idiot of yourself on the pitch, doesn't think you've done a permanent job."
Francis Lee

"Remember, postcards only, please. The winner will be the first one opened."
Brian Moore

"A lot of people in football don't have much time for the press; they say they're amateurs. But I say to those people, 'Noah was an amateur, but the Titanic was built by professionals."
Malcolm Allison

"They must go for it now as they have nothing to lose but the match."
Ron Atkinson

"Kenny Dalglish has about as much personality as a tennis racket."
Mick Channon

"Don't tell those coming the final result of the fantastic match, but let's just have another look at Italy's winning goal."
David Coleman

"If in winning the game we only finish with a draw, we would be fine."
Jack Charlton

"Nottingham Forest are having a bad run....... they've lost six matches now without winning."
David Coleman

"Trevor Brooking floats like a butterfly, and stings like one too."
Brian Clough

"You know, the Brazilians aren't as good as they used to be, or as they are now."
Kenny Dalglish

"Lukic saved with his foot which is all part of the goalkeeper's arm."
Barry Davies

"He hit the post, and after the game people will say, well, he hit the post."
Jimmy Greaves

"If a week's a long time in politics, it is an equinox in football."
Stuart Hall

"The USA are a goal down, and if they don't get a goal, they'll lose."
John Helm

Football's Famous Quotes

Interviewer: *"You've devoted a whole chapter of your book to Jimmy Greaves.*
Pat Jennings: *"That's right. Well, what can you say about Jimmy Greaves?"*

"Sporting Lisbon in their green and white hoops, looking like a team of zebras."
Peter Jones

"Bobby Robson must be thinking of throwing some fresh legs on."
Kevin Keegan

Dickie Davies: *"What's he going to be telling his team at half-time, Denis?*
Denis Law: *"He'll be telling them that there are forty-five minutes left to play."*

"Both of the Villa scorers - Withe and Mortimer - were born in Liverpool, as was the Villa manager - Ron Saunders - who was born in Birkenhead."
David Coleman

"Chesterfield 1, Chester 1. Another score draw there in that local derby."
Desmond Lynam

"The news from Guadalajara, where the temperature is 96 degrees, is that Falcao is warming up."
Brian Moore

"If history is going to repeat itself, I should think we can expect the same thing again."
Terry Venables

"I hear Glenn Hoddle has found God. That must have been one hell of a pass."
Jasper Carrott

"He's (a fellow coach) not so much a coach as a hearse."
Tommy Docherty

"Last time we got a penalty away from home, Christ was still a carpenter."
Lenny Lawrence

"We've got grounds which are a state of the art and administration which is state of the Ark."
PFA chairman Gordon Taylor

"I'm not superstitious or anything like that, but I'll just hope that we'll play our best and put it in the lap of the Gods."
Terry Neill

"My only problem (after his transfer to Italy) seems to be with Italian breakfasts. No matter how much money you've got, you can't get any Rice Krispies."
Luther Blissett

"We fought two wars with the Germans. We probably got on better with the smaller nations like the Dutch, the Belgians, the Norwegians and the Swedes, some of whom are not even in Europe."
Jack Charlton

"There's a hell of a lot of politics in football. I don't think Henry Kissinger would have lasted 48 hours at Old Trafford."
Tommy Docherty

Facts

Football's Famous Quotes

"Manchester United are buzzing around the goalmouth like a lot of red bottles."
David Coleman

"The doctor at Lazio told me I should try drinking wine, because it would be good for me. When I did, he had one look at me and said: 'You'd better go back on the beer.'"
Paul Gascoigne

Football's Famous Quotes

"Well, stone me. We've had cocaine, bribery and Arsenal scoring two goals at home. But just when you thought there truly were no surprises left in football, Vinnie Jones turns out to be an international player."
Jimmy Greaves

"I'm not giving away any secrets like that to Milan. If I had my way, I wouldn't even tell them the time of the kick-off."
Bill Shankly, on delaying his team line-up

"The World Cup - truly an international event."
John Motson

"I have Gary Lineker's shirt up in my hotel room, and it's only stopped moving now."
Mick McCarthy

"With Maradona, even Arsenal would have won it (the 1986 World Cup)."
Bobby Robson

FOOTBALL'S TOP TENS

Football's Top Tens

TEN GREAT FOOTBALL MATCHES

Blackpool 4 Bolton 3 (FA Cup Final, 1953)

'The Matthews Final' is recognised as the most memorable in the competition's history. It was Stanley Matthews who inspired Blackpool to a thrilling win, with Stan Mortensen scoring a hat-trick.

England 3 Hungary 6 (Wembley, 1953)

British fans had never seen football quite like that of the Hungarians as they completely outplayed Walter Winterbottom's side. Led superbly by Puskas, the visitors inflicted England's heaviest ever defeat at Wembley.

Liverpool 4 Newcastle 3 (Anfield, 1996)

Probably the most thrilling game in recent times, the lead changed hands three times before Stan Collymore's last-gasp winner sealed a memorable win for Liverpool.

Real Madrid 7 Eintracht Frankfurt 3 (Hampden Park, 1960)

Once again the mercurial Ferenc Puskas showed the world how the game could be played, his four goals and a hat-trick from Alfred Di Stefano securing the European Cup for the Spanish giants.

Everton 4 Liverpool 4 (Goodison, 1991)

Following a disappointing scoreless draw in the FA Cup Fifth Round, the replay proved to be a classic. Tony Cottee twice denied Liverpool the victory in the dying minutes of both normal and extra time.

England 4 West Germany 2 (Wembley, 1966)

The greatest moment in the history of English football. In a pulsating and controversial match, Geoff Hurst became the only player to score a hat-trick in a World Cup final.

Italy 4 West Germany 3 (Mexico City, 1970)

Italy held the lead throughout the tense World Cup semi-final until a dramatic last minute equaliser by Schnellinger. The game was finally settled in the 112th minute, Rivera sending the elated Italians to the final.

 **Facts** **Football's Top Tens**

Italy 3 West Germany 1 (Madrid, 1982)

Dino Zoff's side played some masterful football as they crushed the West Germans in the 1982 World Cup Final. Paolo Rossi, the prodigal son of Italian football, scored once in a comfortable but stylish win.

Italy 3 Brazil 2 (Barcelona, 1982)

On the way to the final the Italians faced the mighty Brazil in the Group C qualifying stages. A hat-trick from Rossi, who finished as the tournament's leading marksman, secured victory, Falcao and Socrates scoring for the South Americans.

France 1 Brazil 1 (Guadalajara, 1986)

Arguably the finest match of the 1986 Mexico World Cup, it was a tragedy that this quarter-final game had to be decided on penalties. Goals from Careca and Platini took the thrilling encounter to extra-time, France winning the tense shoot-out 4-3.

TEN BEST TOP-FLIGHT STRIKING PARTNERSHIPS

Dixie Dean and Tommy Johnson, 1931-32

Newly-promoted from the Second Division, Everton won the First Division title at the first attempt. The 67 goals from Dean and striking partner Johnson were instrumental in the success.

Ted Drake and Drake and Cliff Bastin, 1934-35

The combination of Drake and Bastin netted 62 goals for Arsenal in the 1934-35 season, steering the North Londoners to their second successive Championship.

Raich Carter and Bob Gurney, 1935-36

Sunderland's last success in the top-flight was in 1935-36 when Johnny Cochrane's side won the old First Division. The pairing of Carter and Gurney was central to the team, scoring 62 goals between them.

Football's Top Tens

Ray Crawford and Ted Phillips, 1961-62

Ipswich won promotion to the top-flight in the 1960-61 season and clinched the First Division title the following year. The 37 goals from Crawford and 24 from Phillips was the reason.

Tommy Thompson and Tom Finney, 1957-58

Despite 60 goals from the partnership of Thompson and Finney, the club's most capped international, Preston North End won no silverware in 1957-58. They were relegated two seasons later.

Dennis Westcott and Dickie Dorsett, 1938-39

The only League club to have been champions of all four Divisions, Wolverhampton Wanderers could not capitalise on the 58 goals scored by Westcott and Dorsett in the 1938-39 season.

Jimmy Greaves and Cliff Jones, 1962-63

Defending champions Tottenham could not hold on to their title in 1962-63 despite 57 goals from Greaves and Jones. However Greaves' five strikes in Europe did steer Spurs to victory in the European Cup Winner's Cup.

Jimmy Greaves and Ron Tindall, 1960-61

Greaves had been in another prolific partnership two seasons before for Chelsea, scoring a total of 57 goals alongside Tindall. Ted Drake's men could not exploit the free-scoring duo and failed to win any trophies.

George Robledo and Jackie Milburn, 1951-52

The pairing of Robledo and Milburn yielded 57 goals for Newcastle in the 1951-52 season. The League eluded the Magpies but Milburn's three goals in the FA Cup helped the St James Park side to Wembley glory.

Dennis Westcott and Jesse Pye, 1946-47

Westcott and Pye scored an impressive 57 goals for Wolves in the 1946-47 season but did could not clinch any silverware for the club. Westcott finished with 38 goals in the League that year which remains a club record.

Quiz Score Sheets

Quiz Score Sheets

Quiz Score Sheets

Quiz Score Sheets

Quiz Score Sheets

Quiz Score Sheets